Fluid Flow and Heat Transfer in Wellbores

Fluid Flow and Heat Transfer in Wellbores

A.R. Hasan
Professor and Chair, Chemical Engineering
U. of North Dakota
Grand Forks, North Dakota

C.S. Kabir
Senior Advisor, Reservoir Management
ChevronTexaco Overseas Petroleum
Bellaire, Texas

Society of Petroleum Engineers

ISBN 978-1-55563-094-2

12 13 14 15 16 17 / 10 9 8 7 6 5 4 3 2

Society of Petroleum Engineers
222 Palisades Creek Drive
Richardson, TX 75080-2040 USA

http://store.spe.org/
books@spe.org
1.972.952.9393

Dedication

To Neelufar and Kumkum

Rashid Hasan is a professor at the U. of Minnesota-Duluth. Previously, he was the Chair of Chemical Engineering at U. of North Dakota and was named the Olson Professor of Engineering. He has also served as a visiting professor at the U. of Texas and was a research fellow at the NASA Glenn Laboratory and the Idaho National Engineering Laboratory. Momentum and energy transport, especially coupled transient transport processes, is Hasan's major research interest. Other interests include the rheology of non-Newtonian fluids, pressure-transient analysis, and cryogenic fluids. He has performed contract research for various organizations and has been sought as a consultant by major oil and service companies. Hasan has published extensively and has served on various SPE committees. He earned a PhD degree in chemical engineering from the U. of Waterloo, Canada in 1979.

Shah Kabir has over 25 years experience in the oil industry, with the last 12 years at Chevron-Texaco. Currently, he is with ChevronTexaco's Mid-Africa Business Unit in Bellaire, Texas. He has lived and/or worked in many producing provinces of the world and contributed to various facets of petroleum engineering. His experience includes transient testing, production logging, production operations, and reservoir/reservoir-simulation engineering. Kabir has published extensively and has served various SPE committees, including editorial review for *SPEPF*, *SPEREE*, and *SPEJ*. He has received commendation as an outstanding technical editor four times for two different journals. In 2002, he received the SPE Western North America Region's Service Award. He holds a Master's degree in chemical engineering from the U. of Calgary.

Preface

Fluid flow in wellbores occurs during various phases of a well's life. Our ability to optimize each flow process depends largely on grasping the underlying physics so that we can mathematically describe the process involved. At a well's inception, drilling operations require mud circulation causing a considerable heat exchange between the colder fluid and the warmer formation. In the event of an unfortunate blowout, because of lost circulation or an unexpected overpressured zone, we encounter transient two-phase flow as the formation interacts with the wellbore prematurely. When we initiate flow from the formation by design, such as in a drill-stem or production test, flow of either a single- or multi-phase fluid occurs. As the fluids ascend the wellbore, the warm formation fluid begins to exchange heat with the colder formation above it. Therefore, heat flow is always coupled with fluid flow in actual wellbores.

In this book, we attempt to address the coupled fluid and heat flow issue as encountered in many practical production-operation problems, including drilling. Both steady and unsteady-state transport problems are considered. Even when steady fluid flow is maintained during circulation, injection, or production modes, unsteady heat transport in the formation occurs nonetheless. Fluid circulation during drilling and workover operations and injection of annular gas in a gas-lift operation are cases in point. We also examine fully transient processes of fluid and heat flows, such as those in drillstem or production testing.

Before we undertake a detailed treatment of each operational problem, we introduce the reader to some basic concepts, starting with the rudiments of single-phase flow (Chap. 1) to more complex issues of two-phase flow modeling (Chaps. 2, 3, and 4). Thereafter, the principles of heat conduction in the formation, and the elements of fluid flow and the associated heat flow are discussed in Chaps. 5, 6, and 7. These chapters provide the ingredients for solving various flow problems that we consider subsequently, termed collectively as application chapters. Field examples are used to illustrate the principles learned in Chaps. 2 through 7, wherever feasible.

In the application chapters, we present the working equations and simple worked-out examples to illustrate their use. Details of the derivation of models are shown in appendices. We endeavored to facilitate application of a piece of technology learned along with its underlying physics and the assumptions involved in developing the model, and therefore its limitations. Overall, we have presented eight different topics in application (Chaps. 8 through 10).

The application chapters vary in scope. Some deal with parameter estimation while others lead to the understanding of a flow process. For example, a section in the drilling chapter shows how the proper heat-transfer modeling can lead to reliable static-formation temperature estimation. By contrast, the production-logging chapter leads one to improved understanding of individual layer contribution, by invoking the principles of flow modeling. In all cases, we attempt to show the linkage between theory, as developed in Chaps. 2 through 7, and practice.

While discussing transient aspects of mass and fluid flow in production testing, we introduced the notion of seamless Nodal or systems analysis. In this context, the significance of non-Darcy flow, often a forgotten entity in oil-well testing, is shown. Because inflow performance is a key parameter that a production engineer uses to seek or to evaluate well remediation, we felt that this treatment was justified. Here, the idea is not to discuss the intricacies of transient-pressure analysis but rather to stress the importance of combining transient testing, production logging, and well-performance analysis needed for reservoir management from a production engineer's viewpoint.

The book is envisioned to serve a variety of readers, from advanced senior and graduate students to practicing engineers. The overall philosophy is to show not just how to solve a given problem but also why the recommended approach is superior. In other words, we attempted to avoid the proverbial cookbook approach. Instead, we strove to strike a balance between theory and practice. Illustrative examples are used to reinforce the principles learned at the end of each major section.

Although hundreds of papers have been written on both topics of multiphase flow and heat transfer over the last five decades, we attempted to present only those that pertain to solving the wellbore flow problems. Thus, this book is not designed to treat either topic in great depth but to acquaint the reader with enough information so that practical oilfield problems can be tackled. In presenting various approaches to solving a problem, we favored physical models, which have been verified with either laboratory and/or field data, over purely empirical correlations. However, in choosing mechanistic models we have leaned toward a simpler approach, rather than delving into complex but rigorous solutions. Here, the motivation was to retain simplicity and engineering accuracy. In this context, we must point out that we have drawn heavily from our experiences, both academic and applied, to present this material. In this compilation effort, our familiarity of material, which is our own, took precedence even though we tried to be objective.

We did not attempt to solve all the coupled fluid and heat flow problems in production operations. This book is simply an attempt to capture a few. Our ardent hope is that the presented material gives both the foundation and examples to tackle other problems.

A.R. Hasan

C.S. Kabir

Acknowledgments

In our quest to grasp various aspects of production operations as practiced in the oilfield, we learned from others, be it through personal interaction or through published work. Our colleagues, in both academia and the industry, enriched our knowledge over the years. We are indebted to them all.

Here, we recognize a few who made the real difference in our learning and the eventual compilation of this book. Dr. Xiaowei Wang, a former graduate student at U. of North Dakota, contributed a great deal to our cause. He was instrumental in developing many pieces of the models presented in Chaps. 6 through 9. In this respect, the contributions of another UND graduate, Dr. Dongqing Lin, are worthy of note. Former graduate student Dr. Mahbub Ameen also contributed significantly to solving the fluid-circulation problems. Many field examples were drawn from hands-on experience that one of us, C.S. Kabir, had in Kuwait. We thank Kuwait Oil Co. for allowing us to present those examples in various SPE papers.

We are grateful to Professor Khalid Aziz of Stanford U. for giving us the much-needed impetus to launch this project. Professor Emeritus James P. Brill of the U. of Tulsa helped broaden our horizons. Professor Cem Sarica of the U. of Tulsa reviewed the manuscript. His timely reviews and insightful comments helped enrich the content, for which we will remain indebted forever. We express our gratitude to our respective organizations, U. of North Dakota and ChevronTexaco, for aiding our pursuit. SPE's Books Committee deserves special recognition for entrusting us with this project. We owe Shelley Nash for her diligence and attention to meticulous details while reviewing the manuscript. Her extraordinary patience was instrumental in minimizing endless imperfections in the manuscript. We are thankful to SPE staff members Jennifer Wegman, for managing and reviewing the manuscript, and Fran Kennedy-Ellis, for overseeing the book's publication.

A few academicians helped shape our understanding of this technology through their exemplary leadership. Professor Graham Wallis of Dartmouth College formalized the drift-flux approach for two-phase flow modeling. Late professors Abraham Dukler of the U. of Houston and Hank Ramey Jr. of Stanford U. laid the foundation for mechanistic modeling of two-phase flow and wellbore heat transfer, respectively.

Last, but not least, our family members, especially our spouses, deserve particular mention for their encouragement and fortitude. Their extraordinary understanding allowed us to steal countless hours from the family time so that we could complete this task. Finally, our parents, who taught us values, inspired us to compile this material. To this end, we hope the reader finds this text stimulating and useful.

Table of Contents

Chapter 1
Overview

1.1 Single-Phase Flow

Fluid flow, in a variety of forms and complexities, is a basic entity that must be dealt with in the production of hydrocarbons. In its rudiments, single-phase gas or oil production and water injection form the core of all flow problems. Therefore, Chap. 1 discusses the mechanical energy balance equation, which relates pressure drop to its various components for single-phase flow. Next, the components of total pressure drop—static, kinetic, and frictional—are discussed. Also, flows in tubing-casing annuli and horizontal wells, which are of particular interest to petroleum engineers, are briefly discussed.

1.1.1 Mechanical Energy Balance.
A simple one-dimensional (1D) analysis of single-phase gas or liquid flow is best made with the aid of a schematic, as shown in **Fig. 1.1.** The channel, inclined at an arbitrary angle (α) with the horizontal, shows upward flow of the fluid. For the present, we consider only the steady-state case and assume that pressure, at any point in the cross-sectional plane normal to flow, remains the same. With these simplifications, we derive the momentum balance equation.

Conservation of Momentum. The sum of forces acting on the fluid element, shown in Fig. 1.1, equals the change of momentum of the fluid. The forces acting on the fluid element are those owing to pressure, p, friction, F, and gravity. Referring to the differential length, dz, of Fig. 1.1, we write $pA - (p+dp) - dF - A(dz)g\rho\sin\theta =$ change of momentum.

If the fluid mass flow rate is w and its velocity is v, then its momentum equals wv. For the general case of transient flow, when both flow rate and velocity change along the flow direction, fluid momentum change is given by $(w+dw)(v+dv)-wv$. Therefore,

$$pA - (p + dp)A - dF - A(dz)g\rho\sin\theta$$

$$= (w+dw)(v+dv) - wv \cdots\cdots\cdots\cdots (1.1)$$

Simplifying, we obtain

$$-A dp - dF - A(dz)g\rho\sin\theta = w dv + v dw \cdots\cdots (1.2)$$

Usually, the mass flow rate is invariant; that is, dw=0, leading to

$$-A dp - dF - A(dz)g\rho\sin\theta = w dv \cdots\cdots\cdots\cdots (1.3)$$

Dividing both sides of Eq. 1.3 by $A dz$, we obtain

$$-(dp/dz) + (dp/dz)_F - g\sin\theta - (w/A)dv/dz = 0$$
$$\cdots\cdots\cdots\cdots\cdots (1.4)$$

or $(dp/dz) = (dp/dz)_F + (dp/dz)_H + (dp/dz)_A$,
$$\cdots\cdots\cdots\cdots\cdots (1.5)$$

where $(dp/dz)_H = g\rho\sin\theta$, $\cdots\cdots\cdots\cdots\cdots (1.6)$

and $-(dp/dz)_A = (w/A)dv/dz = \rho v dv/dz \cdots\cdots (1.7)$

1.1.2 Components of Pressure Gradient.
Eq. 1.5 shows the total pressure gradient is the sum of the frictional gradient $(dp/dz)_F$, the hydrostatic gradient $(dp/dz)_H$, and the accelerational gradient $(dp/dz)_A$. Of these three terms, perhaps the static gradient is the easiest to estimate because it only requires knowledge of the fluid density and well-deviation angle. Because gas density depends on pressure, the static term will vary along the well for gas wells. Usually such variation is small, and relatively simple equations of state can be used to account for it. To some extent, even for single-phase oil production, oil-density variation with well depth, owing to temperature and dissolved gases, must be taken into account. The same comments apply to the estimation procedure for the kinetic head (Eq. 1.7).

For incompressible flow in a straight pipe with no change in cross-sectional area (gases at very high pressures and liquids), the change in fluid velocity with axial distance (dv/dz) is generally negligible. However, for gases at moderate and low pressures, and especially at high velocities, the kinetic energy loss can be a significant portion of the total pressure loss and must be accounted for properly. Computational complications that arise for gas flow have led to a number of correlations for calculating pressure drop in a wellbore. We recommend the widely used Cullender and Smith[1] method for computing pressure drop in a gas well.

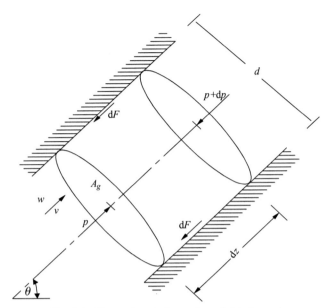

Fig. 1.1—Momentum balance for a fluid element.

The frictional pressure gradient is generally represented by

$$(dp/dz)_F = -fv^2\rho/2g_cd, \quad \dots\dots\dots\dots (1.8)$$

where the Moody friction factor, f, depends on the turbulence of the fluid and also on the pipe roughness. The friction factor is usually expressed as a function of Reynolds number

$$\text{Re} = dv\rho/\mu. \quad \dots\dots\dots\dots\dots\dots (1.9)$$

and roughness factor ε/d. The chart for friction factor as a function of Reynolds number with pipe roughness as a parameter is shown in **Fig. 1.2;** whereas, **Fig. 1.3** presents the chart for estimating relative roughness. Note, k/d represents the relative roughness or ε/d in both figures, and in Fig. 1.3, the units of measure for pipe diameter (d) are ft. We point out that Fig. 1.2 is the Moody friction factor chart. The Fanning friction factor is simply one-fourth the Moody friction factor. Because of its popularity in the oil industry, we use the Moody friction factor throughout this book.

At low-Reynolds numbers (R<2,100), the flowing fluid elements do not interact with each other, and the flow is called laminar. For laminar flow in either rough or smooth pipes, friction factor is inversely related to Reynolds number

$$f = 64/\text{Re} = 64dv\rho/\mu, \quad \dots\dots\dots\dots (1.10)$$

when Re<2,100.

At high-Reynolds numbers (Re>4,000), the flow is termed turbulent. During turbulent flow, the friction factor depends on both the Reynolds number and pipe roughness. For smooth pipes, such as plastic pipes and tubulars coated with PVC lining, friction factor can be estimated reliably from the Blassius equation,

$$f = 0.32(\text{Re})^{-0.25}, \quad \dots\dots\dots\dots (1.11)$$

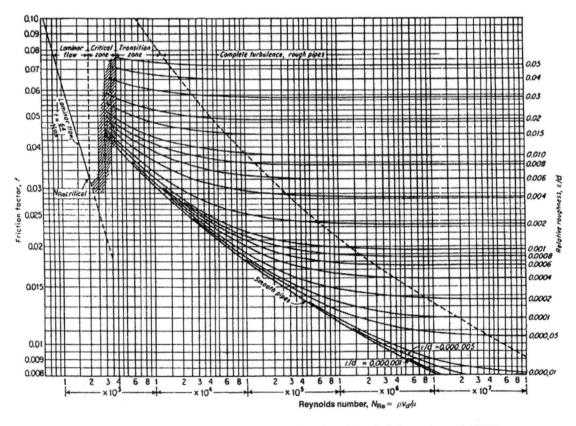

Fig. 1.2—Moody friction factor chart for turbulent flow (from Ref. 3; courtesy of ASME).

FLUID FLOW AND HEAT TRANSFER IN WELLBORES

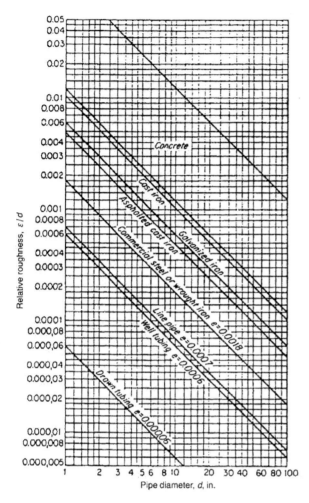

Relative roughness, ε/d

Pipe diameter, d, in.

Fig. 1.3—Relative roughness of pipes (from Ref. 3; courtesy of ASME).

when Re>4,000.

For very high Reynolds numbers (Re>50,000), Eq. 1.11 is slightly modified as $f = 0.184\,(\text{Re})^{-0.2}$.

Eq. 1.11, of course, is invalid for rough pipes. Although a chart is useful for all types of pipe roughness, chart reading is tedious and is not easily amenable to computer calculations. A number of equations, relating friction factor to Reynolds number and pipe roughness, has been proposed over the years and are in fair agreement with the original friction-factor charts. We recommend the following expression proposed by Chen,[2] which yields Fanning friction factor and is given by

$$f = \frac{1}{\left[4\log\left(\dfrac{\varepsilon/d}{3.7065} - \dfrac{5.0452}{\text{Re}}\log\Lambda\right)\right]^2}, \quad \ldots\ldots (1.12)$$

where ε is pipe roughness, and the dimensionless parameter, Λ, is given by

$$\Lambda = \frac{(\varepsilon/d)^{1.1098}}{2.8257} + \left(\frac{7.149}{\text{Re}}\right)^{0.8981} \quad \ldots\ldots\ldots (1.13)$$

Unlike many other expressions, which require iterative solutions for the friction factor, Eq. 1.12 is explicit and, therefore, computationally efficient.

The evaluation of various terms in Eq. 1.12 is relatively easier for flow of single-phase fluids, even for gases, than for two-phase mixtures. In the latter case, estimating the average density and friction factor can be challenging because these are complex functions of fluid properties and flow conditions. Chap. 2 discusses various approaches taken to evaluate these entities in two-phase flow.

1.2 Flow in Nonisothermal Systems

Fluid temperature in the wellbore often varies significantly with depth, and sometimes with time. Many of the fluid properties that influence pressure drop, such as density and viscosity, are greatly influenced by the fluid temperature. Therefore, we cannot overemphasize the importance of accurate fluid temperature estimation as a function of well depth and production or injection time. This calculation can be done by a proper energy balance on the fluid-wellbore system, as shown in Chap. 5. For single-phase flow, the expression for fluid temperature, T_f, simplifies to

$$T_f = T_{ei} + \left[1 - e^{-zL_R}\right]g_G\sin\theta, \quad \ldots\ldots\ldots (1.14)$$

where the parameter, L_R, which is a function of wellbore heat-transfer coefficient U_{to} and formation heat conductivity k_e, is defined by

$$L_R = \frac{2\pi}{c_P w}\left[\frac{r_{to}U_{to}k_e}{k_e + (r_{to}U_{to}T_D)}\right]. \quad \ldots\ldots\ldots (1.15)$$

In Eq. 1.15, T_D represents dimensionless temperature, which is a function of dimensionless time, $t_D = k_e c_e t/\rho_e r_{wb}^2$.

$$T_D = \ln\left[e^{-0.3t_D} + \left(1.5 - 0.3719e^{-t_D}\right)\sqrt{t_D}\right]. \quad \ldots\ldots (1.16)$$

For a complete discussion of Eqs. 1.14 through 1.16, please refer to Chap. 5.

1.3 Flow in Annulus

Although flow through a tubing string is the most common configuration, many completions dictate modeling for flow up the tubing-casing annulus. The presence of two walls makes flow through an annulus different from that through ordinary circular strings. The classical work of Bird et al.[4] shows Eq. 1.8 is also applicable for such geometry, although the correlation for friction factor must be modified to reflect greater wall shear. For laminar flow in a concentric annulus, the Moody friction factor, f_{CA}, is given by[4]

$$f_{CA} = \frac{64}{\text{Re}}\frac{(1-K)^2}{\left[\dfrac{1-K^4}{1-K^2} - \dfrac{1-K^2}{\ln(1/K)}\right]}, \quad \ldots\ldots\ldots (1.17)$$

where K is the diameter ratio, d_t/d_c. Following the studies of Gunn and Darling[5] and Caetano et al.,[6] we recommend expressing turbulent flow in a concentric annulus as

$$\cfrac{1}{\left[\left\{f_{CA}\left(\cfrac{F_p}{F_{CA}}\right)^{0.45\exp\{-(Re-3000)/10^6\}}\right\}^{0.5}\right]}$$

$$= 4\log\left[Re\left\{f_{CA}\left(\cfrac{F_p}{F_{CA}}\right)^{0.45\exp\{-(Re-3000)/10^6\}}\right\}^{0.5}\right] - 0.4,$$

$$\dots\dots\dots\dots\dots (1.18)$$

where F_p is the laminar-flow friction factor geometry parameter and F_{CA} is the ratio of friction factor for the annulus to that of a circular channel with the same d_c. Thus, from Eq. 1.18, F_p, for a concentric annulus, is given by

$$F_P = \frac{(1-K)^2}{\left[\dfrac{1-K^4}{1-K^2} - \dfrac{1-K^2}{\ln(1/K)}\right]} \cdot \dots\dots\dots (1.19)$$

For eccentric annuli, eccentricity (E) is defined as

$$E = D/(d_c - d_t), \quad \dots\dots\dots\dots (1.20)$$

where D is the distance between the pipe centers. The values of F_p, as a function of K and E, are shown in **Fig. 1.4**. For an eccentric annulus, the friction factor equation is similar to that of Eq. 1.18,

$$f_{ECA} = \frac{4}{Re}\frac{4}{\xi\sinh^4\eta_o}\frac{(1-K)^2\left(1-K^2\right)}{1}, \quad \dots\dots\dots (1.21)$$

where η_o and ξ incorporate the effect of eccentricity factor E. A complete treatment of flow through eccentric annuli is beyond the scope of this text; for further details, the reader is referred to the work of Caetano et al.[6] Two-phase flow in an annular geometry is treated in Chap. 4.

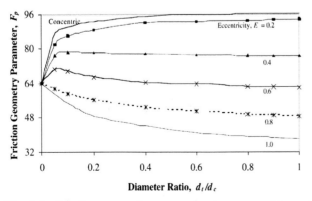

Fig. 1.4—Friction geometry parameter for concentric and eccentric annuli.

1.4 Flow in Horizontal Wells

The recent interest in horizontal wells stems from significant increases in productivity and ultimate recovery in certain cases. Initial efforts[7,8] to couple the wellbore with reservoir using analytic approaches considered frictional effects only. In other words, fluid ingress along the well length leading to momentum and related effects was ignored in those formulations.

Estimating pressure drop in horizontal wells presents a number of difficulties. First, pipe-surface roughness is a difficult entity to discern because of perforations along the well length in a cased borehole. Because most completions occur openhole, complexity increases significantly to ascribe a friction factor for an ill-defined surface—that is, the formation. The second factor revolves around fluid influx or changes in momentum that occur along the well length.

Recent experimental studies[9-11] in perforated horizontal pipes, allowing fluid ingress along the well length, led to the development of several friction-factor correlations. Of these, the results of Ouyang et al.[10] and Yuan et al.[11] are noteworthy.

Ouyang et al.[10] presented the following Moody friction-factor correlations for laminar and turbulent flows, respectively.

$$f = \frac{64}{Re}\left(1 + 0.04304 Re_w^{0.6142}\right), \quad \dots\dots (1.22)$$

$$\text{and } f = f_o\left(1 - 0.0153 Re_w^{0.3978}\right), \quad \dots\dots (1.23)$$

where f_o is the no-wall-flow friction factor, which can be estimated from Eq. 1.12. Note, Re_w represents the wall Reynolds number, which is based on the pipe ID and equivalent inflow velocity per unit wellbore length.

A somewhat different approach led Yuan et al.[11] to obtain the following expression for the total or apparent friction factor, f_T (Moody friction factor), for fluid ingress along the borehole.

$$f_T = a\,Re^{-b} + C_n 2d\varphi\frac{q_i}{q_a}, \quad \dots\dots\dots (1.24)$$

where $a = 10219.5\varphi - 3.25\dfrac{q_i}{q_a} - 8.87\times10^{-4}\varphi^2$

$$+ 5.37\times10^{-2}\varphi - 0.075, \quad \dots\dots (1.25)$$

and $b = \left(-1.24\times10^5\varphi^{-3.075} + 42.4\right)\left(\dfrac{q_i}{q_a}\right)^2$

$$+ 1.577\times10^3\varphi^{-2.63}\frac{q_i}{q_a} - 5\times10^{-4}\varphi^2$$

$$+ 2.31\times10^{-2}\varphi + 0.085 \cdot \quad \dots\dots\dots (1.26)$$

For $(q_i/q_a) < 0.02$, $C_n = 2.3$, and for $(q_i/q_a) > 0.02$, C_n is given by

$$C_n = 4.25\left(\frac{q_i}{q_a}\right)^{-0.099} \quad \dots\dots\dots\dots\dots\dots (1.27)$$

Experiences show that pressure drop in horizontal wells becomes important in high-transmissivity reservoirs, where the pressure drop in the wellbore becomes comparable to that in the formation. When the wellbore pressure drop becomes important, in most cases, the frictional component becomes the dominant mechanism. Chap. 4 discusses two-phase flow in horizontal wells.

Summary

The objective of this introductory chapter is to acquaint the reader with the rudiments of single-phase flow, which forms the backbone for understanding the mechanics of two-phase flow. Here, we attempted to capture some elements of fluid flow through conduits of various complexities, such as annulus and horizontal wells, and when fluid flow is accompanied by heat flow. Subsequent chapters discuss these elements in detail.

Nomenclature

a = parameter defined by Eq. 1.25, dimensionless

A = cross-sectional area for fluid flow, ft^2

A_g, A_l = cross-sectional area available for gas or liquid to flow, ft^2

b = parameter defined by Eq. 1.26, dimensionless

c_e = heat capacity of earth or formation, Btu/(lbm-°F)

c_p = heat capacity of fluid, Btu/(lbm-°F)

C_n = parameter defined by Eq. 1.27, dimensionless

d = pipe or well diameter, in.

d_c, d_t = casing or tubing diameter, in.

D = distance between pipe centers in Eq. 1.20, ft

E = eccentricity factor, dimensionless

f = friction factor, dimensionless

f_o = no-wall friction factor, dimensionless

f_{CA} = friction factor of concentric annulus, dimensionless

f_{ECA} = friction factor of eccentric annulus, dimensionless

f_T = apparent friction factor, dimensionless

F = force, lbm

F_p = friction geometry parameter, dimensionless

g = acceleration due to gravity, ft/sec^2

g_c = conversion factor, 32.17 lbm-ft/lbf-s^2

g_G = geothermal gradient, °F/ft

H = fluid enthalpy, Btu/lbm

k = formation permeability, md

k_e = earth conductivity, Btu/(hr-ft-°F)

K = diameter ratio of annulus to tubing, dimensionless

L_R = relaxation distance parameter, ft^{-1}

p = pressure, psi

(dp/dz) = pressure gradient, psi/ft

$(dp/dz)_A$ = accelerational (kinetic) pressure gradient, psi/ft

$(dp/dz)_F$ = frictional pressure gradient, psi/ft

$(dp/dz)_H$ = static pressure gradient, psi/ft

q_a = average flow rate over incremental length, ft^3/hr

q_i = influx rate from each perforation, ft^3/hr

r_{wb} = wellbore radius, ft

r_{to} = outside tubing radius, ft

Re = Reynolds number [$= dv\rho/\mu$], dimensionless

Re$_g$, Re$_L$ = Reynolds number for the gas ($= \rho_g v_g d/\mu_g$) or liquid phase ($= \rho_L v_L d/\mu_L$), dimensionless

Re$_m$ = Reynolds number for the mixture [$= \rho_m v_m d/\mu_m$], dimensionless

Re$_w$ = wall Reynolds number, dimensionless

t = producing, injecting, or circulation (mud) time, hr

t_D = dimensionless time, $k_e c_e t/\rho_e r_{wb}^2$

T_{ei}, T_e = formation temperature at initial condition or at any radial distance, °F

T_D = dimensionless temperature = $(2\pi k_e)(T_{wb} - T_{ei})/Q$

T_f = fluid temperature, °F

T_{wb} = wellbore fluid temperature, °F

U = overall heat transfer coefficient, Btu/(hr-°F-ft)

v = fluid velocity, ft/hr

w = mass flow rate of fluid, lbm/hr

z = any vertical well depth, ft

Z = gas-law deviation factor, dimensionless

α = wellbore inclination with horizontal, deg

Λ = parameter given by Eq. 1.13, dimensionless

μ = oil viscosity, cp

ε = pipe roughness factor, ft

ϕ = parameter used in Eq. 1.21

φ = perforation density, 1/ft

ρ = density, lbm/ft^3

η = parameter used in Eq. 1.21

Subscripts

c = casing

e = earth or formation

o = oil

t = tubing

to = tubing outside

wb = wellbore

References

1. Cullender, M.H. and Smith, R.V.: "Practical Solution of Gas Flow Equations for Wells and Pipelines With Large Temperature Gradients," *Trans.*, AIME (1956) **207**.

2. Chen, N.H.: "An Explicit Equation for Friction Factor in Pipe," *Ind. Eng. Chem., Fundamentals* (1979) **18**, No. 3, 296.

3. Moody, L.F.: "Friction Factors for Pipe Flow," *Trans.*, ASME (1944) **66**, No. 8, 671.

4. Bird, R.B., Stewart, W.E., and Lightfoot, E.N.: *Transport Phenomena*, John Wiley and Sons, New York City (1973).

5. Gunn, D.J. and Darling, C.W.W.: "Fluid Flow and Energy Losses in Non Circular Conduits," *Trans. Inst. Chem. Eng.* (1963) **41**, 163.

6. Caetano, E.F., Shoham, O., and Brill, J.P.: "Upward Vertical Two-Phase Flow Through an Annulus, Part I: Single-Phase Friction Factor, Taylor Bubble Rise Velocity and Flow Pattern Prediction," *J. Energy Res. Tech.* (March 1992) **114**, 1.

7. Dikken, B.J.: "Pressure Drop in Horizontal Wells and Its Effect on Production Performance," *JPT* (November 1990) 1426.

8. Novy, R.A.: "Pressure Drops in Horizontal Wells: When Can They be Ignored?," *SPERE* (February 1995) 29.

9. Asheim, H., Kolnes, J., and Oudeman, P.: "A Flow Resistance Correlation for Completed Wellbore," *J. Pet. Eng. Sci.* (1992) **8**, 97.

10. Ouyang, L-B., Arbabi, S., and Aziz, K.: "A Single-Phase Wellbore Flow Model for Horizontal, Vertical, and Slanted Wells," *SPEJ* (June 1998) 124.

11. Yuan, H.J., Sarica, C., and Brill, J.P.: "Effect of Perforation Density on Single-Phase Liquid Flow Behavior in Horizontal Wells," *SPEPF* (August 1999) 203.

SI Metric Conversion Factors

Btu	$\times$ 1.055 056	E + 00 = kJ
Btu/lbm	$\times$ 2.326*	E + 03 = J/kg
Btu/(lbm-°F)	$\times$ 4.186 8*	E + 03 = J/(kg·K)
cp	$\times$ 1.0*	E – 03 = Pa s
ft	$\times$ 3.048*	E – 01 = m
ft^2	$\times$ 9.290 304*	E – 02 = m^2
ft^3	$\times$ 2.831 685	E – 02 = m^3
°F	(°F – 32)/1.8	= °C
in.	$\times$ 2.54*	E + 00 = cm
lbf	$\times$ 4.448 222	E + 00 = N
lbm	$\times$ 4.535 924	E – 01 = kg
lbm/ft^3	$\times$ 1.601 846	E + 01 = kg/m^3
lbm/hr	$\times$ 1.259 979	E – 04 = kg/s
psi	$\times$ 6.894 757	E + 00 = kPa

*Conversion factor is exact.

Chapter 2
Multiphase Flow: Introduction

2.1 Introduction

Most installations for petroleum production and testing involve concurrent flow of gas and liquid. A simplified schematic representation of the overall production system is shown in **Fig. 2.1.** The reservoir fluid, entering the wellbore, may contain all three phases (gas, oil, and water), in which case, multiphase flow starts at the perforations. However, gas often enters the wellbore in solution with the oil. Gas comes out as a separate phase, only when fluid moves up enough for the pressure to drop below the bubblepoint pressure, thus leading to gas/liquid, two-phase flow. In a favorable system, the entire fluid mixture may flow freely to the wellhead through a vertical or directional wellbore and then onto the separator through a horizontal or near-horizontal flowline.

Artificial lift is required in low-energy environments and/or when oil production is accompanied by water. When the artificial stimulus is provided by gas injection (gas-lift) through the annulus, the entire tubing production becomes two- or three-phase flow. Similarly, when a sucker-rod or an electrical submersible pump is used for the lift, only liquid is produced through the tubing to sustain high-pump efficiency, while gas is vented through the annulus. Even in this case, a substantial portion of the tubing may experience gas/liquid flow, as well as, three-phase flow. Some production facilities have to contend with the simultaneous flow of solids (sand), liquids (water and oil), and gases (injected and in solution).

Interest in multiphase flow is not restricted to the oil industry. Nuclear, geothermal, and chemical processing plants routinely encounter two-phase flow problems. The diverse interest explains the large number of publications in this area. At the same time, the plethora of publications indicates that the basics of multiphase flow are not completely understood. Often, correlations are published that have no general applicability to any situation other than specific conditions under which those were developed.

One of the reasons multiphase flow is more complicated than single-phase flow is that two or more fluids compete for the available flow area. To model flow behavior, one needs to know how the flow cross section is occupied by each fluid phase. Therefore, understanding physics of multiphase flow demands grasping important concepts, such as flow patterns, in-situ velocity, and volume fractions. In these and subsequent discussions, we focus on systems containing only two phases—gas and liquid. Many of these concepts may be extended to systems experiencing three-phase flow.

2.2 Concepts and Definitions

2.2.1 Flow Pattern. During flow of two or more immiscible fluids, deformable interfaces present complications. Shape and distribution of these interfaces greatly influence flow characteristics. These interfaces tend to be spherical, especially at low relative velocities, owing to surface tension effects. However, at higher relative velocities of the lighter fluid, the bubbles begin to elongate and coalesce, gradually changing into a different flow pattern or flow regime. Thus, bubbly flow, with small bubbles that distribute uniformly across the flow channel, changes to slug flow, with large bubbles that fill the entire channel cross section with slugs of liquid between them. At extremely high-gas rates, all of the gas may flow through the core of the channel, while the liquid flows through the annulus formed by the gas core and pipe wall. This flow pattern is called annular flow because of the dominance of the gas core. Therefore, multiphase flow can be categorized into a number of flow patterns or regimes, whose dynamics differ from each other. The existence of these flow patterns is influenced by many parameters, including fluid velocities, fluid properties, channel geometry, and channel orientation. These flow patterns, their transition from one to another, and their effect on pressure drop will be discussed later in more detail.

2.2.2 Superficial and In-Situ Velocities. Superficial velocity of any phase is the volumetric flow rate of that phase, divided by the total cross-sectional area of the channel. Thus, the superficial liquid velocity, v_{sL}, is given in terms of the volumetric liquid flow rate, q_L, and cross-sectional area, A, of the pipe by

$$v_{sL} = q_L / A \cdot \dots\dots\dots\dots\dots\dots\dots\dots (2.1)$$

Similarly, superficial gas velocity, v_{sg}, is defined in terms of q_g. Note, superficial velocity is a quantity averaged over the flow cross section. Even for single-phase flow, fluid velocity across the channel varies; elements of fluid flowing

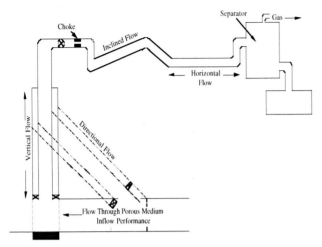

Fig. 2.1—Schematic representation of a production system (from Ref. 1).

close to the wall have much lower velocity than those flowing near the channel center.

As mentioned before, neither phase occupies the entire pipe flow cross section. In other words, the actual velocity of the liquid phase (observe by injecting a colored dye into the channel) will be considerably higher than that given by Eq. 2.1. Because the actual area available for the liquid flow is less than the total area by the extent occupied by the gas, the actual liquid velocity must be higher than its superficial velocity. The actual velocity of any phase is called in-situ velocity and is defined as

$$v_L = q_L / A_L \text{ and } v_g = q_g / A_g, \quad \dots\dots\dots\dots (2.2)$$

where A_g and A_L are cross-sectional areas available for gas and liquid phases to flow, respectively. Obviously, if these are the only two phases flowing, then $A_g + A_L = A$, or $A_L = A - A_g$. Unfortunately, while the pipe cross-sectional area is usually evident, the area (A_g or A_L) in which each phase flows is unknown.

2.2.3 Volume Fraction, Mass Fraction, and Mass Flux.
The relative amount of each phase in the wellbore may be expressed in many ways. We may wish to express the volumetric flow of the gas or liquid phase as a fraction of the total volumetric flow. This volume fraction, calculated from the known flow rates, is different from the in-situ volume fraction discussed in Sec. 2.2.4. The gas volume fraction, C_g, can be calculated from superficial phase velocities as

$$C_g = q_g / (q_g + q_L) = v_{sg} / v_m . \quad \dots\dots\dots\dots (2.3)$$

Similarly, we can define flowing gas mass fraction, x, (called quality in steam/water flow) in terms of the mass flow rates, w_g and w_L, as

$$x = \frac{w_g}{w_g + w_l} = \frac{q_g \rho_g}{q_g \rho_g + q_L \rho_L} = \frac{v_{sg} \rho_g}{v_{sg} \rho_g + v_{sL} \rho_L} . \quad \dots (2.4)$$

Of course, volume and mass fraction for the liquid phase can be described similarly.

Mass flux, G, is the mass flow rate per unit area and is also known as mass velocity. Therefore, for the two-phase mixture, the mixture mass flux, G_m, is given by

$$G_m = \frac{w_L + w_g}{A} = \frac{\rho_L v_{sL} + \rho_g v_{sg}}{A} . \quad \dots\dots\dots\dots (2.5)$$

Similarly, for the liquid and gas phases,

$$G_L = \frac{w_L}{A} = \frac{(1-x)w_m}{A} = (1-x)G_m \text{ and } G_g = xG_m .$$
$$\dots\dots\dots\dots\dots\dots (2.6)$$

2.2.4 Slip, Gas-Volume Fraction, and Liquid Holdup.
During two-phase flow, the actual or in-situ velocities of the phases are unknown, while the superficial velocities, v_{sg} and v_{sL}, are usually evident. In addition, the in-situ velocity of the gas phase is different from that of the liquid phase, even when the volumetric flow rates of the phases are equal. Indeed, in upflow, the lighter gas phase moves faster than the liquid phase, especially in vertical and near-vertical systems. This difference in in-situ velocities is called slip and is defined as

$$v_s = S = v_g - v_L . \quad \dots\dots\dots\dots\dots\dots (2.7)$$

We can relate in-situ velocity to superficial velocity by

$$v_g = q_g / A_g = \frac{q_g}{A} \frac{A}{A_g} . \quad \dots\dots\dots\dots\dots (2.8)$$

Gas in-situ volume fraction (also known as void fraction, f_g) is defined as the fraction of the total cross-sectional area through which gas flows.

$$f_g = A_g / A \cdot \quad \dots\dots\dots\dots\dots\dots\dots (2.9)$$

By combining Eqs. 2.8 and 2.9, we get

$$v_g = \frac{v_{sg}}{f_g} \quad \dots\dots\dots\dots\dots\dots\dots (2.10)$$

Because cross-sectional area is volume per unit length, f_g may be defined as the fraction of the channel volume occupied by the gas. Similarly, we can define a liquid (or the heavier phase) in-situ volume fraction, f_L, as

$$f_L = A_L / A = (A - A_g) / A,$$
$$v_L = v_{sL} / (A_L / A) = v_{sL} / f_L, \quad \dots\dots\dots\dots (2.11)$$

and $f_L = 1 - f_g \cdot \quad \dots\dots\dots\dots\dots\dots (2.12)$

Fig. 2.2 depicts the in-situ volumetric fractions of the two phases in a pipe's cross-sectional area of flow. The figure attempts to illustrate the relative portions of the two phases upon segregation, if a sample is drawn from a given portion of the pipe. The liquid in-situ velocity is generally less than

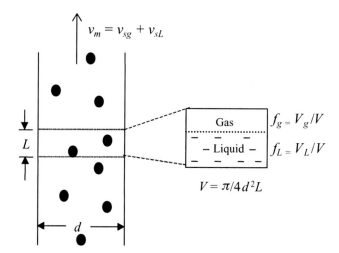

$v_m = v_{sg} + v_{sL}$

$V = \pi/4\, d^2 L$

$f_g = V_g/V$

$f_L = V_L/V$

Fig. 2.2—Schematic of in-situ gas and liquid volume fractions in two-phase flow.

that of the gas phase, which means the liquid is held up. This is why f_L is known as the liquid holdup in the petroleum industry. However, gas is not held up during two-phase flow, and the term gas holdup is a misnomer.

Note, if either slip velocity or in-situ volume fraction is known, the other can be calculated from superficial velocities. Thus,

$$v_s = v_g - v_L = \frac{v_{sg}}{1 - f_L} - \frac{v_{sL}}{f_L} \quad \ldots \ldots \ldots \ldots \ldots (2.13)$$

There are other ways of expressing the slip (or void fraction) phenomenon, such as holdup ratio. However, these definitions are no longer widely used; therefore, they will not be discussed in this text.

2.3 Method of Analysis

The analysis of two-phase flow closely follows the well-established method for single-phase flow. Eq. 1.5, derived for the single-phase flow, applies to two-phase systems with appropriate definition for average properties for the mixture,

$$(dp/dz) = (dp/dz)_F + (dp/dz)_H + (dp/dz)_A \cdot$$
$$\quad \ldots \ldots \ldots \ldots \ldots \ldots \quad (1.5)$$

$$-(dp/dz)_F = \frac{f_m v_m^2 \rho_m}{2 g_c d}, \quad \ldots \ldots \ldots \ldots \ldots (2.14)$$

$$-(dp/dz)_H = \rho_m g \sin\alpha / g_c, \quad \ldots \ldots \ldots \ldots (2.15)$$

and $-(dp/dz)_A = \rho_m v_m (dv_m/dz)/g_c \cdot \quad \ldots \ldots \ldots (2.16)$

Therefore,

$$-\frac{dp}{dz} = \frac{f_m v_m^2 \rho_m}{2 g_c d} + \frac{g \sin\alpha}{g_c}\rho_m + \frac{\rho_m v_m}{g_c}\frac{dv_m}{dz} \cdot \quad \ldots \ldots (2.17)$$

The symbol, f, is widely used for friction factor by engineers of all disciplines. We use the same symbol, subscripted

with m (f_m), to represent the Moody friction factor for the mixture in Eqs. 2.14 and 2.17 and in subsequent parts of this book. When viewed in the appropriate context, there should be no confusion with the usage of f for friction and f_L and f_g for in-situ volume fraction of the phases.

By definition, mixture density is the mass of gas and liquid in a unit volume of the mixture. Of course, in a cubic foot of the mixture, there is f_L ft³ of liquid and $(1-f_L)$ ft³ of gas. Therefore, in-situ density of the two-phase mixture, ρ_m, is based upon the in-situ volume fraction of each phase and is given by

$$\rho_m = f_L \rho_L + (1 - f_L)\rho_g \cdot \quad \ldots \ldots \ldots \ldots \ldots (2.18)$$

Estimating density (or liquid holdup) and friction factor for the fluid mixture becomes complicated for two-phase flow. Two different approaches, generalized and flow-pattern based, may be taken to express frictional, accelerational, and potential pressure gradient during multiphase flow. The simpler of the two—the generalized approach—attempts to develop methods for computing pressure drop and liquid holdup that will be applicable to all types of flow geometry and patterns. Within the generalized approach, two types of flow models can be used—homogeneous flow and separated flow.

The homogeneous flow model is the simplest. The model assumes that the multiphase mixture behaves much like a homogeneous single-phase fluid, with property values that are some type of average of the constituent phases. Once one decides the kind of averaging procedure to use (e.g., mass- or volume-weighted average) the computation problem becomes identical to that of a single-phase system. Note, the assumption of homogeneity presupposes a condition of no slip; that is, all the phases move with the same in-situ velocity. Consequently, in-situ liquid fraction or liquid holdup, f_L, is the same as the input fraction, C_L.

In contrast, the separated flow model recognizes that the phases are segregated and that they move with unequal velocities. Therefore, the slip between the phases (or liquid holdup) needs to be known in addition to the frictional interaction of the phases with the wall and among themselves. In the simpler versions of the separated flow model, the frictional interactions among the phases are ignored. Consequently, even for the simplest model in this category, empirical correlations for computing liquid holdup and wall shear are needed, unlike the homogeneous model, where only wall shear is required.

In the flow-pattern-based approach, an attempt is made to develop a mathematical model consistent with the observed physical phenomena for each flow regime. While modeling, only the most dominant processes are recognized, and unimportant effects, which do not add significantly to the solution accuracy, are neglected. As flow patterns are somewhat different for horizontal, vertical, and inclined flows, pipe orientations are usually treated separately. Various flow patterns arise because of different hydrodynamic conditions. The consensus is that this approach leads to the development of accurate working equations, which are much more suitable for extrapolation and interpolation than the generalized approach. However, this method requires determining all relevant flow patterns beforehand. In most oil industry applications, the flow-pattern visualization is either impossible or uncertain; therefore, the pattern must be inferred based upon measured data, thereby introducing a possible source of error. A number of empirical or semitheoretical correlations or maps are available for flow pattern delineation. Much progress has been made recently to model flow-pattern transition.

To summarize, the homogeneous model requiring the input of only one entity (the wall friction) is the simplest of all models and yields reasonable estimates of pressure drop under favorable conditions. However, the model is unrealistic for vertical and near-vertical flow of gas/liquid mixtures. The separated flow model, requiring estimates of friction and liquid holdup, is more sophisticated and usually more accurate than the homogeneous model. This model, however, is more complex and time-consuming from a computational standpoint than the homogeneous model. The flow-pattern approach is the most sophisticated of all models and is generally recognized as the most accurate method. The method requires estimating flow pattern, wall friction, and liquid holdup. This chapter discusses the homogeneous and the separated flow models. A detailed exposition of the flow-pattern-based approach will be given in Chaps. 3 and 4.

2.4 Homogeneous Models

As the name implies, this model assumes fluids in the system to be perfectly mixed, forming a homogeneous mixture with no slip between the phases. The no-slip assumption treats the two-phase mixture essentially as a single-phase fluid. In general, earlier attempts to compute pressure loss in wellbores (e.g., Poettmann and Carpenter[2]) used this simplifying assumption to estimate mixture density and friction factor.

Because the model assumes no slip between the phases, $v_s = 0$, and Eq. 2.12 yields

$$\frac{v_{sg}}{v_{sL}} = \frac{1 - f_L}{f_L}. \quad\dots\dots\dots\dots\dots\dots\dots (2.19)$$

Adding one to both sides, we get $v_m/v_{sL} = 1/f_L$. Therefore, the homogeneous model allows us to compute liquid holdup from

$$f_L = \frac{q_L}{q_g + q_L} = \frac{v_{sL}}{v_m} = C_L. \quad\dots\dots\dots\dots (2.20)$$

Similarly,

$$f_g = \frac{q_g}{q_g + q_L} = \frac{v_{sg}}{v_m} = C_g. \quad\dots\dots\dots\dots (2.21)$$

The mixture density, ρ_m, can be computed from Eq. 2.18, and f_L and f_g, using Eqs. 2.20 and 2.21, respectively. Those equations, in turn, allow us to express the mixture density in terms of gas mass-fraction and the density of the individual phases by

$$\frac{1}{\rho_m} = \frac{x}{\rho_g} + \frac{1-x}{\rho_l}. \quad\dots\dots\dots\dots\dots\dots (2.22)$$

With known mixture density, an expression for mixture friction factor is all that is needed to compute pressure drop in two-phase flow. Poettmann and Carpenter,[2] in their classical work published in 1945, presented a graph of friction factor vs. pseudo-Reynolds number, defined as $dv_m\rho_m$. They developed the friction-factor chart based on field data, collected from 49 vertical wells. During formulation, they subtracted the static head, calculated with Eq. 2.15 from the measured total pressure drop and attributed the rest to the frictional head. Using Eq. 2.14, they then calculated friction factor, which, in turn, was correlated to the pseudo-Reynolds number. The exclusion of fluid viscosity from friction-factor correlation makes this method theoretically deficient, leading to unreliable pressure-drop estimation. For instance, data gathered by Baxendell and Thomas[3] deviates significantly from the Poettmann-Carpenter correlation. Fancher and Brown[4] modified the Poettmann-Carpenter correlation to account for the effect of gas/liquid ratio on mixture friction factor, which was evident from the extensive data they gathered from a 8,000-ft well. Their data indicate a decrease in f_m with an increase in the gas/liquid ratio (GLR). Hagedorn and Brown[5] also noted a similar trend in f_m with GLR.

The effect of GLR and liquid viscosity on two-phase friction factor is explained by noting that the gas has much lower viscosity than the liquid. Thus, the actual mixture viscosity decreases with increasing GLR, especially when the liquid is highly viscous crude. Consequently, the actual (not the pseudo) Reynolds number of the mixture increases with an increase in the GLR, accounting for the lower value of f_m. Therefore, a two-phase average mixture viscosity is needed to correlate the two-phase friction factor properly. A number of researchers have defined such mixture viscosity using various averaging approaches. Definitions proposed by Cicchiti et al.,[6] Dukler et al.,[7] and McAdams et al.[8] are presented.

$$\mu_m = x\mu_g + (1-x)\mu_L \text{ (Cicchitti)}, \quad\dots\dots\dots (2.23)$$

$$\mu_m = \rho_m \left[\frac{x\mu_g}{\rho_g} + \frac{(1-x)\mu_L}{\rho_L} \right] \text{ (Dukler)}, \quad\dots\dots (2.24)$$

and $\dfrac{1}{\mu_m} = \dfrac{x}{\mu_g} + \dfrac{(1-x)}{\mu_L}$ (McAdams) $\dots\dots\dots (2.25)$

Any of the three methods presented in Eqs. 2.23–2.25 will work better than the Poettmann and Carpenter[2] approach. We recommend the Cicchitti[6] correlation (Eq. 2.23) because of its simplicity.

Apart from the problem of defining a proper two-phase viscosity or a two-phase Reynolds number, the homogeneous model also suffers from the unrealistic assumption regarding slip and liquid holdup. As stated earlier, the no-slip assumption for vertical and near-vertical systems can lead to significant underestimation of the liquid holdup because the in-situ velocity of the liquid phase is much lower than that of the gas phase. This fact implies that the actual liquid holdup, f_L, is higher than the input volume fraction, C_L, of the liquid phase. Therefore, the actual static head is higher than that when calculated using the homogeneous model. The Poettmann-

Carpenter[2] and related correlations were developed using data from vertical wells. They computed static head using the homogeneous model, leading to its underestimation. Therefore, their friction-factor correlation, obtained by subtracting these low-static-head values from the total pressure drop, was too high. In other words, these correlations compensate one error by the other; therefore, caution should be taken when contemplating these applications.

2.5 Separated Flow Models

Unlike the homogeneous models, the separated flow model makes a more realistic assumption in that the two phases are segregated and flow at different velocities. As with the homogeneous model, Eq. 2.13 gives the density of the mixture, but liquid holdup, f_L, cannot be assumed to be given by Eq. 2.14 and must be estimated. The estimation of the two important parameters (f_L and Moody friction factor, f_m) has led to the development of many correlations. Three useful correlations are discussed in this section.

2.5.1 Lockhart-Martinelli Correlation.

In the Lockhart-Martinelli correlation[9], the frictional component of the pressure gradient is expressed in terms of a two-phase friction multiplier, ϕ_L^2, and the single-phase (generally liquid phase) frictional pressure gradient, which will be obtained if that (liquid) phase was flowing alone in the channel. In other words,

$$-\left(\frac{dp}{dz}\right)_F = -\left[\left(\frac{dp}{dz}\right)_F\right]_L \phi_L^2 = \frac{f_L \rho_L v_{sL}^2}{2g_c d}\phi_L^2 \cdot \quad \dots \dots (2.26)$$

One may use a gas-phase friction multiplier, ϕ_g^2, with a gas-phase frictional pressure gradient, instead of ϕ_L^2. Note, in Eq. 2.24, the term, $\rho_L v_{sL}^2$, can be replaced by $G_m^2(1-x)^2/\rho_L$ or (G_L^2/ρ_L).

Calculating frictional pressure gradient using Eq. 2.26, requires estimating the two-phase friction multiplier, ϕ_L^2. In addition, liquid holdup estimates are needed to calculate the

static head. In the 1940's, Lockhart, Martinelli, and their coworkers[9-12] proposed a generalized method to compute the values of the two-phase friction multiplier and liquid holdup for isothermal two-component flow. They defined a parameter, X^2, as the ratio of liquid-phase to gas-phase friction pressure drop given by

$$X^2 = \left[\left(\frac{dp}{dz}\right)_F\right]_L \Bigg/ \left[\left(\frac{dp}{dz}\right)_F\right]_g , \quad \dots \dots \dots (2.27)$$

and correlated ϕ_L and ϕ_g as unique functions of X. When both phases are flowing in a turbulent manner, which is often the case in most wells, a simple expression for the parameter, X, may be derived by writing the single-phase frictional-pressure gradients and using the Blasius equation.

$$X^2 = \left(\frac{1-x}{x}\right)^{1.8}\frac{\rho_g}{\rho_L}\left(\frac{\mu_L}{\mu_g}\right)^{0.2} . \quad \dots \dots \dots (2.28)$$

Lockhart and Martinelli[9] expressed their findings as four distinct curves for ϕ_L vs. X, depending on the viscous (laminar) or turbulent nature of the gas and liquid flows, and a single curve for f_L vs. X. These curves are reproduced in **Fig. 2.3**, where the first subscript of ϕ represents the turbulent or viscous nature of the liquid phase, while the second one denotes the same for the gas phase. For example, ϕ_{tt} represents turbulent liquid/turbulent gas flow ($\text{Re}_L = Gd(1-x)/\mu_L > 1{,}000$ indicates turbulent liquid flow), while ϕ_{vt} represents viscous (laminar, $\text{Re}_L < 1{,}000$) liquid-turbulent gas flow. These curves can be represented by Eq. 2.28,

$$\phi_L^2 = 1 + \frac{C}{X} + \frac{1}{X^2} , \quad \dots \dots \dots (2.29)$$

where the value of C varies; $C_{tt}=20$, $C_{vt}=12$, $C_{tv}=10$ and $C_{vv}=5$. Their void-fraction correlation may be represented at low pressures and low values of the Lockhart-Martinelli parameter, X ($X<10$), by

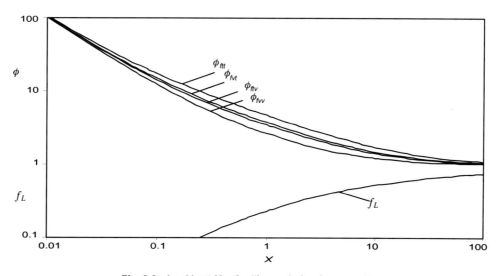

Fig. 2.3—Lockhart-Martinelli correlation for ϕ_L and f_L.

$$f_L = 1 - f_g = 1 - \left(1 + X^{0.8}\right)^2 . \quad \ldots\ldots\ldots\ldots (2.30)$$

Gregory[14,15] shows that the liquid holdup, computed by the Lockhart-Martinelli correlation, agrees with his data quite well.

The Lockhart-Martinelli correlation is specifically derived for horizontal flow without significant acceleration. Its application to other situations, where frictional gradient is comparatively small (e.g., vertical systems), can lead to errors. One aspect of the Lockhart-Martinelli correlation is that it skirts the flow-pattern issue. This simplification has the advantage of avoiding the flow-pattern discontinuities at the transition boundaries, although at a cost of model performance. Another well-known deficiency of the model is its unsatisfactory representation of the effects of system variables, in particular, flow rate. The effect of flow rate upon the curves of ϕ_L vs. X, originally not considered in the Lockhart-Martinelli correlation, was reported by some investigators.[13,16]

The extensive comparison, made by Idsinga et al.[17] against a large data bank, shows that the Lockhart-Martinelli correlation is quite reliable in computing pressure drop in channels of various orientations, if modification for mass effect is made. Even the unmodified correlation is preferable to the homogeneous model in vertical and near-vertical systems.

2.5.2 Duns and Ros Correlation. In the early 1960's, Ros[18] and Duns and Ros[19] developed an empirical correlation from a large set of laboratory data. Their method does not strictly fall in the generalized correlation category because they define four different flow regimes and assign individual correlations for slip between the phases for each regime. However, the flow regimes they defined are quite different from those that are understood today.

They defined Region I as the flow regime where the liquid is the continuous phase and, therefore, includes bubble, froth (presumably dispersed bubbly), plug, and some slug flow. Region II covers situations when neither phase is continuous and, hence, includes the rest of the slug and froth flows, as well as heading or pulsating flow. When gas becomes the continuous phase, as in annular flow, it is termed Region III. Duns and Ros also included a transition region (probably corresponding to churn flow) between Region II and Region III.

The Duns and Ros flow regime map is based on the gas velocity number, $v_{gd} = v_{sg}(\rho_L/g\sigma)^{1/4}$, the liquid velocity number, $v_{Ld} = v_{gd}(v_{sL}/v_{sg})$ and the pipe diameter number, $N_d = d(\rho_L g/\sigma)^{1/2}$. **Table 2.1** shows the transition criteria for the various regions. Note, the gas and liquid velocity numbers, v_{gd} and v_{Ld}, are phase superficial velocities made dimensionless by dividing with the bubble-rise velocity, v_∞, because v_∞ is proportional to $(g\sigma/\rho_L)^{1/4}$.

Duns and Ros defined a slip-velocity number, $N_s = S(\rho_L/g\sigma)^{1/4}$, to estimate liquid holdup in any region. Once N_s and, hence, the slip are determined, the liquid holdup can be calculated. The correlation for N_S, however, is different in each region. For example, for Region I

TABLE 2.1—TRANSITION BOUNDARIES OF THE DUNS-ROS MODEL

Region	Limit	Parameters
I	$v_{gd} < L_1 + L_2 v_{Ld}$	L_1 and L_2 are functions of pipe diameter number, $N_d = d(r_L g/S)^{1/2}$
II	$v_{gd} > L_1 + L_2 v_{Ld}$ & $v_{gd} < L_S$	$L_S = 50 + 36 v_{Ld}$
Transition	$L_M > v_{gd} > L_S$	$L_M = 75 + 84 v_{Ld}^{3/4}$
III	$v_{gd} > L_M$	

$$N_s = F_1 + F_2 v_{Ld} + F_{3'}\left[\frac{N_s}{1 + N_s}\right]^2 ,$$

$$\text{where } F_{3'} = F_3 - \frac{F_4}{N_d} . \quad \ldots\ldots\ldots\ldots\ldots (2.31)$$

The factors F_1, F_2, F_3, and F_4 are given as functions of the liquid viscosity number, $N_L = \mu_L(g/\rho_L S^3)^{1/4}$. The frictional gradient is calculated in the following manner.

$$-\left(\frac{dp}{dz}\right)_F = \frac{2f_m v_{sg}^2 \rho_g}{g_c d}\left[1 + \frac{v_{sL}}{v_{sg}}\right] . \quad \ldots\ldots\ldots (2.32)$$

The two-phase friction factor, f_m, is estimated using the expression

$$f_m = f_1 f_2 / f_3 , \quad \ldots\ldots\ldots\ldots\ldots (2.33)$$

where f_1 is the conventional single-phase friction factor based upon Reynolds number, calculated from the superficial liquid velocity and liquid properties. The friction factor-Reynolds number relationship is slightly modified in the transition range, $700 < Re_{sL} < 3,000$. The factors f_2 and f_3 are intended to correct for the effect of holdup. The factor f_2 is correlated in terms of f_L, v_{sg}/v_{sL}, and the diameter number, N_d. The factor f_3 is a secondary correction factor for high viscosity ($\mu_L/\rho_L > 50$ centistoke) liquids and is given by

$$f_3 = 1 + f_1\sqrt{\frac{v_{sg}}{50 v_{sL}}} . \quad \ldots\ldots\ldots\ldots\ldots (2.34)$$

For Region II, Duns and Ros proposed the correlation for the slip velocity number as

$$N_s = \left(1 + F_5\right)\frac{v_{gd}^{0.982} + F_{6'}}{\left(1 + F_7 v_{Ld}\right)^2},$$

$$\text{where } F_{6'} = 0.029 N_d + F_6 . \quad \ldots\ldots\ldots\ldots (2.35)$$

The factors F_5, F_6, and F_7 are functions of the liquid viscosity number, N_L. The frictional pressure drop in Region II is calculated using an approach similar to that used in Region I. The accelerational pressure loss is neglected for both Regions I and II.

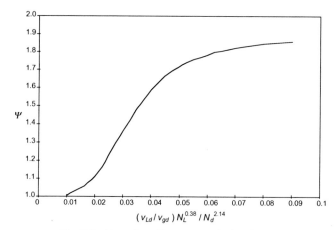

Fig. 2.4—Hagedorn-Brown correlation for ψ.

For the Transition Region, Duns and Ros suggested that the average fluid density and the frictional gradient be calculated by linear interpolation between Region II and Region III boundaries with respect to v_{gd}. Thus,

$$\rho_m = \frac{L_M - v_{gd}}{L_M - L_S}(\rho_m)_{II} + \frac{v_{gd} - L_S}{L_M - L_S}(\rho_m)_{III}. \quad \ldots \ldots \ldots (2.36)$$

A similar expression can be written for the frictional pressure gradient.

For Region III, slip is assumed to be zero and liquid holdup is estimated from $f_L = v_{sL}/v_m$. The frictional loss is calculated from

$$-\left(\frac{dp}{dz}\right)_F = \frac{f_m v_g^2 \rho_g}{2 g_c d}, \quad \ldots \ldots \ldots \ldots \ldots \ldots (2.37)$$

where the friction factor, f_m, is calculated from the total Reynolds number, $d v_m \rho_L / \mu_L$, and a roughness factor, ε/d. Duns and Ros gave the correlation for the roughness factor as

$$\frac{\varepsilon}{d} = \frac{34\sigma}{\rho_g v_g^2 d}, \text{ if } N_w < 0.005,$$

$$\text{and } \frac{\varepsilon}{d} = 174 \frac{\sigma N_w^{0.302}}{\rho_g v_g^2 d}, \text{ if } N_w > 0.005,$$

$$\text{where } N_w = 4.52 \times 10^{-7} \left(\frac{v_g \mu_L}{\sigma}\right)^2 \left(\frac{\rho_g}{\rho_L}\right). \quad \ldots \ldots \ldots (2.38)$$

Duns and Ros limit the value of ε/d to be no smaller than 0.001 and no greater than 0.50. Friction factor is estimated from the ε/d value calculated from Eq. 2.37 and using a standard friction-factor chart for single-phase flow, as shown in Chap. 1. When the calculated ε/d is outside the limits, the limiting value is used.

2.5.3 Hagedorn and Brown Method. Hagedorn and Brown[5,1] recognized that for vertical and near-vertical systems, the static-head loss accounts for most of the total pressure drop and that any reasonable estimate of the frictional

component would suffice, as long as the liquid holdup is estimated accurately. They assumed that the friction factor-Reynolds number relationship for two-phase flow is the same as for single-phase flow and arbitrarily defined two-phase viscosity as

$$\mu_m = \mu_L^{f_L} \times \mu_g^{f_g}, \quad \ldots \ldots \ldots \ldots \ldots \ldots \ldots (2.39)$$

where f_L and f_g are liquid holdup and gas-volume fraction, respectively.

Hagedorn and Brown[5] developed their correlation for effective liquid holdup using data obtained from a 1,500-ft vertical experimental well that used air as the gas phase and four different liquids. They subtracted the frictional component, calculated it with Eq. 2.14 in combination with Eq. 2.38, and attributed the rest to the static head. The effective liquid holdup, f_L, so calculated, was then related to the dimensionless numbers proposed by Duns and Ross[19] (v_{Ld}, v_{gd}, N_d, and N_L) and a pressure ratio, p/p_a.

The Hagedorn and Brown[5] correlation for liquid holdup is shown in **Fig. 2.4** in terms of the correlating coefficients ψ, C, and various dimensionless numbers. Variation of ψ with the dimensionless number is shown in **Fig. 2.5** and that of C with N_L in **Fig. 2.6**.

Over the years, modifications have been proposed to the original Hagedorn and Brown correlation to overcome some of its deficiencies. The most serious of these problems is that the correlation sometimes estimates lower liquid holdup (f_L), than the no-slip holdup value (C_L). This suggests liquid slips past the gas phase—a physical impossibility during two-phase upflow. In those situations, when the computed f_L is greater than C_L, the procedure should be set to $f_L = C_L = v_{sL}/v_m$. Another recommendation is to use the Orkiszewski[20] correlation for bubbly flow in that region. A third proposal is to use the Duns and Ros method to compute pressure gradient, but only if Regime III is prevalent, to account for accelerational effects.

Example 2.1. A 5,151-ft vertical well produces 23° API dry oil at 1,140 STB/D through a 2.99-in. ID tubing. The gas/oil ratio (GOR) is 450 scf/STB, and the gas gravity is 0.80. The following property values and computed fluid parameters, which are available at the wellhead where pressure is 505 psig, are:

$v_{sL} = 1.601$ ft/sec
$v_{sg} = 2.824$ ft/sec
$\rho_L = 55.042$ lbm/ft³
$\rho_g = 2.19$ lbm/ft³
$\mu_L = 13.09$ cp
$\mu_g = 0.019$ cp
$\sigma = 31.6$ dynes/cm $= 0.0696$ lbm/sec²

Calculate the pressure gradient at this point.

The Hagedorn-Brown Correlation.

$v_{Ld} = v_{sL}(\rho_L/g\sigma)^{0.25} = 1.601(55.042/32.2 \times 0.0696)^{0.25} = 3.56.$

$v_{gd} = v_{sg}(\rho_L/g\sigma)^{0.25} = 2.824(55.042/32.2 \times 0.0696)^{0.25} = 6.29.$

$N_d = d(g\rho_L/\sigma_L)^{0.5} = (0.25)(55.042 \times 32.2/0.0696)^{0.5} = 39.75.$

$N_L = 0.15726\mu_L(1/\rho_L\sigma_L{}^3)^{0.25} = 0.15726\times13.693$
$\times\{1/(55.042\times31.6^3)\}^{0.25} = 0.0594.$

$v_{gd}N_L{}^{0.38}/N_d{}^{2.14} = 6.29\times0.0594^{0.38}/39.75^{2.14} = 8.12\times10^{-4}.$
Hence, from Fig. 2.4, $\psi = 1.$

$C_{NL}=\exp\{-4.895-1.0775\ln(N_L)-0.80822[\ln(N_L)^2]-0.1597$
$\ln(N_L)^3-0.01019\ln(N_L)^4\}=\exp\{-4.895-1.0775\ln(0.0594)$
$-0.80822[\ln(0.0594)]^2-0.1597\ln(0.0594)^3-0.01019$
$\ln(0.0594)^4\}=0.0048.$

$N_f=(v_{Ld}/v_{gd}{}^{0.575})(p/14.65)^{0.1}\,C_{NL}(10^6/N_d)= (3.56/6.29^{0.575})$
$(519.7/14.65)^{0.1}\,0.0048(10^6/39.75)=211.4.$

$f_L = \psi\{\exp(-3.6372)+0.8813(\ln N_f)-0.1335(\ln N_f)^2$
$+0.018534(\ln N_f)^3-0.001066(\ln N_f)^4\}=0.46.$

$\mu_m=(\mu_L)^{fL}\times\mu_g{}^{fg}=(13.693)^{0.46}\times0.019^{0.54}=0.388\text{ cp}.$

$q_g=v_{sg}A=(2.824)\{(3.1416/4)\times0.25^2\}=0.1377\text{ ft}^3/\text{sec}.$

$q_L=v_{sL}A=(1.601)\{(3.1416/4)\times0.25^2\}=0.078\text{ ft}^3/\text{sec}.$

$C_L=q_L/(q_L+q_g)=0.362.$

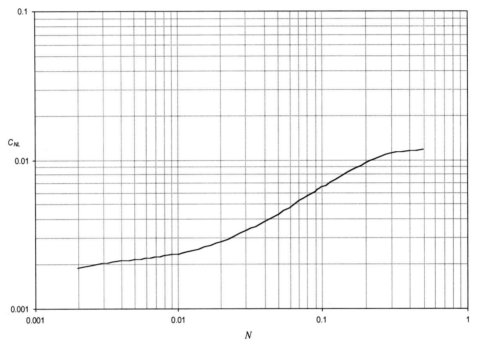

Fig. 2.5—Hagedorn-Brown correlation for C_{NL}.

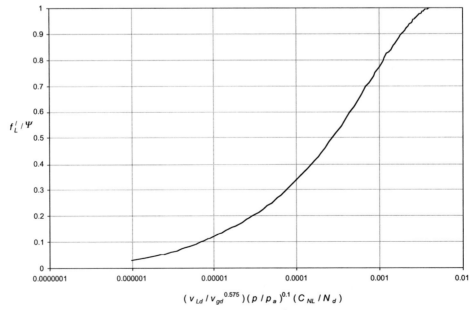

Fig. 2.6—Hagedorn-Brown correlation for f'_L/ψ.

FLUID FLOW AND HEAT TRANSFER IN WELLBORES

$\rho_n = \rho_L C_L + (1-C_L)\rho_g = 55.042(0.362) + (1-0.362)2.19 = 21.3$ lbm/ft³.

$v_m = v_{sL} + v_{sg} = 4.425$ ft/sec.

$\text{Re} = \rho_n v_m d/\mu_m = 1,488(28.07)(3.43)(0.25)/(0.388) = 90,024.$

$f = 0.184(\text{Re})^{-0.2} = 0.184 (90,024)0.25 = 0.019$

$\rho_s = \rho_L f_L + (1-f_L)\rho_g = 55.042(0.46) + (1-0.46)2.19$
$= 26.5$ lbm/ft³.

$-(dp/dz)_F = f\rho_n^2 v_m^2/(2\rho_s g_c d)$
$= 0.019 \times 21.3^2 \times 4.42^2/(2 \times 26.5 \times 32.174 \times 0.25)$
$= 0.394$ psf/ft.

$-(dp/dz)_H = \rho_s g/g_c = 26.42$ psf/ft.

$-dp/dz = 0.394 + 26.42 = 26.82$ psf/ft $= 0.1862$ psi/ft total pressure gradient at wellhead.

The Lockhart-Martinelli Correlation.

$G_m = v_{sg}\rho_g + v_{sL}\rho_L = 94.32$ lbm/ft²sec.

$x = (v_{sg}\rho_g)/G_m = 0.066.$

$X^2 = \{(1-x)/x]^{1.8}(\rho_g/\rho_L)(\mu_L/\mu_g)^{0.2}\} = \{(1-0.066)/0.066]^{1.8}$
$(2.19/55.042)(13.69/0.019)^{0.2}\} = 17.52.$

$f_g = (1+X^{0.8})^{-0.378} = 0.584.$

$v_m = x(v_{sg}/f_g) + (1-x)(v_{sL}/f_L) = 0.066\{(2.824/0.584)$
$+(1-0.066)(1.60/(1-0.584))\} = 3.9$ ft/sec.

$\rho_m = \rho_g f_g + f_L\rho_L = 24.15$ lbm/ft³ and $C_{tt} = 20.$

$\phi_L^2 = 1 + C/X + 1/X^2 = 5.835.$

$\text{Re}_L = (dv_{sL}\rho_L/\mu_L) = 1,488(0.25 \times 55.04 \times 1.605/13.09) = 2,385.$

$f_L = 0.32(\text{Re})^{-0.25} = 0.0454.$

$-(dp/dz)_F = f_L(\rho_g f_g G_m)^2(1-x)^2\phi_L^2/(2\rho_L g_c d) = 2.364$ psf/ft
$= 0.0164$ psi/ft.

$-(dp/dz)_H = (\rho_g f_g + \rho_L f_L)g/g_c = 24.2$ psf/ft $= 0.1677$ psi/ft.

$-dp/dz = 0.0164 + 0.1677 = 0.1840$ psi/ft total pressure gradient at wellhead.

The Homogeneous Model.

$\mu_m = \mu_L(1-x) + \mu_g x = 13.69(1-0.066) + 0.019(0.066) = 12.8$ cp.

$1/\rho_m = (1-x)/\rho_L + x/\rho_g = (0.934/55.042) + (0.066/2.19)$
$= 0.0472$ ft³/lbm

$\rho_m = 21.17$ lbm/ft³.

$\text{Re}_m = G_m d/\mu_m = 94.32(0.25)/(12.6 \times 0.000672) = 2,732.$

$f_m = 0.32(\text{Re})^{-0.25} = 0.0442.$

$-(dp/dz)_F = f_m G_m^2/(2\rho_m g_c d) = 1.158$ psf/ft $= 0.008$ psi/ft.

$-(dp/dz)_H = \rho_m g/g_c = 21.17$ psf/ft $= 0.1470$ psi/ft.

$-dp/dz = 0.1552$ psi/ft total pressure gradient at wellhead.

Although the estimated pressure gradient at the wellhead is about the same for all three methods, **Fig. 2.7** shows that

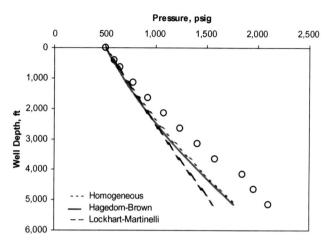

Fig. 2.7—Performance comparison of three correlations.

the Lockhart-Martinelli (LM) method becomes unreliable with increasing depth. Indeed, this empirical method, developed from steam/water and air/water data, estimates lower liquid holdup near the bottomhole than is estimated using the homogeneous model. In other words, the LM method suggests that the oil "slips" past gas in high-pressure, gas/oil vertical systems, clearly violating basic physical principles. Our experience with data from other sources reinforces that the LM method is unreliable for oil wells. We introduced the LM method because we make appropriate reference in Chap. 4.

By contrast, the homogeneous model provides a reasonable agreement with field data, yielding BHP of 1,770 psig, compared to the measured value of 2,105 psig. This underestimation of pressure loss by the homogeneous model is expected because the model neglects gas slippage resulting in an underestimation of mixture density. For a low-rate well, performance of the homogeneous model tends to be even poorer than this example indicates. Nonetheless, the usefulness of this model is that it provides a lower limit of BHP estimation and that computations can be done very easily to check the validity of other complex models, discussed in Chap. 3.

Here, the Hagedorn-Brown (H-B) correlation uncharacteristically underestimates the BHP by about 15%. Experience of most researchers with the H-B correlation is generally much better than this example illustrates. Note that available proprietary commercial software packages quite often apply modifications to the "standard" H-B correlation, which are usually not transparent to the user. Here, we used the modified form of the H-B correlation discussed in the text.

Summary

This chapter provides ingredients for understanding the fundamentals of two-phase flow. For instance, concepts of superficial and in-situ velocities, in-situ and input volume fractions, and slip between phases were explored. To model flow behavior, we discussed three approaches—homogeneous, separated flow, and flow-pattern-based. Here, we addressed the first two types. Chaps. 3 and 4 will discuss the modern flow-pattern-based approach.

Among the correlations presented, we strongly recommend the Hagedorn-Brown method with the modifications mentioned. Developed for the oil industry, the modified Hagedorn and Brown method is more appropriate than the LM method. The method is also less complicated than the Duns and Ross correlation. Perhaps more important, a comprehensive study by Ansari et al.[21] showed that when the above modifications are incorporated, the Hagedorn and Brown correlation mimics data from several sources very well. Indeed, the performance of the modified correlation appears to be better than most available correlations.

Nomenclature

A = cross-sectional area for fluid flow, ft^2

A_g, A_L = cross-sectional area available for gas or liquid to flow, ft^2

C = constant in Lockhart-Martinelli parameter, dimensionless

C_g = input volume fraction of the gas phase, dimensionless

C_L = input volume fraction of the liquid phase, dimensionless

C_{NL} = parameter used in Hagedorn-Brown method to compute dimensionless viscosity number, N_L, dimensionless

C_{tt} = constant in Lockhart-Martinelli parameter, C, for turbulent gas and turbulent liquid flow, dimensionless

C_{tv} = constant in Lockhart-Martinelli parameter, C, for turbulent gas and viscous (laminar) liquid flow, dimensionless

C_{vt} = constant in Lockhart-Martinelli parameter, C, for viscous gas and turbulent liquid flow, dimensionless

C_{vv} = constant in Lockhart-Martinelli parameter, C, for viscous gas and viscous liquid flow, dimensionless

d = pipe or well diameter, in.

f = friction factor, dimensionless

f_g = gas in-situ volume fraction (void fraction), dimensionless

f_L = liquid holdup or in-situ volume fraction, dimensionless

f_m = friction factor of the mixture, dimensionless

F = force, lbf

g = acceleration owing to gravity, ft/sec^2

g_c = conversion factor, 32.17 (lbm-ft)/lbf/sec^2

G = mass flux, mass flow rate per unit area, ρv, lbm/(hr-ft^2)

G_m = mixture mass flux, $\rho_m v_m$, lbm/(hr-ft^2)

L = total vertical well depth, ft

L_M = parameter in Duns and Ros regime transition criteria, dimensionless

L_s = total length of a cell in slug flow, ft

L_S = parameter in Duns and Ros regime transition criteria, dimensionless

N_d = diameter number, dimensionless

N_f = inverse viscosity number [= $gd^3 \rho_L(\rho_L-\rho_g)]^{1/2}/\mu_L$], dimensionless

N_L = liquid viscosity number [=$\mu_L(g/\rho_L\sigma^3)$], dimensionless

N_s = Duns and Ros slip velocity [= $S(\rho_L/g\sigma)^{1/4}$], dimensionless

N_w = parameter in Duns and Ros correlation for calculating roughness factor, dimensionless

p = pressure, psi

dp/dz = pressure gradient, psi/ft

$(dp/dz)_A$ = accelerational (kinetic) pressure gradient, psi/ft

$(dp/dz)_F$ = frictional pressure gradient, psi/ft

$(dp/dz)_H$ = static pressure gradient, psi/ft

q_g, q_L = gas or liquid flow rate at standard conditions, MMscf/D or STB/D

Re_g, Re_L = Reynolds number for the gas (=$\rho_g v_g d/\mu_g$) or liquid phase (=$\rho_L v_L d/\mu_L$), dimensionless

S = slip between the phases [=v_g-v_L], ft/sec

v = fluid velocity, ft/sec

$v_\infty, v_{\infty T}$ = terminal rise-velocity of bubbles in bubbly flow or a Taylor bubble in slug flow, ft/sec

v_g, v_L = gas or liquid in-situ velocity, ft/sec

v_{gd}, v_{Ld} = dimensionless phase velocities

v_m = mixture velocity, ft/sec

v_s = [=S]

v_{sg}, v_{sL} = superficial gas or liquid in-situ velocity, ft/sec

V = volume, ft^3

w = mass flow rate of fluid, lbm/sec

w_m = mixture mass flow rate, lbm/sec

x = gas mass fraction in tubing fluid mixture, dimensionless

X = Lockhart-Martinelli parameter, dimensionless

z = any vertical well depth, ft

ε = pipe roughness factor, ft

μ = oil viscosity, cp

μ_m = mixture viscosity, cp

ρ = density, lbm/ft^3

ρ_g, ρ_L = gas or liquid phase density, lbm/ft^3

ρ_m = density of gas/liquid mixture, lbm/ft^3

ρ_L = liquid density, lbm/ft^3

ρ_n = mixture density assuming no slip between phases, lbm/ft^3

ϕ_g, ϕ_L = friction multiplier in the Lockhart-Martinelli correlation, based on gas or liquid flowing alone in the channel, dimensionless

ϕ_{tt} = friction multiplier in the Lockhart-Martinelli correlation for turbulent gas and turbulent liquid flow, dimensionless

ϕ_{vt} = friction multiplier in the Lockhart-Martinelli correlation for viscous gas and turbulent liquid flow, dimensionless

σ = surface tension, lbm/sec^2

σ_L = surface tension of the liquid phase, lbm/sec^2

ψ = Hagedorn-Brown flow parameter, dimensionless

References

1. Brown, K.E. *et al.:* "Production Optimization of Oil and Gas Wells by Nodal Systems Analysis," *Technology of Artificial Lift Methods*, PennWell Publishing Co., Tulsa, Oklahoma (1984).
2. Poettmann, F.H. and Carpenter, P.G.: "The Multiphase Flow of Gas, Oil, and Water Through Vertical Flow Strings," *API Dril. and Prod. Prac.* (1952) 257.
3. Baxendell, P.B. and Thomas, R.: "The Calculation of Pressure Gradient in High Rate Flowing Wells," *JPT* (1961) 1023; *Trans.*, AIME, **222**.
4. Fancher, G.H. and Brown, K.E.: "Prediction of Pressure Gradients for Multiphase Flow in Tubing," *SPEJ* (1963) 59; *Trans.*, AIME, **228**.
5. Hagedorn, A.R. and Brown, K.E.: "Experimental Study of Pressure Gradients Occurring During Continuous Two-Phase Flow in Small-Diameter Conduits," *JPT* (April 1965) 475; *Trans.*, AIME, **234**.
6. Cicchitti, A. *et al.:* "Two-Phase Cooling Experiments— Pressure Drop, Heat Transfer and Burnout Measurements," *Energia Nucleare* (1960) **7**, No. 6, 407.
7. Dukler, A.E., Wicks, M., and Cleveland, R.G.: "Frictional Pressure Drop in Two-Phase Flow: A Comparison of Existing Correlations for Pressure Loss and Hold-Up," *AIChE J.* (1964) 38.
8. McAdams, W.H. *et al.:* "Vaporization Inside Horizontal Tubes—Part II—Benzene-Oil Mixtures," *Trans.*, ASME (1942) 193.
9. Lockhart, R.W. and Martinelli, R.C.: "Proposed Correlation of Data For Isothermal Two-Phase Two Component Flow in Pipes," *Chem. Eng. Prog.* (1949) 39.
10. Martinelli, R.C. *et al.:* "Isothermal Pressure Drop for Two-Phase Two-Component Flow in Horizontal Pipes," *Chem. Eng. Prog.* (1944) 139.
11. Martinelli, R.C., Putnam, J.A., and Lockhart, R.W.: "Two-Phase Two-Component Flow in the Viscous Region," *Trans.*, AIChE (1946) 681.
12. Martinelli, R.C. and Nelson, D.B.: "Prediction of Pressure Drop During Forced Circulation Boiling of Water," *Trans.*, ASME (1948) 695.
13. Chisholm, D. and Sutherland, L.A.: "Prediction of Pressure Gradients in Pipeline Systems During Two-Phase Flow," Paper 4 presented at the 1969 Symposium of Fluid Mechanics and Measurements in Two-phase Flow Systems, University of Leeds, Leeds, U.K., September.
14. Gregory, G.A.: "Comments on the Prediction of Liquid Holdup for Gas-liquid Flow in Inclined Pipes," *Cdn. J. Chem. Eng.* (1974) 463.
15. Gregory, G.A.: "Comparison of Methods for Comments on the Prediction of Liquid Holdup for Upward Gas-liquid Flow in Inclined Pipes," *Cdn. J. Chem. Eng.* (1975) 384.
16. Hasan, A.R. and Rhodes, E.: "Effect Of Mass Flux and System Pressure on Two-Phase Friction Multiplier," *Chem. Eng. Comm.* (1984) **27**.
17. Idsinga, W., Todreas, N., and Bowring, R.: "An Assessment of Two-Phase Pressure Drop Correlations for Steam-Water Systems," *Int. J. Multiphase Flow* (1977) 401.
18. Ros, N.C.J.: "Simultaneous Flow of Gas and Liquid As Encountered in Well Tubing," *JPT* (October 1961) 1037.
19. Duns, H. and Ros, N.C.J.: "Vertical Flow of Gas and Liquid Mixtures in Wells," *Proc.*, 6th World Pet. Congress, Tokyo (1963) 451.
20. Orkiszewski, J.: "Predicting Two-Phase Pressure Drops in Vertical Pipes," *JPT* (June 1967) 829; *Trans.*, AIME, **240**.
21. Ansari, A.M. *et al.:* "A Comprehensive Mechanistic Model for Upward Two-Phase Flow in Wellbores," *SPEPF* (May 1994) 143; *Trans.*, AIME, **297**.

SI Metric Conversion Factors

cp $\times$ 1.0*	E – 03	= Pa s
dyne $\times$ 1.0*	E – 02	= m
ft $\times$ 3.048*	E – 01	= m
ft^2 $\times$ 9.290 304*	E – 02	= m^2
ft^3 $\times$ 2.831 685	E – 02	= m^3
ft^3/sec $\times$ 2.831 685	E – 02	= m^3/s
in. $\times$ 2.54*	E + 00	= cm
lbf $\times$ 4.448 222	E + 00	= N
lbm $\times$ 4.535 924	E – 01	= kg
lbm/ft^3 $\times$ 1.601 846	E + 01	= kg/m^3
lbm/hr $\times$ 1.259 979	E – 04	= kg/s
psi $\times$ 6.894 757	E + 00	= kPa

*Conversion factor is exact.

Chapter 3
Multiphase Flow: Mechanistic Models for Vertical Wells

3.1 Introduction

The methods described in Chap. 2 for calculating liquid holdup and pressure drop during two-phase flow are largely empirical. Empirical approaches can potentially give inaccurate results, when applied to situations different from the database in which they are derived. A more satisfactory approach models flow mechanics and develops governing equations, which are then tested against laboratory and field data.

Gas flowing simultaneously with a liquid can take many configurations or patterns. Sometimes, when liquid flows as the continuous medium, the gas flows as discrete bubbles of various shapes and sizes. In other cases, the gas may flow through the channel core as the continuous medium, carrying liquid droplets along with it. Dynamics of each flow pattern are unique and generally require individual treatment.

This chapter examines the mechanistic models used to estimate in-situ-phase volume fractions and pressure drop. Major flow pattern characteristics are then discussed, followed by the procedures that determine flow regime, as well as estimate holdup and pressure drop. Flow pattern during multiphase flow is strongly influenced by channel orientation. Chap. 3 presents the vertical cocurrent upflow of gas and liquid. A discussion of flow in deviated wellbores follows in Chap. 4. Effects of other flow variables and geometry, such as flow through annuli and three-phase flow, will also be discussed in that chapter.

3.1.1 Flow Patterns in Vertical Cocurrent Systems.
To study flow patterns in heated and isothermal channels, various techniques are available. At low velocities, in transparent pipes, it is possible to distinguish flow patterns by direct observation. When flow patterns become indistinct at higher velocities, flash and cine photography can be used. However, reflection and refraction at multiple interfaces often make the interpretation of visual observations and photographs open to considerable uncertainty. This observation is particularly true at high flow rates. Other ingenious observation techniques have also been used, such as looking down the axis of a tube containing a two-phase mixture, to examine flow patterns in boiling systems at high pressures. Thus, to aid in the study of flow structure, various probes, such as—electrical, hot-wire, pressure, and optical—were developed. Signals from these probes provide indirect information, which leads to the identification of flow patterns.

Because the name given to a flow pattern is somewhat subjective, a multitude of terms has evolved to describe the various possible phase distributions. In this text, we consider the four major flow patterns—bubbly, slug, churn, and annular. These flow patterns are clearly distinguishable and are generally recognized by all researchers. However, subdivisions do exist, but transitions between these subpatterns are seldom well defined. The flow patterns encountered in vertical upward cocurrent flow are shown schematically in **Fig. 3.1.**

Bubbly Flow. In bubbly flow, the gas or vapor phase is distributed as discrete bubbles in a continuous liquid medium. At one extreme, the bubbles may be small and spherical, and on the other, they may be large with a spherical cap and a flat tail. In the latter state, although the size of bubbles does not approach the diameter of the pipe, potential for confusion with slug flow exists. In vertical bubbly flow, bubbles are uniformly distributed throughout the liquid at low gas velocities. Boiling water in a beaker or a kettle provides an example of everyday occurrence of bubbly flow.

Slug Flow. In slug flow, the gas or vapor bubbles have approximately the same diameter as that of the channel and are known as Taylor bubbles. The nose of the Taylor bubble has a characteristic spherical cap, and the gas in the bubble is separated from the pipe wall by a slowly descending thin film of liquid. The liquid flow is contained in liquid slugs that separate successive gas bubbles. These slugs often contain smaller entrained gas bubbles, carried in the wake of a large Taylor bubble. The length of the main gas (Taylor) bubble, as well as the liquid slug, can vary considerably. Some designate this pattern as plug or piston flow (low flow rates with well-defined gas/liquid boundaries) and as slug flow (higher flow rates with less clear boundaries). Slug flow can sometimes be observed, while pouring liquid from a large bottle.

Churn Flow. Churn flow forms by the breakdown of Taylor bubbles in slug flow. The gas or vapor flows in a chaotic manner through the liquid, which is mainly displaced to the channel wall. The flow has an oscillatory or

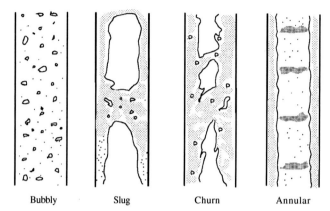

Fig. 3.1—Flow patterns in vertical upward flow (from Ref. 1). Used with permission of the American Institute of Chemical Engineers.

Bubbly Slug Churn Annular

time varying character, hence, the descriptive name—churn flow. This region is also sometimes referred to as semi-annular, annular-slug transition, or froth flow.

Annular Flow. In annular flow, the gas phase flows through the core of the channel, forming a continuous phase. The liquid phase is dragged along the pipe wall and appears to flow through the annulus, formed by the channel wall and the vapor core. The gas core generally carries entrained liquid droplets along with it. Large, amplitude-coherent waves are usually present on the surface of the liquid film, and the continuous breakup of these waves forms a source for droplet entrainment. Droplet entrainment occurs in varying amounts in the central gas core. The droplets can be separated or agglomerated and appear as irregular filaments or wisps. Because strong drag forces are needed to maintain liquid droplets in suspension, annular flow occurs only at high gas rates.

3.1.2 Flow Patterns in Wellbores. The large variation in pressure and temperature along a wellbore suggests that different flow patterns would exist at various depths. For example, near the bottomhole, we might only have the liquid phase or two liquid phases consisting of oil and water. Because hydrocarbon crude is a mixture of a large number of compounds, the liquid phase usually contains a significant amount of dissolved gases—chiefly, methane and ethane. As the fluid moves upward, the pressure on it gradually decreases. At a point where the pressure becomes less than the bubblepoint pressure, the gas starts to come out of solution, resulting in bubbly flow. As pressure decreases further with upward movement of fluids, more gas comes out of solution, and the whole range of flow patterns may be visible (**Fig. 3.2**). However, in oil wells, gas flow is rarely high enough for annular flow to exist. Indeed, most multiphase flow patterns in oil wells are limited to bubbly, slug, and churn flow. Therefore, these three flow patterns are important for oil wells.

Gas production may also involve flow of more than one phase, either because of coproduction of condensate or water, or both. The gas flow rate is generally high enough to sustain annular flow. In the lower flow rate limit, liquid unloading

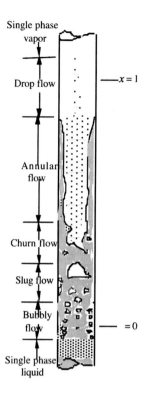

Fig. 3.2—Flow patterns in a wellbore (from Ref. 2).

becomes a real practical issue. Annular flow is also prevalent in geothermal wells producing saturated water and steam.

3.2 Flow-Pattern Delineation

Determining the type of flow that will occur under a given flow situation is essential for mechanistic modeling of multiphase flow. A completely satisfactory general method to correctly establish a flow pattern for a specified local condition is yet to be developed. One reason for this difficulty is the lack of agreement in describing and classifying flow patterns. The flow is often chaotic and difficult to describe, allowing room for individual judgment and interpretation.

Primary variables determining the pattern of flow are the velocities of the individual phases and their in-situ volume fractions. Besides the dominating influences of phase velocities and volume fractions, secondary variables contribute to the subjective flow-pattern classification. These variables include the method of formation of two-phase flow, the amount of departure from local hydrodynamic equilibrium, and the presence of trace contaminants in the system. One example is the formation of bubbly flow by injecting air through a porous wall into water. Close to the injector, bubbly flow will exist up to relatively high gas-volume fractions. Downstream of the injector, in relatively pure tap water, coalescence of bubbles will result in bubbly-slug or slug flow. In water containing trace amounts of a surface-active agent, this coalescence may be inhibited.

Despite these deficiencies, many methods have been proposed to delineate flow pattern during gas/liquid, two-phase flow. Some of these methods can be extended to liquid/liquid systems, with lesser accuracy. One method of representing various transitions is in the form of flow-pattern maps. We may represent individual patterns as areas on a two-dimensional (2D) graph, where coordinates are the actual superficial phase velocities (v_{sL}, v_{sg}) or generalized parameters containing these velocities. Obviously, the influence of secondary variables cannot be represented easily on a 2D map. In the second approach, efforts are directed toward modeling mechanisms that cause one type of flow pattern to change into another. Therefore, modeling flow-pattern transition implies defining individual transition criteria. We will present these two approaches to flow-pattern delineation, flow-regime maps, and individual transition criteria, in the next section.

3.2.1 Flow-Pattern Maps.

A number of flow-pattern maps has been proposed over the last few decades, some of which are quite accurate and have found wide usage in the industry. Most of these works attempt to generalize the map by choosing parameters that will represent the effect of some secondary variables influencing pattern transitions. **Fig. 3.3** shows the flow-pattern map of Hewitt and Roberts,[3] who have used superficial momentum fluxes ($v_{sL}^2\rho_L$ and $v_{sg}^2\rho_g$) of the two phases for the axes. The momentum fluxes may also be expressed in terms of total mass flux and mass fraction of the phases (e.g., $\rho_L v_{sL}^2 = G^2(1-x)^2/\rho_L$ and $\rho_g v_{sg}^2 = G^2 x^2/\rho_g$). The map is based on low-pressure air/water and high-pressure steam/water data from small diameter (1- to 3-cm) tubes. Inclusion of fluid density, instead of merely superficial velocities in the axes of the map, appears to allow for the effect of pressure on flow pattern transition quite well. However, because the map was developed from air/water and steam/water data, the effect of fluid properties in an oil well may not be captured very well. In addition, the small diameter pipe used to gather the data also makes the map less appealing for gas/oil flow, particularly because of the influence of pipe diameter on bubbly and slug flows.

Fig. 3.4 is the generalized map of Govier and Aziz.[4] The axes used are the modified superficial phase velocities, Yv_{sL} and Xv_{sg}, where

$$Y = \left(\rho_L \sigma_{wA} / \rho_w \sigma\right)^{1/4},$$

$$\text{and } X = Y\left(\rho_g / \rho_A\right)^{1/3}. \quad \dots \dots \dots \dots \dots \dots (3.1)$$

In Eq. 3.1, σ represents surface tension and ρ represents fluid density. Subscripts L, g, w, and A represent liquid, gas, water, and air, respectively, at standard conditions. The curves for various transitions may be represented by equations

$$Yv_{sL} = 0.01\,(1.96Xv_{sg})^{5.81} \text{ (Bubbly-Slug)},$$

$$Yv_{sL} = 0.263\,(Xv_{sg}-8.61) \text{ (Slug-Froth/Churn)},$$

$$Xv_{sg} = 26.5 \text{ (Slug-Annular)},$$

$$\text{and } Yv_{sL} = 0.01\,(Xv_{sg}/70)^{-6.17} \text{ (Froth-Annular)} \cdot$$

$$\dots \dots \dots \dots \dots \dots \dots (3.2)$$

Fig. 3.4 is based on air/oil and air/water data and may predict pattern transition in hydrocarbon systems better. However, the effect of pressure, which is very important for application to wellbores, may be poorly represented on this map.

A number of sophisticated flow-pattern maps has been advanced in recent years. For example, Weisman, Kang and coworkers[5] proposed a generalized map for vertical and inclined systems. The axes of their map contain property groups, reflecting the influence of pipe orientation, flow direction, and other parameters. We defer this discussion until the next chapter because of its use in inclined systems, although it is applicable to vertical systems as well. The Taitel et al.[1] flow-pattern map, based on physics of individual pattern transition, is discussed in Sec. 3.2.2.

Limitations of maps, in representing all flow-pattern transitions, arise because of the influence of secondary variables, which cannot be easily represented on a 2D graph. The use of superficial phase velocities for the axes of the map restricts its application to a particular situation. Any attempt to generalize the map requires choosing adequate parameters that represent various flow-pattern transitions. Because differing hydrodynamic conditions and balance of forces govern different transitions, a truly generalized map is very difficult to construct.

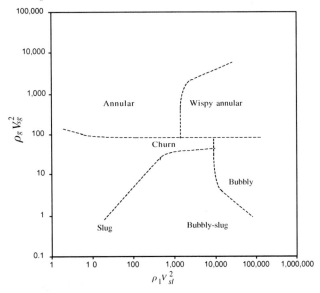

Fig. 3.3—Flow-pattern map of Hewitt and Roberts (from Ref. 3).

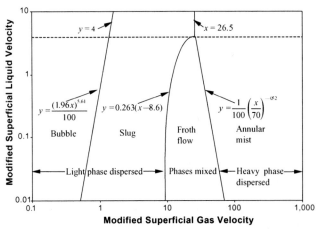

Fig. 3.4—Flow-pattern map of Govier and Aziz (from Ref. 4). Used with permission from the Petroleum Society. No copies may be made without written consent.

FLUID FLOW AND HEAT TRANSFER IN WELLBORES

3.2.2 Individual Transition Criteria.

An alternative and more flexible approach to empirical flow-pattern maps is to examine each pattern transition and develop criteria valid for that specific transition. In the last few years, this approach has made enormous progress. Because examining specific transitions allows physical modeling of individual flow patterns, this is probably the most reliable approach available today. We will now discuss transition criteria based on this approach, with special emphasis to bubbly-slug flow transition, because of its importance to the petroleum industry.

Bubbly-Slug Flow Transition. Transition from bubbly flow to slug flow requires the small, dispersed bubbles to agglomerate or coalesce to become large enough to fill the entire pipe cross section. Most bubbles, except the very small ones, follow a zigzag path when rising through a liquid. This movement results in collisions among bubbles, with consequent bubble agglomeration and formation of larger bubbles. Obviously, collision frequency and bubble agglomeration increases with increasing gas flow rate. At gas-volume fractions, higher than 0.25 (i.e., liquid holdup, $f_L < 0.75$), the collision frequency becomes extremely high and transition to slug flow is certain.[6] Experimental verification that the transition to slug flow occurs at a volume fraction of about 0.25 has been offered by many.[7-9] Hasan et al.[7] also found the transition to take place at a volume fraction of about 0.25, even when the flow occurs in tubing-casing annuli.

Therefore, $f_g = 0.25$ ($f_L = 0.75$) may be taken as the criterion for transition between bubbly and slug flow. We can express the transition criterion of $f_g = 0.25$ in terms of such measured variables as superficial velocities using an expression for the gas-volume fraction. The expression for volume fraction in bubbly flow (to be developed later) is given by

$$f_g \equiv 1 - f_L = \frac{v_{sg}}{C_o v_m + v_\infty} \quad \cdots \cdots \cdots \cdots \cdots \cdots \cdots \cdots \quad (3.3)$$

By re-arranging Eq. 3.3, one can obtain a linear relationship between the in-situ gas velocity and its superficial velocity. **Fig. 3.5** captures the $v_g - v_{sg}$ linear behavior, which also shows transition to slug flow. Because $f_g = 0.25$ for this transition, Eq. 3.3 gives

$$v_{sg} = \frac{C_o v_{sL} + v_\infty}{4 - C_o} \quad \cdots \cdots \cdots \cdots \cdots \cdots \cdots \cdots \quad (3.4)$$

By using a value of 1.2 for the flow parameter, C_o, as suggested by many,[8-10] we get

$$v_{sg} = 0.429 v_{sL} + 0.357 v_\infty \quad \cdots \cdots \cdots \cdots \cdots \cdots \quad (3.5)$$

We recommend use of the Harmathy[11] equation for estimating single-bubble, terminal-rise velocity, v_∞.

$$v_\infty = 1.53 \left[g \left(\rho_L - \rho_g \right) \sigma / \rho_L^2 \right]^{1/4} \quad \cdots \cdots \cdots \cdots \quad (3.6)$$

For an air/water system at room temperature, Eq. 3.6 calculates a terminal-rise velocity of 0.80 ft/sec (for oil with $\rho_L = 1$ g/cm^3 and $\sigma = 20$ dynes/cm, $v_\infty \sim 0.60$ ft/sec ~ 0.18 m/s). There-

fore, for a stagnant water column, Eq. 3.5 suggests that slug flow will occur whenever superficial air velocity exceeds 0.29 ft/sec (0.088 m/s).

Taitel et al.[1] arrived at the following expression for transition to slug flow, assuming that the slip between the phases equals v_∞.

$$v_{sg} = 0.33 v_{sL} + 0.25 v_\infty \quad \cdots \cdots \cdots \cdots \cdots \cdots \quad (3.7)$$

Although Eq. 3.7 has been adopted by Ansari et al.,[10] we recommend the use of Eq. 3.5 for bubble-slug pattern transition because slip between the phases generally does not equal terminal rise velocity. However, differences in the results of Eqs. 3.5 and 3.7 are small, particularly at low-phase velocities characteristic of this pattern transition. Various uncertainties, involved in the transition from bubbly to slug flow, probably overshadow that difference. Additionally, the bubbly-slug transition is gradual. Therefore, applicability of the holdup relationship for bubbly flow, up to the point of transition—implicit in deriving Eq. 3.5—is unlikely. If the expression for holdup for slug flow is assumed at the transition point, the terminal-rise velocity, v_∞, for small bubbles will have to be replaced by the Taylor bubble-rise velocity, $v_{\infty T}$, in Eq. 3.5. However, the difference in the rise velocities of a small bubble and a Taylor bubble is usually small, and Eq. 3.5 is quite adequate in representing the transition between bubbly and slug flow.

Fig. 3.6 shows the bubbly-slug transition data from a number of sources. The agreement between Eq. 3.5 with these data appears good. Of particular interest is the data reported by Sadatomi et al.[12] for both circular-annular and rectangular channels. The excellent agreement of these data with Eq. 3.5 indicates the applicability of this transition criterion for noncircular geometry. We explore this point further in Chap. 4.

If the pipe diameter is very small or if the fluid velocities are very high, the transition criterion given by Eq. 3.5 (or Eq. 3.7) may not apply. These two exceptions are discussed next.

Pipe Diameter Effect. An interesting aspect of the channel diameter on the transition between bubbly and slug flows

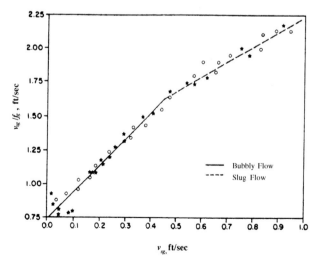

Fig. 3.5—Gas in-situ and superficial velocities bear a linear relationship in bubbly and slug flow (from Ref. 8).

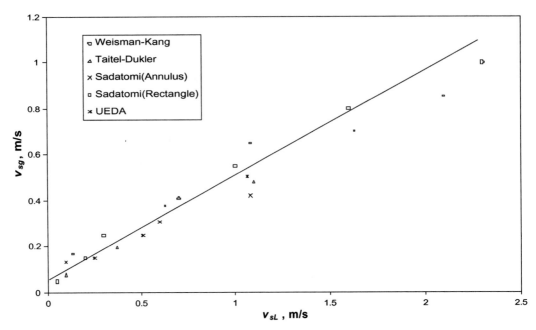

Fig. 3.6—Eq. 3.5 represents bubbly-slug transition data from several sources.

was pointed out by Taitel *et al.*[1] They observed that the terminal-rise velocity of small bubbles, given by Eq. 3.6, is unaffected by the channel diameter. In contrast, the rise velocity of a Taylor bubble, $v_{\infty T}$, is strongly dependent on the pipe diameter, as shown by the expression for $v_{\infty T}$, proposed by Nicklin *et al.*,[13]

$$v_{\infty T} = 0.35\sqrt{gd\left(\rho_L - \rho_g\right)/\rho_L} \cdot \quad\quad \text{......}(3.8)$$

When $v_{\infty T}$ is greater than v_{∞}, the nose of the Taylor bubble sweeps the smaller bubbles ahead of it. But, when $v_{\infty T}$ is less than v_{∞}, which is possible in small pipes, the rising smaller bubbles approach the back of the Taylor bubble, coalesce with it, increase its size, and ultimately cause a transition to slug flow. Taitel *et al.*[1] claimed that bubbly flow cannot exist under the condition $v_{\infty T} < v_{\infty}$; that is, when

$$1.53\left[g\left(\rho_L - \rho_g\right)\sigma/\rho_L^2\right]^{1/4} > 0.35\sqrt{gd\left(\rho_L - \rho_g\right)/\rho_L} \,,$$

$$\text{or } d < 19.1\sqrt{\sigma_L/g\left(\rho_L - \rho_g\right)} \cdot \quad\quad \text{...........}(3.9)$$

This fact is also evident from the Hewitt and Roberts[3] map. Here, data were gathered with 10- to 25-mm ID tubes for which $v_{\infty T}$ is smaller than v_{∞}. Bubbly flow cannot exist at low liquid rates in the Hewitt and Roberts[3] map, supporting Taitel *et al.*'s[1] contention.

Dispersed Bubbly Flow. At higher flow rates, shear stress caused by turbulence tends to break up the larger bubbles. Such breakups of larger bubbles may inhibit transition to slug flow even when gas-volume fraction exceeds 0.25. This type of bubbly flow resulting from the breakdown and dispersion of larger bubbles in the liquid is known as dispersed bubbly flow. Mechanics of dispersed bubbly flow were analyzed by Taitel *et al.*[1] and Shoham.[14] Based on the maximum bubble diameter analysis, which is possible under highly turbulent

conditions, they arrived at the expression for the onset of dispersed bubbly flow,

$$2v_m^{1.2}\left(\frac{f}{2d}\right)^{0.4}\left(\frac{\rho_L}{\sigma}\right)^{0.6}\sqrt{\frac{0.4\sigma}{g\left(\rho_L - \rho_g\right)}} = 0.725 + 4.15\sqrt{\frac{v_{sg}}{v_m}} \cdot$$

$$\text{.....................}(3.10)$$

Therefore, if the mixture velocity is greater than the velocity calculated with Eq. 3.10, bubbly flow will persist, even when $f_g > 0.25$. However, Taitel *et al.*[1] showed that even for small gas bubbles, the gas-volume fraction could be 0.52, at most. At higher volume fractions, transition to slug or churn flow must take place, even though v_m exceeds that when calculated with Eq. 3.10.

We note that for air/water systems at 25°C in a 2-in. (50.8-mm) pipe, one computes a mixture velocity of about 12 ft/sec (3.6 m/s) [~4,000 B/D or 609 m³/d] with Eq. 3.10, above the velocity for bubbly flow, which will only persist up to $f_g = 0.52$. For 100-cp oil under similar conditions, the mixture velocity must exceed 8.5 ft/sec (2.6 m/s). Also, at least half of this volumetric rate must be owing to the liquid phase because bubbly flow can exist only when $f_g < 0.52$. Such high velocities are rare in oil wells, and the transition to slug flow usually takes place when v_{sg} exceeds the value given by Eq. 3.5. However, geothermal wells, producing saturated water at high rates, offer the potential for occurrence of dispersed bubbly flow.

Slug-Churn Flow Transition. In slug flow, Taylor bubbles, formed by the agglomeration of smaller bubbles, occupy most of the pipe cross-sectional area. A liquid slug, in which small bubbles are dispersed axially, separates the Taylor bubbles. The liquid confined by the Taylor bubble and the tube wall flows around the bubble as a falling film. With an increasing flow rate, the interaction between the falling film and rising Taylor bubble increases. The upper limit of the slug flow occurs when the interaction becomes high enough to break-up the long bubbles, thus, causing the transition to churn flow. This breakup of Taylor bubbles is similar to the phenomenon of flooding during countercurrent flow of gas and liquid.

Many investigators have examined slug/churn transition with empirical,[15] semitheoretical,[5] and theoretical[16] analysis. However, none appears satisfactory for oilwell applications. The most promising model for this transition is probably the one proposed by Brauner and Bornea.[17] They analyzed the condition of the liquid slug following the Taylor bubble just before transition to churn flow occurs. If the mixture velocity is high enough for dispersed bubbly flow to occur, the local in-situ gas-volume fraction in the liquid slug can attain a maximum value of 52%. In other words, for transition to churn flow, the mixture velocity, v_m, must be higher than that predicted by Eq. 3.10, and the gas velocity must be high enough so that the gas-volume fraction is greater than 52%. In addition, they noted that at high flow rates, characteristic of this flow regime, the in-situ volume fraction may be approximated by the no-slip volume fraction so that $f_g = v_{sg}/v_m$. Therefore, for transition to churn flow

$$\frac{v_{sg}}{v_{sg}+v_{sg}} > 0.52 \, ,$$

or $v_{sg} > 1.08\, v_{sL}$ $\cdots\cdots\cdots\cdots\cdots\cdots$ (3.11)

Brauner and Bornea[17] presented data that lend support to the equation they proposed. They also show how this criterion can be modified for inclined two-phase flow. Ansari et al.[10] recommended a higher value of 0.76 for the limiting gas-volume fraction proposed by Scott and Kouba,[18] which leads $v_{sg} > 3.17\, v_{sL}$ for the superficial gas velocity needed for the transition to churn flow. Performance of Eq. 3.11 may be improved by noting that the gas-volume fraction may be better represented by Eq. 3.3, $f_g = v_{sg}/(C_o v_m + v_\infty)$. For example, Hasan and Kabir[8] proposed that the flow parameters for dispersed bubbly flow, C_o and v_∞, have the same values as those for ordinary bubbly flow. Recently, Kaya et al.[19] recommended an even higher limiting void fraction of 0.78 for the existence of slug flow. Using $f_g = v_{sg}/(1.2 v_{sL} + v_{\infty T})$, as proposed by Hasan and Kabir, they show that when v_{sg} exceeds $12.9\,(1.2 v_{sL} + v_{\infty T})$, transition from slug to churn flow should occur. Their proposed method, with appropriate modification for rise velocity, is also applicable for deviated wells and is discussed in Chap. 4. Note that in any case, for churn flow to take place, v_m must exceed the value given by Eq. 3.10.

Despite these efforts to characterize churn flow, uncertainties remain. For instance, Mao and Dukler,[20] deriving support from their experimental measurements, concluded that churn flow is really a manifestation of slug flow and that it may not exist as a separate entity. However, Hewitt and Jayanti,[21] citing their earlier work,[22] contended that flooding waves are formed within the Taylor bubbles in slug flow, as the churn flow transition is approached. Our experience shows that churn flow can be treated much like slug flow for oil field applications, as we discuss later.

Transition to Annular Flow. At high gas flow rates, transition from churn or slug flow to annular flow takes place. The liquid flows upward along the tube wall, while the gas flows through the center of the tube. The liquid film on the wall has a wavy interface, which can be broken by the gas and carried away as entrained droplets.

The transition between churn (or slug) and annular flow can be understood by visualizing a long vertical tube with a porous section at the middle. If the liquid is fed through the porous section at the middle and gas from the bottom, then at low gas flow rates, the liquid will flow down the tube as a film. However, at high gas flow rates, the shear force of the gas on the liquid will pull it upward, just as in the case of annular flow. Wallis,[23] among others, proposed criteria for transition to annular flow, based on the minimum gas velocity needed for reversal in the direction of the liquid flow.

A different physical model was adopted by Taitel et al.,[1] who examined the drag force, necessary to keep the entrained liquid droplets in suspension. They suggested that when the gas velocity is not sufficient to keep the liquid droplets in suspension, the droplets will fall back, accumulate, and form a bridge, leading to churn or slug flow. The minimum velocity required to keep a droplet with an average diameter, d, in suspension can be determined from a balance of the drag force on the droplet and the gravitational force acting on it. This analysis leads to the following expression for gas velocity, beyond which annular flow is expected.

$$v_{sg} > 3.1 \left[g\sigma(\rho_L - \rho_g)/\rho_g^2 \right]^{1/4} \cdots\cdots\cdots\cdots (3.12)$$

Taitel et al.[1] presented data from various sources that appear to agree with the results of Eq. 3.12 quite well. Note that both Eq. 3.12 and the Hewitt-Roberts map[3] suggest that the transition to annular flow is not affected by the liquid flow rate. For an air/water system at standard conditions, Eq. 3.12 predicts a gas velocity of about 50 ft/sec (15 m/s), above the velocity in which annular flow exists, while the Hewitt and Roberts map suggests a gas velocity of about 35 ft/sec. In practical applications, such high gas flow rates occur only in gas and geothermal wells.

When the liquid film at the wall is thick and a significant amount of liquid is entrained in the gas, the liquid might bridge the gas core. Bornea[16] proposed the following correlation for f_{LF}, the maximum liquid holdup beyond that in which annular flow cannot exist, even if v_{sg} is higher than that given by Eq. 3.12.

$$\left[f_{LF} + (E_{Lc} A_c / A) \right] > 0.12 \cdots\cdots\cdots\cdots (3.13)$$

From geometrical considerations,

$$f_{LF} = 4\underline{\delta}(1-\underline{\delta}) \cdots\cdots\cdots\cdots\cdots\cdots (3.14)$$

In Eq. 3.14, the dimensionless liquid film thickness, $\underline{\delta}$, equals δ/d, where δ is the actual film thickness. Also, E_{Lc} represents the fraction of flowing liquid that is entrained in the gas core, and A_c is the average cross-sectional area of the gas core.

The liquid holdup, f_{LF}, depends on the combined momentum equation,

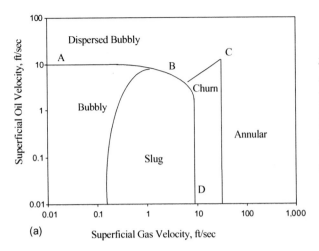

Fig. 3.7a—Flow-pattern map at standard conditions.

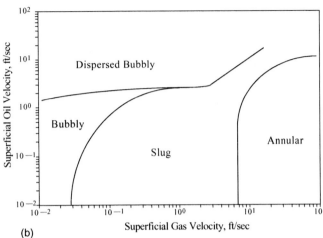

Fig. 3.7b—Flow-pattern map at 1,000 psi.

$$Y_M = \frac{f_i/f_c}{\left(1-f_{LF}\right)^{2.5} f_{LF}} - \frac{X_M^2}{f_{LF}^3} \quad \ldots \ldots \ldots \ldots \ldots (3.15)$$

In Eq. 3.15, the dimensionless parameter, Y_M, represents the ratio of static to frictional pressure gradient in the gas core.

$$Y_M = \frac{g\sin\theta\,(\rho_L - \rho_c)}{(dp/dz)_c} \quad \ldots \ldots \ldots \ldots \ldots (3.16)$$

X_M represents the Lockhart-Martinelli parameter defined in Chap. 2, modified here to reflect the fact that the liquid flow rate in the film is reduced by the liquid entrained in the gas core.

$$X_M = \sqrt{(1-E)^2 (f_F/f_{sL}) \frac{(dp/dz)_{fL}}{(dp/dz)_c}} \quad \ldots \ldots \ldots (3.17)$$

The procedure for calculating interfacial-friction factor, f_c, fraction of liquid entrained, E, and core cross-sectional area, A_c, is discussed later.

Flow-Pattern Map in an Oil Well. The individual transition criteria discussed so far are presented in the form of two flow-pattern maps in **Figs. 3.7a** and **3.7b** for a 30°API oil flowing in a 3-in. ID pipe. The fluid properties used are: $\gamma_g = 0.75$, $\rho_L = 54.67$ lbm/ft³, $\sigma = 0.0685$ lbm/sec², and $\mu_g = 0.0103$ cp. Fig. 3.7a shows the map at the standard (14.7 psia and 60°F) conditions. Note that the dispersed bubbly flow pattern is represented by two transition lines. The segment represented by AB is given by Eq. 3.10, while the BC segment is based on Eq. 3.11. The segment BD, representing the slug-churn transition, is a continuation of the line AB. As mentioned earlier, the line BD is the locus of constant mixture velocity for a given set of fluid properties. On the right of the BD line, mixture velocity is high enough for dispersed bubbly flow, but the in-situ gas-volume fraction is higher (below line BC) than 0.52; therefore, churn flow results.

Fig. 3.7b represents a condition likely to be prevalent in an oil well with a pressure of 1,000 psia and a temperature of 100°F in which the following property values were used:

$\rho_g = 3.77$ lbm/ft³, $\rho_L = 54$ lbm/ft³, $\sigma = 0.0316$ lbm/sec² and $\mu_g = 0.0127$ cp. At this higher pressure, the gas density is significant; therefore, transition to annular flow occurs at a much lower superficial gas velocity of 6.8 ft/sec, compared to 44.4 ft/sec at standard conditions. Note also that the bubbly flow area shrinks and the churn flow regime vanishes entirely.

3.3 Liquid Holdup and Pressure Drop

In the analysis of multiphase flow in vertical and near-vertical systems, the estimation of static head becomes very important. In most vertical flow situations, the static head is the major contributor to the total pressure gradient and can account for more than 90% of the total pressure drop. Because the mixture density and, therefore, the static head are directly dependent on the liquid holdup, f_L, an accurate estimation is of paramount importance.

The success of the flow pattern-based approach stems from the fact that slip between the phases depends upon the buoyancy of the lighter phase and its tendency to flow through the center of the channel. The effect of buoyancy and the channeling tendency of the gas phase depend, in turn, on the particular flow pattern that exists under the given conditions of flow, pressure, and channel geometry. One may surmise that the dynamics of flow are different for each flow regime and that individual modeling for each regime should lead to better insights into flow behavior and, therefore, more reliable computational tools. We will now discuss the modeling approach for each of those four regimes.

3.3.1 Bubbly Flow.
In bubbly flow, gas bubbles tend to flow mostly through the center of the channel. At the channel center, the mixture velocity is significantly higher than the cross-sectional average velocity, which means that gas bubbles are moving faster than the average velocity of the mixture, v_m. In addition, the density difference between the phases gives rise to a drift-flux, v_d, which adds a velocity, v_d/f_g, to the lighter phase.

Holdup. If we assume that the velocity at the channel center is C_o multiplied by the cross-sectional average velocity, we can write the expression for in-situ gas velocity, v_g, as

FLUID FLOW AND HEAT TRANSFER IN WELLBORES

$$v_g = C_o v_m + v_d / f_g \cdot \quad \cdots\cdots\cdots\cdots\cdots\cdots\cdots \quad (3.18)$$

Because in-situ velocity is equal to the superficial velocity, v_{sg}, divided by the gas volume fraction, f_g, we have a simple relation between volume fraction and phase velocities.

$$f_g = \frac{v_{sg}}{C_o v_m + v_d / f_g} \cdot \quad \cdots\cdots\cdots\cdots\cdots\cdots \quad (3.19)$$

Eq. 3.19 expresses gas volume fraction in an implicit form and requires an expression for drift-flux, v_d. For upward vertical flow of small bubbles or particles in liquids, Zuber and Findlay[9] and Wallis[23] suggest the following semitheoretical expression for drift-flux in terms of the volume fraction, f_g, and terminal rise velocity, v_∞.

$$v_d = v_\infty f_g \left(1 - f_g\right)^n \cdot \quad \cdots\cdots\cdots\cdots\cdots\cdots \quad (3.20)$$

For gas/liquid flow in vertical pipes, we recommend a value of zero for the exponent n, as noted by many researchers.[8,9] Therefore, for gas/liquid flow, the expression for drift-flux simplifies to $v_d = v_\infty f_g$, and Eq. 3.19 can be rewritten as

$$f_g = \frac{v_{sg}}{C_o v_m + v_\infty} \cdot \quad \cdots\cdots\cdots\cdots\cdots\cdots \quad (3.21)$$

Therefore, the liquid holdup f_L $(=1-f_g)$ is given by

$$f_L = 1 - \frac{v_{sg}}{C_o v_m + v_\infty} \cdot \quad \cdots\cdots\cdots\cdots\cdots\cdots \quad (3.22)$$

Eq. 3.21 can be recast in the form,

$$v_g \equiv v_{sg} / f_g = v_{sg} /(1-f_L) = C_o v_m + v_\infty \cdot \quad \cdots\cdots\cdots \quad (3.23)$$

Eq. 3.23 shows that the in-situ gas velocity varies linearly with the mixture velocity with a slope, C_o, and an intercept, v_∞. Eqs. 3.21 and 3.22 have the advantage of being explicit in form for holdup.

Ansari *et al.*[10] used a value of 0.5 for the exponent n in Eq. 3.20, which leads to the implicit expression for liquid holdup,

$$f_L = 1 - \frac{v_{sg}}{C_o v_m + v_\infty f_L^{0.5}} \cdot \quad \cdots\cdots\cdots\cdots\cdots \quad (3.24)$$

The use of either Eq. 3.22 or 3.24 requires estimates of the flow parameter, C_o, and the terminal-rise velocity, v_∞. Next, we discuss the values of these parameters.

Terminal-Rise Velocity, v_∞. A single gas bubble rising through an infinite liquid medium soon attains a constant rise velocity owing to the balance of drag and buoyancy forces on it. Separate approaches taken by Peebles and Garber[24] and Harmathy[11] result in different final expressions for v_∞. Because of its simplicity and accuracy, the Harmathy equation, Eq. 3.6, is used in this book. We point out that the bubble-rise velocity could be significantly lower if the bubble diameter approaches that of the pipe wall.

Many researchers have used Eq. 3.23 to correlate their holdup data without gathering independent rise-velocity data. In such cases, the value used for v_∞ is essentially a correlating parameter for the data and is often slightly different from the value estimated from the Harmathy equation. We recommend the use of Eq. 3.6.

Flow Parameter, C_o. Analysis of velocity and bubble concentration profiles may allow estimation of C_o. For a vast majority of multiphase flow applications, the flow can be assumed turbulent so that the maximum velocity at the channel axis is 1.2 times the average velocity. In addition, the velocity profile is quite flat for a portion of the central section of the pipe. Although not all bubbles flow through the channel center because only a few flow close to the wall, 1.2 has been found to be a reasonable value for C_o. The classic work of Zuber and Findlay[9] established a value of $C_o = 1.2$ for an air/water system in a 2-in. pipe. Many studies, in a variety of systems since then, have firmly established this value of C_o.

An exception to this C_o value occurs for bubbly flow in large-diameter pipes (>100 mm) with standing liquid columns. The upward motion of gas bubbles through the central portion of the channel causes the liquid surrounding them to move upward. Because net liquid movement is zero in a stagnant liquid column, backflow of liquid occurs along the channel wall. The resulting liquid recirculation in a stagnant column leads to a significantly higher ratio of maximum to average velocity, resulting in a higher value of the flow parameter in such cases.

Analyzing holdup data with Eq. 3.23, Rahman[25] reported a C_o value of 2.0 for a stagnant-liquid column in a 127-mm vertical pipe. Earlier, some investigators, Zahradnik and Kastanek,[26] for example, determined C_o to be 1.95 for large-diameter (>127-mm) bubble columns. Our work[27] also suggested that $C_o = 2.0$ is appropriate, not only for stagnant liquid columns, but also for very low liquid rates ($v_{sL} < 0.01$ ft/sec). Similarly, data from a 5.5-in. (140-mm) ID tube at moderate liquid velocities show a value of 1.6 for C_o.

Therefore, a C_o value of 2.0 is applicable for large-diameter pipes in stagnant or near-stagnant liquid systems. However, $C_o = 1.2$ appears to be well established for bubbly flow in small diameter pipes, even with stagnant liquid columns. Unfortunately, the precise pipe size, at which the change in value for C_o occurs, has not been investigated nor do we know if the transition is gradual or abrupt. Clearly, the dependence of C_o on liquid velocity in near-stagnant, large-diameter columns needs investigation.

Eq. 3.21 reproduces bubbly flow data quite well, such as that shown in Ref. 8. **Fig. 3.8** provides the testimony. The figure also shows that the simplified slug flow model, given by Eq. 3.26, is capable of reproducing laboratory data satisfactorily.

For estimating holdup in dispersed bubbly flow, we propose to use Eq. 3.22 with $C_o = 1.2$ and v_∞ as given by the Harmathy[11] equation. Dispersed bubbly flow is therefore treated similar to ordinary bubbly flow. Many researchers, including Ansari *et al.*,[10] have used a homogeneous flow approach in calculating holdup and pressure drop in a dispersed bubbly flow regime. However, we think that large

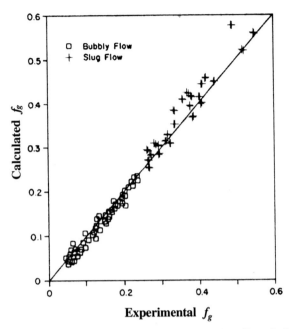

Fig. 3.8—Eqs. 3.21 and 3.26 mimic laboratory data (from Ref. 8).

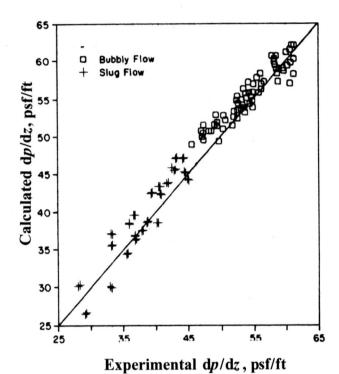

Experimental dp/dz , psf/ft

Fig. 3.9—Laboratory data lend support to pressure gradient calculations in bubbly and slug flows (from Ref. 8).

superficial velocities, involved in dispersed bubbly flow, make the fluids more homogeneous but do not necessarily lead to a no-slip condition. In other words, the gas phase still flows mostly through the channel center at a velocity higher than the average mixture velocity.

Pressure Drop. As mentioned in Chap. 2, the general expression for total pressure gradient during two-phase flow is given by

$$-\frac{dp}{dz} = \frac{g}{g_c}\rho_m + \frac{f_m v_m^2 \rho_m}{2 g_c d} + \frac{\rho_m v_m}{g_c}\frac{dv_m}{dz} , \quad \dots\dots (2.17)$$

where the average mixture density ρ_m is given by

$$\rho_m = \rho_L f_L + \rho_g\left(1 - f_L\right), \quad \dots\dots\dots\dots (2.18)$$

and the liquid holdup f_L is given by Eq. 3.22 or 3.24.

Wall friction contributes very little pressure drop during vertical bubbly flow. Using the homogeneous model for estimating friction pressure drop reduces calculation complexity without introducing any significant inaccuracy. The well may be assumed to be smooth, allowing us to use the simple Blassius equation for estimating the friction factor,

$$f_m = 0.32\mathrm{Re}_m^{-0.25} = 0.32(dv_m\rho_m / \mu_m)^{-0.25}. \quad \dots\dots (1.11)$$

One may use any of the three methods (Eqs. 2.21 through 2.23) suggested in Chap. 2 to estimate mixture average viscosity, μ_m. Considering the insignificance of the friction term, Govier and Aziz[4] suggested the use of liquid density and viscosity values, instead of the mixture property values for estimating f_m, as

$$f_m = 0.32\left(dv_m\rho_L / \mu_L\right)^{-0.25}. \quad \dots\dots\dots (3.25)$$

Fluid acceleration during bubbly flow is very small, and the last term in Eq. 2.15 is often neglected. A good estimate of this term can be obtained by taking the difference in mixture velocity over a finite depth of the well to calculate the mixture velocity gradient, dv_m/dz.

Fig. 3.9 exhibits the quality of match obtained, when pressure gradients were computed for both bubbly and slug flows.

3.3.2 Slug Flow. Fluid configuration in slug flow is quite different from that in bubbly flow. As **Fig. 3.10** illustrates, there are two distinct zones during slug flow; one is dominated by the large Taylor bubble and the other consisting of small bubbles dispersed in the liquid slug. The Taylor bubble rises up against a falling liquid film at a velocity much higher than that of the small bubbles in the liquid slug. This difference in drift velocities makes the application of the simple drift-flux model, developed for bubbly flow to slug flow, difficult. One can still develop a simple expression for liquid holdup in slug flow by neglecting these differences in drift velocities.

Holdup. Assuming differences in these drift velocities to be negligible, one[8] can derive the following expression for holdup using $v_{\infty T}$ for the rise velocity of a Taylor bubble.

$$f_L = 1 - \frac{v_{sg}}{C_o v_m + v_{\infty T}} \quad \dots\dots\dots\dots\dots\dots (3.26)$$

If the gas content in the liquid slug is a small fraction of the total gas phase and the difference in drift velocities between the slug and the Taylor bubble is not large, Eq. 3.26 estimates f_g with good accuracy.

However, in many instances of slug flow, the liquid slug might be quite large compared to the Taylor bubble, casting

FLUID FLOW AND HEAT TRANSFER IN WELLBORES

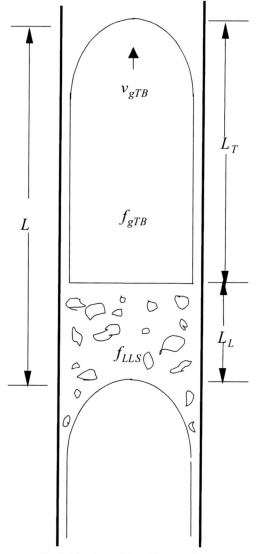

Fig. 3.10—A model cell in slug flow.

In addition to simplifying the computation procedure, an advantage of using this average rise velocity becomes apparent when we consider the calculated values of liquid holdup and pressure drop in bubbly and slug flow regimes near the transition zone. Use of separate rise velocities in the two flow regimes results in different values of the holdup and pressure gradient, even if the same fluid velocities are used. This approach causes an abrupt change in the computed pressure gradient in a well, as the flow regime changes from bubbly to slug flow. The continuous nature of Eq. 3.28 avoids this problem, thereby conforming to the measured wellbore pressure profiles.

However, the contrast in rise velocities is not the only difference between the two zones—Taylor bubble and the liquid slug—of the slug unit. The velocity profile and, therefore, the flow parameter in the two zones can also differ. To rigorously account for these differences between the liquid slug and the Taylor bubble, a few hydrodynamic models have been advanced for vertical circular pipes.[29,30] Fig. 3.10 shows a model cell of length, L, consisting of a Taylor bubble of length, L_T, and a liquid slug of length, L_L. Denoting the in-situ gas fraction in the Taylor bubble portion by f_T and that in the liquid slug portion by f_s, we derive at the expression for the average gas-volume fraction for the cell, which is written as

$$f_g = \beta f_T + (1-\beta)f_s , \quad\cdots\cdots\cdots\cdots\cdots\cdots(3.29)$$

where $\beta = L_T/L$. Eq. 3.29 requires estimates of gas-volume fraction in the Taylor bubble zone and in the liquid slug, besides requiring an estimate of β. A number of approaches[29,30] has been suggested for estimating the liquid slug volume fraction and other parameters required for the model. Caetano et al.[31] successfully extended this approach to a vertical annular channel. Hasan and Kabir[32] presented a simplified cellular approach using data and correlations from the literature to estimate β. However, the model presented by Ansari et al.[10] is perhaps the most accurate. In the following, we present their analysis.

The Ansari[10] model is based on a material balance for the liquid and the gas in the Taylor bubble zone, denoted by the subscript, $_{TB}$, and the liquid slug zone, denoted by the subscript, $_{LS}$. Density of the individual phases are assumed to remain constant in the cell, thereby allowing us to write the volumetric flow balance as

$$v_{sg} = \beta v_{gTB}(1-f_{LTB}) + (1-\beta)v_{gLS}(1-f_{LLS}) , \quad\cdots(3.30)$$

$$\text{and } v_{sL} = (1-\beta)v_{LLS}f_{LLS} - \beta v_{LTB}f_{LTB} \cdots\cdots\cdots\cdots(3.31)$$

The difference in velocities between the Taylor bubble and liquid film, and between the bubble and the wall will cause liquid to flow downward from the Taylor bubble section into the liquid slug. The Taylor bubble is assumed to have an in-situ velocity, v_{TB}, which is given by (analogous to that given by Eq. 3.23)

$$v_{TB} = 1.2v_m + v_{\infty T} \cdot \quad\cdots\cdots\cdots\cdots\cdots\cdots\cdots(3.32)$$

doubt on the accuracy of Eq. 3.26. One simple way to account for different drift velocities in slug flow is to use some type of an average rise velocity for all gas bubbles, large and small, in the system. Therefore, for estimating in-situ gas-volume fraction during slug flow, we modify Eq. 3.26 as

$$f_L = 1 - \frac{v_{sg}}{C_o v_m + \overline{v}_\infty} \cdot \quad\cdots\cdots\cdots\cdots\cdots\cdots(3.27)$$

The average rise velocity is expressed in terms of the Taylor bubble-rise velocity, small bubble-rise velocity, and bubbly-slug-transition velocity as

$$\overline{v}_\infty = v_\infty\left(1-e^{-v_t/v_{sg}}\right) + v_{\infty T}e^{-v_t/v_{sg}} , \quad\cdots\cdots\cdots(3.28)$$

where the superficial gas velocity for transition to slug flow is given by Eq. 3.5, $v_t = 0.429\,v_{sL} + 0.357\,v_\infty$. This approach was used successfully to compute laboratory liquid-holdup data during countercurrent slug flow.[28]

We defer discussion on estimation procedure for the rise velocity of a Taylor bubble, $v_{\infty T}$. The volumetric rate of liquid moving into the slug is $(v_{TB}+v_{LTB})f_{LTB}$, where f_{LTB} is the fraction of a Taylor bubble section volume that is liquid. This rate must equal the increase in the flow rate of the liquid slug; that is

$$\left(v_{TB} + v_{LTB}\right)f_{LTB} = \left(v_{TB} - v_{LLS}\right)f_{LLS} \cdot \quad \cdots\cdots\cdots (3.33)$$

A similar equation is written for the gas-phase mass balance.

$$\left(v_{TB} - v_{gTB}\right)\left(1 - f_{LTB}\right) = \left(1.2v_m + v_{\infty T} - v_{gLS}\right)\left(1 - f_{LLS}\right) \cdot$$
$$\cdots\cdots\cdots\cdots\cdots (3.34)$$

For the in-situ velocity of the gas phase in the liquid slug, v_{gLS}, Ansari et al.[10] used

$$v_{gLS} = 1.2v_m + v_\infty f_{LLS}^{1/2}, \quad \cdots\cdots\cdots\cdots (3.35)$$

where v_∞ is the small bubble rise velocity estimated with the Harmathy[11] correlation. For the falling liquid film velocity, v_{LTB}, they use the expression proposed by Brotz.[33]

$$v_{LTB} = 9.916\left[gd\left(1 - \sqrt{f_{gTB}}\right)\right]^{1/2} \cdot \quad \cdots\cdots\cdots (3.36)$$

Ansari et al.[10] calculated the liquid holdup in the liquid slug, $f_{gLS} = 1 - f_{LLS}$, based on the correlation of Schmidt[34] data,

$$f_{gLS} = \frac{v_{sg}}{2.65v_m + 0.425}, \quad \cdots\cdots\cdots\cdots (3.37)$$

where the velocities are in SI units (m/s). By combining Eqs. 3.29–3.35, one obtains

$$\left(9.916\sqrt{gd}\right)\left(1 - \sqrt{f_{gTB}}\right)^{1/2} f_{LTB} + \overline{A} = v_{TB}\left(1 - f_{LTB}\right),$$
$$\cdots\cdots\cdots\cdots\cdots (3.38)$$

where $\overline{A} = v_{TB}f_{gLS} + \left(1 - f_{gLS}\right)\left[v_m - f_{gLS}\left(v_\infty\left(1 - f_{gLS}\right)^{1/2}\right)\right] \cdot$
$$\cdots\cdots\cdots\cdots\cdots (3.39)$$

The solution procedure is detailed in Brill and Mukherjee.[35] To solve for f_{LTB}, using a successive iterative approach, we can rewrite Eq. 3.38 as

$$v_{LTB}f_{LTB} + v_{TB}f_{LTB} = v_{TB} - \overline{A} \cdot$$

That is, $f_{LTB} = \dfrac{v_{TB} - \overline{A}}{v_{LTB} + v_{TB}} \cdot \quad \cdots\cdots\cdots\cdots (3.40)$

We show the application of the model with an example problem at the end of this chapter.

Ansari et al.[10] also used the presence of a developing slug flow zone, where the Taylor bubble has a cap that is a very large fraction of its total length. For detail of the delineation of this zone and estimating various flow parameters for it, the reader is referred to Ansari et al.[10] and/or Brill and Mukherjee.[35]

Taylor Bubble Rise Velocity. Following the classic work of Davies and Taylor[36] and Nicklin et al.,[13] the Taylor bubble rise velocity in vertical circular channels, $v_{\infty T}$, in slug flow is written as

$$v_{\infty T} = C_2\sqrt{gd\left(\rho_L - \rho_g\right)/\rho_L} \cdot \quad \cdots\cdots\cdots\cdots (3.41)$$

Analyses and data presented by a number of researchers show that the constant C_2 is influenced by the forces of inertia, viscosity, and surface tension. Wallis[23] showed that

$$C_2 = 0.345\left[1 - e^{-0.029N_f}\right]\left[1 - e^{(3.37 - 0.029E_o)/m}\right], \quad \cdots (3.42)$$

where N_f is the inverse viscosity number and Eo represents the Eotvos number.

$$N_f = \sqrt{d^3 g\left(\rho_L - \rho_g\right)\rho_L/\mu_L^2}, \quad \cdots\cdots\cdots\cdots (3.43)$$

$$\text{and } E_o = d^2 g\left(\rho_L - \rho_g\right)/\sigma \cdot \quad \cdots\cdots\cdots\cdots (3.44)$$

The value of the parameter m depends on N_f.

$$m = 10, \text{ for } N_f > 250$$
$$= 69N_f^{-0.35}, \text{ for } 18 < N_f < 250$$
$$= 25, \text{ for } 18 < N_f \cdot \quad \cdots\cdots\cdots\cdots (3.45)$$

For large values of N_f (>300) and Eo (>100), Eq. 3.41 reduces to $C_2 = 0.345$.

For air/water flow through a 2-in. pipe at standard conditions, $N_f = 35,000$ and Eo=322. For a 100-cp oil under similar conditions (with $\sigma = 30$ dynes/cm), $N_f = 350$ and Eo=817. Therefore, for most practical purposes, $C_2 = 0.345$ and Eq. 3.41 for Taylor bubble rise velocity becomes

$$v_{\infty T} = 0.345\sqrt{gd\left(\rho_L - \rho_g\right)/\rho_L} \cdot \quad \cdots\cdots\cdots\cdots (3.46)$$

Often $\rho_L >> \rho_g$, in which case Eq. 3.45 further simplifies to $v_{\infty T} = 0.345\sqrt{gd}$.

Pressure Gradient. The total pressure gradient during slug flow can be obtained by adding the three components as shown in Eq. 2.15, making use of Eq. 3.27 to estimate holdup. Because accelerational and frictional contribution to the total pressure drop is small, the homogeneous model may be used to estimate these two components, as in the case of bubbly flow.

Ansari et al.[10] and others[37] suggested that the wall shear stress around a Taylor bubble can be ignored. That is because some liquid flows downward as a film against the Taylor bubble, while most of the liquid flows upward in the liquid slugs. Therefore, they recommended that the frictional drop for the liquid slug, using the mixture density of the slug, ρ_{LS}, and its length, $(1-\beta)z$, be used to calculate frictional loss for the entire cell. For estimating the static head component, Ansari et al.[10] suggested that we assume the entire Taylor bubble section is 100% gas, while the liquid slug contains f_{gLS} fraction gas. Thus, in their model, the liquid slug density, ρ_{LS}, the static head, $(dp/dz)_H$, and the friction head, $(dp/dz)_F$, are

$$\rho_{LS} = \rho_L f_{LLS} + \rho_g (1 - f_{LLS}) , \quad\ldots\ldots\ldots\ldots\ldots (3.47)$$

$$\left(\frac{dp}{dz}\right)_H = \frac{g}{g_c}\left[\rho_{LS}(1-\beta) + \beta\rho_g\right], \quad\ldots\ldots\ldots\ldots (3.48)$$

$$\text{and } \left(\frac{dp}{dz}\right)_F = \frac{f_{LS}\rho_{LS}(1-\beta)v_m^2}{2d\,g_c} \quad\ldots\ldots\ldots\ldots\ldots (3.49)$$

Ansari et al.[10] neglected acceleration in this flow regime. Note that because $\rho_{LS}(1-\beta)$ is approximately equal to ρ_m, the frictional component estimated with Eq. 3.48 is not very different from that given by Eq. 2.15.

3.3.3 Churn Flow.
The chaotic nature of churn flow causes difficulty not only in delineating this flow regime but also in modeling it. Consequently, this flow pattern has not been investigated extensively. However, a number of investigators[2,7,8] suggested that the drift-flux model may be applied to the churn flow pattern. Earlier, Govier and Aziz[4] recommended that the equations developed for slug flow be used for the churn flow regime. This approach is also suggested by Fernandes et al.[30] for circular channels and by Kelessidis and Dukler[38] and Caetano et al.[31] for annuli. Recent experimental observations of Mao and Dukler[20] also lend credence to this suggestion. Kaya et al.[19] used a modification of this approach in vertical and deviated wells.

Although the bubble shape during churn flow is quite different from that in slug flow, the rise velocities in these two regimes are probably not very different. In addition, because the mixture velocity is much higher than the bubble rise velocity during churn flow, a small error in estimating v_{tT} does not significantly affect holdup estimation. However, an accurate estimation of the flow parameter, C_o, is important for computing holdup in churn flow. The bubble concentration profile is likely to be different from that in slug flow because of the characteristic churning motion of this flow regime, which tends to make the mixture velocity and gas concentration profiles flat. This argument leads to a C_o value lower than 1.2. We recommend a value of 1.15 for C_o.

3.3.4 Annular Flow.
In annular flow, gas flows through the central core of the pipe, while liquid flows along the wall as a film. Therefore, the system can be viewed as single-phase flow of gas through a pipe, in which its walls are formed by the liquid film. If we assume that no liquid is being carried as droplets in the gas phase and that the gas/liquid interface is smooth, then the problem reduces to estimating pressure drop in single-phase gas flow. For such an ideal annular flow, we do not need to estimate holdup, as we are modeling a true single-phase flow, except that the pipe diameter must be reduced somewhat. The liquid film thickness is typically less than 10% of the pipe diameter, thus introducing a negligible error.

Unfortunately, annular flow is rarely ideal. Usually, a certain fraction of the liquid is carried as droplets in the gas stream. Often, the amount of entrained liquid is a substantial

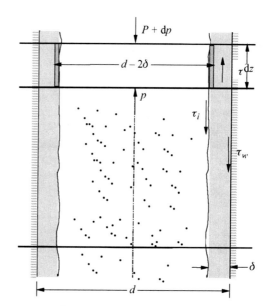

Fig. 3.11—Vertical annular flow.

portion of the total liquid flow. The existence of liquid droplets in the gas core requires the core fluid density to properly account for the droplets. Existence of the liquid droplets also makes the core fluid velocity, v_c, larger than the gas velocity, v_g. More importantly, the gas/liquid interface is usually wavy, thereby causing difficulty while establishing an appropriate friction factor. Frictional loss constitutes a very large fraction of the total pressure gradient; consequently, an accurate estimation of the friction factor becomes very important.

Consider the gas core, as shown in **Fig. 3.11,** and assume the liquid droplet velocity to be equal to that of the gas in the core. Using v_c for the core fluid in-situ velocity and v_g for the gas in-situ velocity, we can write the equation for the total pressure gradient during annular flow as

$$-\frac{dp}{dz} = \frac{1}{g_c}\left[g\rho_c + \frac{f_c v_c^2 \rho_c}{2d(1-2\delta)} + \rho_c v_g \frac{dv_g}{dz}\right]. \quad\ldots\ldots (3.50)$$

The differential, dv_g/dz, in the acceleration term may be rewritten as $-v_g(dp/dz)$ using the gas law, which results in the expression for pressure gradient,

$$-\frac{dp}{dz} = \frac{1}{g_c}\frac{g\rho_c + \left(f_c v_c^2 \rho_c / \{2(1-\delta)d\}\right)}{1 - \left(\rho_c v_c^2\right)/(pg_c)} \quad\ldots\ldots\ldots (3.51)$$

The problem then reduces to that of estimating the density of the fluid in the core, ρ_c, the friction factor, f_c, for gas flowing through a rough pipe, and the liquid film thickness, δ.

Entrainment Estimation. To determine the density of the fluid flowing through the core, we must estimate the fraction of total liquid that is entrained in the gas core. Entrainment is defined as the fraction, E, of the input liquid that is entrained in the vapor core. We recommend the correlation Steen and Wallis[39] present for E, as a function of critical gas velocity, v_{sgc}. The following expression represents the graphical correlation they presented.[37]

$$E = 1 - e^{-0.125(v_{sgc}-15)} , \quad \dots \dots \dots \dots \dots \dots (3.52)$$

$$\text{where } v_{sgc} = \frac{10^4 v_{sg}\mu_g}{\sigma}\sqrt{\rho_g/\rho_L} . \quad \dots \dots \dots \dots (3.53)$$

Once entrainment is estimated, the core fluid density is determined by considering the gas core as the system. In that case, the superficial-gas velocity remains equal to v_{sg}, but the superficial liquid velocity becomes Ev_{sL} because only the entrained fraction of the liquid is in this system. Therefore, we define superficial core-fluid velocity, v_{sc}, in-situ core fluid velocity, v_c, and core fluid density, ρ_c, as

$$v_{sc} = v_{sg} + Ev_{sL} \quad v_c = v_{sc}/(1-2\underline{\delta})^2 , \quad \dots \dots \dots (3.54)$$

$$\text{and } \rho_c = \left(\rho_L Ev_{sL}/v_{sc}\right) + \left(\rho_g v_{sg}/v_{sc}\right) . \quad \dots \dots \dots (3.55)$$

Film Friction Factor. There are a number of correlations available for predicting the liquid film roughness or film friction factor, f_c. Probably the best correlation is the one proposed by Wallis,[23] which relates the film friction factor to the wall friction factor, f, and the dimensionless liquid-film thickness, $\underline{\delta}(=\delta/d)$. The wall-friction factor is the one that gas would experience flowing through a smooth pipe. The equation for this correlation is written as

$$f_c = f\left[1 + 300\underline{\delta}\right] . \quad \dots \dots \dots \dots \dots \dots (3.56)$$

From geometrical considerations, $4\underline{\delta}$ equals liquid holdup, f_L. Thus, Eq. 3.56 is rewritten as

$$f_c = f\left[1 + 75f_L\right] , \quad \dots \dots \dots \dots \dots \dots (3.57)$$

where f is estimated with the Blassius equation, $f = 0.32/\text{Re}_c^{0.25}$. Ansari *et al.*[10] pointed out that the following expression for f_c, proposed by Whalley and Hewitt,[40] is more accurate when entrainment, E, is smaller than 0.9. For example,

$$f_c = f\left[1 + 24\underline{\delta}\left(\rho_L/\rho_g\right)^{1/3}\right], \text{ if } E < 0.9 \quad \dots \dots \dots (3.58)$$

An accurate estimation of the liquid-film thickness, δ, or the liquid holdup, f_L, is needed because the core friction factor is very sensitive to this entity. For this purpose, f_L can be computed with the separated flow model, as described in Chap. 2 (Eq. 2.30). To estimate f_L with Eq. 2.30, the effective liquid and gas mass fluxes must be used.

Rigorous models for annular flow have been developed in recent years. These models incorporate velocity profiles in the liquid film and the gas core, in an attempt to better relate the interfacial friction. Although complex, some of these models are two-dimensional in nature, which allow a better description of physics of flow. In the following, we describe the model proposed by Ansari *et al.*[10]

The method proposed by Ansari *et al.*[10] is similar to the one previously described (Eq. 3.50), although they neglected the accelerational component. They wrote the expression for pressure gradient for the gas core as

$$-\left[\frac{dp}{dz}\right]_c = \frac{g\rho_c}{g_c} + \frac{f_c v_c^2 \rho_c}{2dg_c(1-2\underline{\delta})} . \quad \dots \dots \dots \dots (3.59)$$

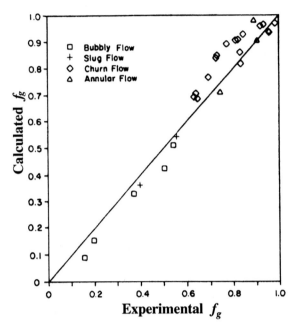

Fig. 3.12—Laboratory data show good agreement with calculations in all flow regimes (from Ref. 8).

For estimating core density, they use Eq. 3.55, along with Eq. 3.52. For friction factor computation, they recommended the use of Eq. 3.56 when $E > 0.9$, and Eq. 3.58 when $E \leq 0.9$. To calculate the liquid-film thickness, δ, Ansari *et al.*[10] noted that the pressure gradient for the gas core must equal to that for the liquid film. Analogous to Eq. 3.59, they wrote the expression for $(dp/dz)_L$ as

$$-\left[\frac{dp}{dz}\right]_L = \frac{g\rho_L}{g_c} + \frac{2f_{LF}v_{sL}^2(1-E)^2\rho_L}{64g_c d\underline{\delta}^3(1-2\underline{\delta})^3} - \frac{f_c v_c^2(1-2\underline{\delta})\rho_c}{2g_c d\underline{\delta}(1-\underline{\delta})} .$$

$$\dots \dots \dots \dots \dots \dots \dots (3.60)$$

Equating $(dp/dz)_L$ and $(dp/dz)_c$, Ansari *et al.*[10] arrived at the expression,

$$\frac{f_c v_c^2 \rho_c}{2g_c d\underline{\delta}(1-\underline{\delta})(1-2\underline{\delta})} = \frac{g(\rho_L-\rho_c)}{g_c} + \frac{2f_{LF}v_{sL}^2(1-E)^2\rho_L}{64g_c d\underline{\delta}^3(1-2\underline{\delta})^3} .$$

$$\dots \dots \dots \dots \dots \dots (3.61)$$

Eq. 3.60 is solved iteratively for the single unknown $\underline{\delta}$.

More recently, Gomez *et al.*[41] and Xiao *et al.*[42] proposed a similar method, based on the two-fluid approach. Because the authors claim the model to be applicable to all inclination angles, we discuss it under horizontal annular flow in Chap. 4.

Figs. 3.12 and **3.13** show that the simple mechanistic approach used by Hasan and Kabir[8] (Eqs. 3.23, 3.26, and 3.57) estimate the liquid holdup and pressure drop data in all four flow regimes with engineering accuracy. The newer and rigorous mechanistic models perform even better as discussed in Sec. 3.3.

3.4 Discussion

In this chapter, our emphasis has been on mechanistic modeling. That is because this approach, besides being accurate over a variety of situations, provides insights into mechanics

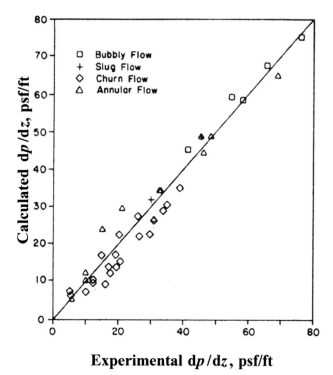

Fig. 3.13—Laboratory data lend support to pressure gradient calculations in all flow regimes (from Ref. 8).

mechanistic model under certain circumstances. **Table 3.1,** reproduced from Ansari *et al.*,[10] sheds light on the relative performance of eight models. This comparative study included flow-pattern-based models of Aziz *et al.*,[2] Duns and Ros,[44] Hasan-Kabir,[32] and Ansari *et al.*[10] Other models considered were Hagedorn-Brown,[43] Beggs-Brill,[45] Orkiszewski,[46] and Mukherjee-Brill.[47]

Note that the numbers in Table 3.1 reflect relative performance factors (RPF).[10] RPF combines six statistical parameters and can assume a value ranging from 0 to 6. The lower the RPF the better is the model with respect to others. Results show that the Ansari *et al.*[10] model outperformed all others. This comparison does not include the recent models of Gomez *et al.*[42] or Kaya *et al.*,[19] which appear to perform even better. Because these models[19,42] are applicable to wells of any deviation angle, we discuss them in Chap. 4. However, the overall performance of other methods, such as Hagedorn-Brown, Aziz *et al.*, Duns-Ros, and Hasan-Kabir are comparable to that of the Ansari *et al.* model. Thus, computational complexity may tip the balance for choosing a simpler model or correlation over a more rigorous one. In addition, as the table shows, performance of different models depends on the flow regime prevailing in the wellbore. As shown in Chap. 9, Secs. 9.1 and 9.2, the Hasan-Kabir model performs well when bubbly flow dominates, thereby testing the conclusion reached in Table 3.1. Similarly, Chap. 10 shows the superiority of mechanistic models over empirical correlations while solving liquid/liquid flow problems. When annular flow is encountered, such as in gas wells producing gas and condensate or gas and water, and in gas-lift wells, the Ansari *et al.* model will clearly outperform all others. In slug flow, however, the Hagedorn-Brown correlation has a slight edge over all others. Note that this correlation owes its success to the large database used in its development and the subsequent

of flow while solving field problems. Application chapters will make this point amply clear. Nonetheless, questions arise as to which approach is most suitable to solve a given problem. Unfortunately, there is no single answer. Although our preference is to recommend the use of a mechanistic model to solve all flow problems, the Hagedorn-Brown[43] empirical correlation appears to outperform even the Ansari *et al.*[10]

TABLE 3.1—RELATIVE PERFORMANCE OF TWO-PHASE FLOW MODELS											
Models	EDB	VW	DW	VNH	ANH	AB	AS	VS	SNH	VSNH	AAN
n	1712	1086	626	755	1381	29	1052	654	745	387	70
Ansari	0.70	1.121	1.378	0.081	0.000	0.143	1.295	1.461	0.112	0.142	0.000
HagBr	0.585	0.600	0.919	0.876	0.774	2.029	0.386	0.485	0.457	0.939	0.546
Aziz	1.312	1.108	2.085	0.803	1.062	0.262	1.798	1.764	1.314	1.486	0.214
DunRos	1.719	1.678	1.678	1.711	1.792	1.128	2.056	2.028	1.582	2.296	1.213
HasKab	1.940	2.005	2.201	1.836	1.780	0.009	2.575	2.590	2.044	1.998	1.043
BegBrl	2.982	2.908	3.445	3.321	3.414	2.828	2.883	2.595	3.261	3.282	1.972
Orkis	4.284	5.273	2.322	5.838	4.688	1.226	3.128	3.318	3.551	4.403	6.000
MukBrl	4.883	4.647	6.000	3.909	4.601	4.463	5.343	5.140	4.977	4.683	1.516

n = number of data points; EDB=Entire Data Bank; VW=Vertical Well Cases; DW=Deviated Well Cases; VNH=Vertical Well Cases w/o Hagedorn-Brown data; ANH=All Well Cases w/o Hagedorn-Brown data; AB=All Well Cases 75% Bubbly Flow; AS=All Well Cases with 100% Slug Flow; VS=Vertical Well Cases with 100 Slug Flow; SNH=All Well Cases with 100% Slug Flow w/o Hagedorn-Brown data; VSNH=Vertical Well Cases with 100% Slug Flow w/o Hagedorn-Brown data; AAN=All Well Cases with 100% Annular Flow; Ansari=Ansari *et al.* Mechanistic Model; HagBr=Hagedorn-Brown Correlation; Aziz=Aziz *et al.* Correlation; DunRos=Duns and Ros Correlation; HasKab=Hasan and Kabir Mechanistic Model; BegBrl=Beggsand Brill Correlation; Orkis=Orkiszewski; MukBrl=Mukherjee and Brill Correlation.

modifications that it has undergone.[35] A comparative study by Pucknell *et al.*[48] involving eight North Sea fields showed that mechanistic models, particularly that of Ansari *et al.*, provided the overall superior results in both oil and gas wells. Similar success was reported by Gomez *et al.*[41] while testing their mechanistic model with field data.

Based on the preceding discussion and experience to date, we recommend the use of the Ansari *et al.*[10] model for its mechanistic basis and overall performance, while solving steady-state flow problems. Although the Gomez *et al.* and the Kaya *et al.* models promise to be even better than the Ansari *et al.* model, independent validation will help solidify their positions. However, whenever solution of a particular problem is sought, selective use of other methods may be made based on the dominant flow regime for superior results. One problem, common to most methods, is the lack of smooth transition from one flow regime to another. Abrupt transitions cause discontinuities, which may appear in wellbore pressure profiles and may also precipitate problems, while solving transient flow problems. They are discussed in Chap. 7. To alleviate this awkward flow-regime transition problem, we presented Eq. 3.28 to address the bubbly-slug flow transition. The slug-churn transition issue is handled implicitly. Therefore, the only remaining problem with the Hasan-Kabir model lies in the churn-annular transition. Note that Pucknell *et al.*[48] reported that the Hasan-Kabir model provided the smoothest transition, even before the introduction of Eq. 3.28.

3.4.1 Field Example. A 5,151-ft vertical well produces 23° API dry oil at 1,140 STB/D through a 2.99-in. ID tubing. The gas/oil ratio (GOR) is 450 scf/STB, and the gas gravity is 0.80. The following property values and computed fluid parameters are available at the wellhead where pressure is 505 psig:

$$v_{sL} = 1.601 \text{ ft/sec}$$
$$v_{sg} = 2.824 \text{ ft/sec}$$
$$\rho_L = 55.042 \text{ lbm/ft}^3$$
$$\rho_g = 2.19 \text{ lbm/ft}^3$$
$$\mu_L = 13.09 \text{ cp}$$
$$\mu_g = 0.019 \text{ cp}$$
$$\sigma = 31.6 \text{ dynes/cm} = 0.0696 \text{ lbm/s}^2$$

Calculate the pressure gradient at this point.

Solution—Flow Pattern. Transition Criteria.

Eq. 3.6: $v_\infty = 1.53 [g\sigma(\rho_L - \rho_g)/\rho_L^2]^{0.25}$
$= 1.53 [(32.2)(0.0696)(52.85/55.042)^2]^{0.25} = 0.680$ ft/sec.

Eq. 3.8: $v_{\infty T} = 0.345 [gd (\rho_L - \rho_g)/\rho_L]^{0.5}$
$= 0.345 [(32.2)(0.25)(52.85)/55.042]^{0.5} = 0.958$ ft/sec.

Because $v_{\infty T} > v_\infty$, Eq. 3.5 would apply for transition from bubbly to slug flow.

Eq. 3.5: $v_t = 0.429 v_{sL} + 0.357 v_\infty$
$= (0.429)(1.601) + (0.357)(0.680) = 0.930$ ft/sec.

Because the actual $v_{sg} > 0.93$ ft/sec, the flow pattern is not bubbly. Let us test each flow regime before moving forward

with any calculations. First, use Eq. 3.10 to compute the minimum mixture velocity needed for dispersed bubbly flow to exist. Note that the actual mixture velocity is $v_{sg} + v_{sL} = 4.425$ ft/sec. Eq. 3.10 requires an estimate of the friction factor. We use a value of $f = 0.04$; its computation will be shown later.

The left-hand side (LHS) of Eq. 3.10 is: $2(4.425)^{1.2}$ $(0.04/0.5)^{0.4}(55.042/0.0696)^{0.6} \{0.4(0.0696)/$ $[(32.2)(52.85)]\}^{0.5} = 0.9629.$

The right-hand side (RHS) of Eq. 3.10 is: $0.725 + 4.15$ $(2.824/4.425)^{0.5} = 4.0405.$

Therefore, the mixture velocity is too low (LHS is too low compared to the RHS) to support dispersed bubbly flow. This test also implies that the flow pattern is not churn.

Transition to Annular Flow. To check if the flow pattern is annular, we use Eq. 3.12 to find the minimum gas velocity needed to sustain annular flow.

Eq. 3.12: $v_{sg} = 3.1 [(32.2)(0.0696)(52.85)/2.19^2]^{1/4}$
$= 6.913$ ft/sec.

Eq. 3.12 shows the required superficial gas velocity for annular flow to be 6.913 ft/sec, while the actual v_{sg} is 2.19 ft/sec. Thus, flow is not annular.

This process of elimination leads us to slug flow occurring at the wellhead.

Solution—Gas-Volume Fraction and Pressure Gradient. The Hasan-Kabir Model.

Gas-Volume Fraction:

$x = v_{sg} \rho_g / (v_{sg} \rho_g + v_{sl} \rho_l) = (2.824)(2.19)/[(2.824)(2.19) + (1.601)(55.042)] = 0.066.$

Eq. 3.28: $\bar{v}_\infty = 0.958 [e^{-0.93/2.824}] + 0.68(1 - e^{-0.93/2.824}) = 0.88$ ft/sec.

Eq. 3.27: $f_g = 2.824 /[1.2(4.425) + 0.88] = 0.4568.$ Holdup: $f_L = 0.5432.$

Pressure Gradient:

Eq. 2.18: $\rho_m = 55.042 (0.5432) + 2.19 (0.4568)$
$= 30.82$ lbm/ft^3.

Eq. 2.15: $(dp/dz)_H = \rho_m g/g_c = 30.82$ psf/ft $= 0.214$ psi/ft.

Eq. 2.23: $\mu_m = 0.934(13.09) + 0.066(0.019) = 12.296$ cp.
$\text{Re}_m = (0.25)(4.425)(30.84)/(12.296 \times 0.000672)$
$= 3,973.$

Eq. 1.11: $f_m = 0.032 (3,973)^{-0.25} = 0.04.$

Eq. 2.14: $(dp/dz)_F = (0.04)(4.425)^2(30.84)/[2(32.2)(0.25)]$
$= 1.516$ psf/ft $= 0.0105$ psi/ft.

Eq. 2.17: $dp/dz = 0.214 + 0.0105 = 0.2246$ psi/ft $=$ total pressure gradient at wellhead.
The Ansari et al. *Model.*

Gas-Volume Fraction:

Eq. 3.37: $f_{gLS} = 2.824/[2.65(4.425) + (0.425/0.3048)]$
$= 0.215; f_{LLS} = 1 - 0.215 = 0.785.$

FLUID FLOW AND HEAT TRANSFER IN WELLBORES

TABLE 3.2—PRESSURE-TRAVERSE CALCULATION			
Depth, ft	Pressure, psig		
	Data	Hasan-Kabir	Ansari *et al.*
0	505	505	505
400	587	593	586
650	647	654	641
1,150	777	781	758
1,650	920	918	885
2,150	1,074	1,063	1,021
2,650	1,237	1,212	1,165
3,150	1,407	1,369	1,316
3,650	1,582	1,530	1,473
4,150	1,850	1,695	1,634
4,650	1,960	1,864	1,799
5,151	2,105	2,034	1,968

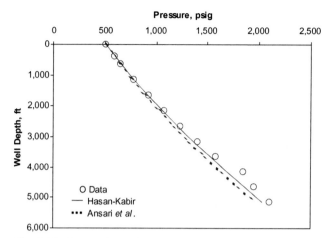

Fig. 3.14—Comparison of mechanistic models with field data.

Eq. 3.35: $v_{gLS} = 1.2(4.425) + (0.68)(0.785)^{0.5} = 5.912$ ft/sec; $v_{TB} = 1.2(4.425) + 0.958 = 6.28$ ft/sec.

Eq. 3.39: $\bar{A} = (6.28)(0.215) + (0.785)\{4.425 - 0.215 [0.68(0.785)^{0.5}]\} = 4.72$ ft/sec.

Eq. 3.36: $v_{LTB} = 9.916[32.2(0.25)\{1 - \sqrt{f_{gTB}}\}]^{0.5} = 28.13(1 - \sqrt{f_{gTB}})^{0.5}$.

Eq. 3.40: $f_{LTB} = [6.28 - 4.72]/[6.28 + v_{LTB}]$.

However, $f_{LTB} = 1 - f_{gTB}$, requiring simultaneous solutions of Eqs. 3.36 and 3.40.

Trial and error gives $f_{LTB} = 0.118$; $v_{LTB} = 6.93$ ft/sec.

Eq. 3.33: $(6.28 + 6.93)(0.118) = (6.28 - v_{LLS})(0.785)$; hence, $v_{LLS} = 4.30$ ft/sec.

Eq. 3.34: $(6.28 - v_{gTB})(1 - 0.118) = (6.28 - v_{gLS})(0.215)$; $v_{gTB} = 6.19$ ft/sec.

Eq. 3.30: $2.824 = \beta(6.19)(1 - 0.118) + (1 - \beta)(5.912)(1 - 0.785) => \beta = 0.37$.

Pressure Gradient:

Eq. 3.47: $\rho_{LS} = 55.042(0.785) + 2.19(0.215) = 43.7$ lbm/ft³.

Eq. 3.48: $(dp/dz)_H = [\rho_{LS}(1 - \beta) + \rho_g \beta]g/g_c = 28.30$ psf/ft $= 0.1965$ psi/ft.

$\mu_{LS} = \mu_g f_{gLS} + \mu_L(1 - f_{gLS}) = 10.75$ cp

$Re_{LS} = dv_m \rho_{LS}/\mu_{LS} = 6,664$; $f_{LS} = 0.0316$.

Eq. 3.49: $(dp/dz)_F = (0.0316)(4.425)^2(43.7)(1 - 0.37)/[2(32.2)(0.25)] = 1.06$ psf/ft $= 0.00737$ psi/ft.

Eq. 2.17: $dp/dz = 0.1965 + 0.00737 = 0.204$ psi/ft $=$ total pressure gradient at wellhead.

Calculations shown in the Field Example for the two mechanistic models were done for the conditions prevailing at the wellhead of an actual well. **Table 3.2** presents the results of pressure-traverse calculations, and **Fig. 3.14** compares the same information with measured data. This example is a continuation of the example discussed in Chap. 2, where we compare the solutions of simplified models.

Note that because the computation was done top-down, discrepancy occurs at the well bottom. Experience shows that when computations are done along the direction of flow; that is bottom up, errors decrease significantly. In this example we wanted to show the complex computations involved for the slug flow pattern existing at the wellhead condition. To compare the results from all models and correlations at this point, we decided on a top-down calculation. The use of fluid property correlations inevitably influences the computed results. In all examples in this book, presenting simplified spreadsheet calculations, we used the Standing[49] correlation for bubblepoint pressure and formation volume factor, Dranchuk and Abou-Kassem[50] correlation for gas-law deviation factor (z-factor), Beggs and Robinson[51] correlation for dead- and live-oil viscosity, and Baker and Swerdloff[52] correlation for oil surface tension.

Note that friction factors and frictional pressure gradients calculated by the two approaches are quite different on a percentage basis. However, because friction contributes only a small fraction to the total pressure drop, the differences in the pressure profiles computed by the two models depend almost totally on the computed static heads. This observation reinforces our belief that great sophistication for calculating friction pressure drop is unwarranted for most vertical and near-vertical wells.

Summary

In this chapter, we presented a mechanistic approach for two-phase flow modeling in vertical systems. Models have been developed for all four major flow regimes—bubbly, slug, churn, and annular. These models use flow-pattern maps and individual transition criteria for discerning flow regimes.

The slip between the phases is modeled by noting the effect of buoyancy and the tendency of the gas phase to flow through the channel center. The flowing mixture densities, calculated from these expressions, are useful for pressure gradient calculations. Note that the static head, $g\rho_m/g_c$, is quite often the major contributor to the total head loss for vertical two-phase flow in wellbores. A number of researchers are in good agreement with the performance of the models presented in this chapter, showing data from both the laboratory[10] and the field.[48,53]

Nomenclature

A = cross-sectional area for fluid flow, ft^2

A_c = core cross-sectional area

C = constant in Lockhart-Martinelli parameter, dimensionless

C_o = flow parameter in bubbly flow, dimensionless

d = pipe or well diameter, in.

(dp/dz) = pressure gradient, psi/ft

$(dp/dz)_c$ = pressure gradient for the core fluid, psi/ft

$(dp/dz)_{fL}$ = pressure gradient for the liquid film, psi/ft

$(dp/dz)_F$ = frictional pressure gradient, psi/ft

$(dp/dz)_H$ = static pressure gradient, psi/ft

$(dp/dz)_L$ = pressure gradient for liquid flowing alone in the channel, psi/ft

E = entrainment

Eo = Eotvos number [$=gd^2(\rho_L-\rho_g)/\sigma$], dimensionless

f = friction factor, dimensionless

f_c = film friction factor for the gas core in annular flow, dimensionless

f_g = gas in-situ volume fraction (void fraction), dimensionless

f_{gLS} = gas in-situ volume fraction in the liquid slug portion of the cell, dimensionless

f_{gTB} = gas in-situ volume fraction in the Taylor bubble portion of the cell, dimensionless

f_i = interface friction factor, dimensionless

f_L = liquid holdup or in-situ volume fraction, dimensionless

f_{LF} = friction factor for the liquid film, dimensionless

f_{LLS} = liquid holdup in the liquid slug portion of the cell, dimensionless

f_{LTB} = liquid holdup in the Taylor bubble portion of the cell, dimensionless

f_m = two-phase mixture friction factor, dimensionless

f_s = in-situ gas volume fraction in the liquid slug during slug flow, dimensionless

f_T = in-situ gas volume fraction in the Taylor bubble during slug flow, dimensionless

g = acceleration owing to gravity, ft/sec^2

g_c = conversion factor, 32.17 lbm-ft/lbf-sec^2

G = mass flux = mass flow rate per unit area, lbm/ft^2

L = length, ft

L_s, L_T = length of the liquid slug or Taylor bubble in slug flow, ft

L_{sB} = length of liquid slug

L_{TB} = length of a Taylor bubble

m = mass of fluid in a control volume, lbm

m = parameter defined by Eq. 3.45, dimensionless

N_f = inverse viscosity number [$=gd^3\rho_L(\rho_l-\rho_g)]^2/\mu_l$], dimensionless

p = pressure, psi

Re_m = Reynolds number for the mixture [$=\rho_m v_m d/\mu_m$], dimensionless

v = fluid velocity, ft/hr

$v_\infty, v_{\infty T}$ = terminal rise-velocity of bubbles in bubbly flow or a Taylor bubble in slug flow, ft/hr

v_c = core fluid velocity, ft/hr

v_d = drift velocity of the lighter phase, ft/hr

v_g, v_L = gas or liquid in-situ velocity, ft/hr

v_{gd}, v_{Ld} = dimensionless phase velocities

v_{gLS} = in-situ gas velocity in the liquid slug portion of the cell, ft/hr

v_{gTB} = in-situ gas velocity in the Taylor bubble portion of the cell, ft/hr

v_{LLS} = in-situ liquid velocity in the liquid slug portion of the cell, ft/hr

v_{LTB} = in-situ liquid velocity in the Taylor bubble portion of the cell, ft/hr

v_m = two-phase mixture velocity, ft/hr

v_∞ = terminal rise velocity of single bubble, ft/hr

$\bar{v}_\infty$ = average rise velocity of small bubbles, ft/hr

v_{sg}, v_{sL} = superficial gas or liquid in-situ velocity, ft/hr

v_{sgc} = critical superficial gas velocity given by Eq. 3.53

v_t = superficial gas velocity needed for transition from bubbly to slug flow, ft/hr

v_{TB} = in-situ velocity of the Taylor bubble, ft/hr

$v_{\infty T}$ = rise velocity of Taylor bubbles, ft/hr

X = Lockhart-Martinelli parameter, dimensionless

X_M = modified Lockhart-Martinelli parameter for annular flow defined by Eq. 3.17, dimensionless

Y_M = ratio of gravitational to gas-phase frictional gradient, dimensionless

z = any vertical well depth, ft

δ = liquid-film thickness, ft

$\underline{\delta}$ = dimensionless liquid-film thickness ($= \delta/d$)

θ = well deviation from horizontal, degree

μ_L = liquid phase viscosity, cp

μ_m = two-phase mixture viscosity, cp

μ_g = gas viscosity, cp

β = ratio of the length of Taylor bubble to the total cell, L_T/L, dimensionless

ρ = density, lbm/ft^3

ρ_w = water density, lbm/ft^3

ρ_A = air density, lbm/ft^3

ρ_c, ρ_e = core fluid or earth (formation) density, lbm/ft^3

ρ_g, ρ_L = gas or liquid phase density, lbm/ft^3

ρ_{LS} = density of the fluid in liquid slug, lbm/ft^3

ρ_m = two-phase mixture density, lbm/ft^3

σ = surface tension, lbm/sec^2

$\sigma_{wA} =$ surface tension between air and water, lbm/sec^2
$\gamma_g =$ gas specific gravity (air $= 1.0$)

Subscripts

$A =$ air
$g =$ gas
$L =$ liquid
$w =$ water

Superscripts

$N =$ exponent used in Eq. 3.20, dimensionless

References

1. Taitel, Y., Bornea, D. and Dukler, A.E.: "Modeling Flow Pattern Transition For Steady Upward Gas-Liquid Flow in Vertical Tubes," *AIChE J.* (May 1980) 345.
2. Aziz, K., Govier, G.W. and Fogarasi, M.: "Pressure Drop in Wells Producing Oil and Gas," *Cdn. J. Pet. Tech.* (July–September 1972) 38.
3. Hewitt, G.F. and Roberts, D.N.: "Studies of Two-Phase Flow Patterns by Simultaneous X-Ray and Flash Photography," AERE-M 2159, HMSO (1969).
4. Aziz, K., Govier, G.W., and Fogarasi, M.: "Pressure Drop in Wells Producing Oil and Gas," *Cdn. J. Pet. Tech.* (July–September 1972).
5. Weisman, J. and Kang, S.Y.: "Flow Pattern Transitions in Vertical and Upwardly Inclined Lines," *Int. J. Multiphase Flow* (1981) **7**, 271.
6. Radovicich, N.A. and Moissis, R.: "The Transition From Two-Phase Bubble Flow to Slug Flow," Report No. 7-7673-22, Dept. of Mech. Eng., MIT, Cambridge, Massachusetts (1962).
7. Hasan, A.R., Kabir, C.S. and Rahman, R.: "Predicting Liquid Gradient in a Pumping-Well Annulus," *SPEPE* (February 1988) 113; *Trans.*, AIME, **285**.
8. Hasan, A.R. and Kabir, C.S.: "A Study of Multiphase Flow Behavior in Vertical Wells," *SPEPE* (May 1988) 263; *Trans.*, AIME, **285**.
9. Zuber, N. and Findlay, J.: "Average Volumetric Concentration in Two-Phase Flow Systems," *Trans., ASME J. Heat Transfer* (1965) **87**, 453.
10. Ansari, A.M., *et al.*: "A Comprehensive Mechanistic Model for Upward Two-Phase Flow in Wellbores," *SPEPF* (May 1994) 143.
11. Harmathy, T.Z.: "Velocity of Large Drops and Bubbles in Media of Infinite or Restricted Extent," *AIChE J.* (1960) **6**, 281.
12. Sadatomi, M., Sato, Y., and Saruwatari: "Two-Phase Flow in Vertical Non-Circular Channels," *Int. J. Multiphase Flow* (1982) **8**, 641.
13. Nicklin, D.J., Wilkes, J.O. and Davidson, J.F.: "Two-Phase Flow in Vertical Tubes," *Trans., Inst. Chem. Engrs.* (1962) 61.
14. Shoham, O.: "Flow Pattern Transition and Characterization in Gas-liquid Two-phase Flow in Inclined Pipes," PhD dissertation, U. of Tel Aviv, Tel Aviv, Israel (1982).
15. Hasan, A.R.: "Void Fraction in Bubbly, Slug, and Churn Flow in Vertical Two-Phase Up-Flow," *Chem. Eng. Comm.* (April 1988) 101.
16. Bornea, D.: "A Unified Model for Predicting Flow Pattern Transition For the Whole Range of Pipe Inclination," *Int. J. Multiphase Flow* (1987) **13**, 1.
17. Brauner, N. and Bornea, D.: "Slug/Churn Transition in Upward Gas-Liquid Flow," *Chem. Eng. Sci.* (1986) **40**, 139.
18. Scott, S.L. and Kouba, G.E.: "Advances in Slug Flow Characterization for Horizontal and Slightly Inclined Pipelines," paper SPE 20628 presented at the 1990 SPE Annual Technical Conference and Exhibition, New Orleans, 23–26 September.
19. Kaya, A.S., Sarica, C., and Brill, J.P.: "Mechanistic Modeling of Two-Phase Flow in Deviated Wells," *SPEPF* (August 2001) 156.
20. Mao, Z.S. and Dukler, A.E.: "The Myth of Churn Flow?," *Int. J. Multiphase Flow* (1993) **19**, 377.
21. Hewitt, G.F. and Jayanti, S.: "To Churn or Not to Churn," *Int. J. Multiphase Flow* (1993) **19**, 527.
22. Jayanti, S. and Hewitt, G.F.: "Prediction of the Slug-to-Churn Flow Transition in Vertical Two-Phase Flow," *Int. J. Multiphase Flow* (1992) **18**, 847.
23. Wallis, G.B.: *One Dimensional Two-Phase Flow*, McGraw-Hill Book Co. Inc., New York City (1969) 93.
24. Pebbles, R.N. and Garber, H.J.: "Studies in the Motion of Gas Bubbles in the Liquids," *Chem. Eng. Prog.* (1953) **35**, 88.
25. Rahman, R.: "Void Fraction During Gas Flow Through a Stagnant Liquid Column in Annular Geometry," MS thesis, U. of North Dakota, Grand Forks, North Dakota (1984).
26. Zahradnik, J. and Kastanek, F.: "Gas Holdup in Uniformly Aerated Bubble Column Reactors," *Chem. Eng. Comm.* (1979) **3**, 413.
27. Kabir, C.S. and Hasan, A.R.: "Two-Phase Flow Correlations as Applied to Pumping Well Testing," *J. Energy Res. Tech.* (June 1994) **116**, 121.
28. Hasan, A.R., Kabir, C.S., and Srivastava, S.: "Countercurrent Bubbly and Slug Flows in Vertical Pipes," *Chem. Eng. Sci.* (1994) **49**, No. 16, 2567.
29. Sylvester, N.D.: "A Mechanistic Model for Two-Phase Slug Flow In Pipes," *J. Energy Res. Tech.* (December 1987) **109**, 206.
30. Fernandes, R.C., Semiat, R., and Dukler, A.E.: "Hydrodynamic Model for Gas-liquid Slug Flow in Vertical Tubes," *AIChE J.* (1986) **32**, 981.
31. Caetano, E.F., Shoham, O. and Brill, J.P.: "Upward Vertical Two-Phase Flow Through an Annulus, Part II: Modeling Bubble, Slug, and Annular Flow," *J. Energy Res. Tech.* (March 1992) **114**, 14.
32. Hasan, A.R. and Kabir, C.S.: "Two-Phase Flow in Vertical and Inclined Annuli," *Int. J. Multiphase Flow* (1992) **18**, No. 2, 273.
33. Brotz, W.: "Uber die Vorausberechnung der Absorptionsgeshwindigkeit von Gasen in Stromenden Flussingkeitsschichten," *Chem. Ing. Tech.* (1954) **26**, 470.
34. Schmidt, Z.: "Experimental Study of Two-phase Flow in a Pipeline Riser Pipe System," PhD dissertation, U. of Tulsa, Tulsa, Oklahoma (1977).
35. Brill, J.P. and Mukherjee, H.: *Multiphase Flow in Wells*, Society of Petroleum Engineers, Monograph Vol. 7, Richardson, Texas (1999).
36. Davies, R.M. and Taylor, G.: "The Mechanics of Large Bubbles Rising Through Extended Liquids and Through Liquids in Tubes," *Proc. of Royal Soc.*, London (1949) **2000A**, 375.
37. Collier, J.G.: *Convective Boiling and Condensation*, 2nd. ed., McGraw-Hill Book Co. Inc., New York City (1981) 72.
38. Kelessidis, V.C. and Dukler, A.E.: "Modeling Flow Pattern Transition for Upward Gas-liquid Flow in Vertical Concentric and Eccentric Annuli," *Int. J. Multiphase Flow* (1989) **15**, 173.
39. Steen, D.A. and Wallis, G.B.: "Pressure Drop and Liquid Entrainment in Annular-Two-Phase Flow," AEC Report No. NYO-3114-2 (1964).

40. Whalley, P. and Hewitt, G.F.: "The Correlation of Liquid Entrainment Fraction and Entrainment Rate in Annular Two-Phase Flow," UKAEA Report, AERE-R9187, Harwell, Oxfordshire, England (1978).

41. Gomez, L.E., *et al.*: "Unified Mechanistic Model for Steady-State Two-Phase Flow: Horizontal to Vertical Upward Flow," *SPEJ* (September 2000) 339.

42. Xiao, J.J., Shoham, O., and Brill, J.P.: "A Comprehensive Mechanistic Model for Two-Phase Flow in Pipelines," paper SPE 20631 presented at the 1990 SPE Annual Technical Conference and Exhibition, New Orleans, 23–26 September.

43. Hagedorn, A.R. and Brown, K.E.: "Experimental Study of Pressure Gradients Occurring During Continuous Two-Phase Flow in Small Diameter Vertical Conduits," *JPT* (April 1965) 475.

44. Duns, H., Jr.,and Ros, N.C.J.: "Vertical Flow of Gas and Liquid Mixtures in Wells," *Proc.*, Sixth World Pet. Cong., Tokyo (1963) 451.

45. Beggs, H.D. and Brill, J.P.: "A Study of Two-Phase Flow in Inclined Pipes," *JPT* (May 1973) 607.

46. Orkiszewski, J.: "Predicting Two-Phase Pressure Drops in Vertical Pipes," *JPT* (June 1967) 829.

47. Mukherjee, H. and Brill, J.P.: "Pressure-Drop Correlations for Inclined Two-Phase Flow," *J. Energy Resources Tech.* (December 1985) **107**, 549.

48. Pucknell, J.K., Mason, J.N.E., and Vervest, E.G.: "An Evaluation of Recent Mechanistic Models of Multiphase Flow for Predicting Pressure Drops in Oil and Gas Wells," paper SPE 26682 presented at the 1993 Offshore European Conference, Aberdeen, 7–10 September.

49. Standing, M.B.: *Volumetric and Phase Behavior of Oil Field Hydrocarbon Systems*, ninth edition, SPE, Richardson, Texas (1981).

50. Dranchuk, P.M. and Abou-Kassem, J.H.: "Calculation of Z-factors for Natural Gases Using Equations-of-State," *J. Cdn. Pet. Tech.* (July–September 1975) **14**, 34.

51. Beggs, H.D. and Robinson, J.R.: "Estimating the Viscosity of Crude Oil Systems," *JPT* (September 1975) 1140.

52. Baker, O. and Swerdloff, W.: "Finding Surface Tension of Hydrocarbon Liquids," *Oil & Gas J.* (2 January 1956) 125.

53. Kabir, C.S. and Hasan, A.R.: "Performance of a Two-Phase Gas/Liquid Model in Vertical Wells," *J. Pet. Sci. Eng.* (1990) **4**, 273.

SI Metric Conversion Factors

cp	$\times$ 1.0*	E – 03 = Pa·s
ft	$\times$ 3.048*	E – 01 = m
ft^2	$\times$ 9.290 304*	E – 02 = m^2
ft^3	$\times$ 2.831 685	E – 02 = m^3
°F	(°F – 32)/1.8	= °C
in.	$\times$ 2.54*	E + 00 = cm
lbf	$\times$ 4.448 222	E + 00 = N
lbm	$\times$ 4.535 924	E – 01 = kg
lbm/ft^3	$\times$ 1.601 846	E + 01 = kg/m^3
psi	$\times$ 6.894 757	E + 00 = kPa

*Conversion factor is exact.

Chapter 4
Multiphase Flow: Deviated and Horizontal Wells and Other Systems

4.1 Introduction

Increased offshore production, by definition, makes multiphase flow from deviated wells a very common occurrence. Advances in horizontal and multilateral well technology demand understanding of multiphase flow in complex well architectures. Besides flow in wellbores, pipeline transportation of produced fluids in an undulating terrain, either on seabed or at surface, clearly present significant challenges in understanding both the fluid and heat transport behavior for optimal design.

The models and correlations developed for flow in vertical wells are not always applicable for inclined or horizontal flow. Wellbore deviation adds another dimension to the already complex flow phenomena, generally observed in vertical wells. Modeling flow pattern transitions and pressure drop in deviated and horizontal wells requires that we account for the effect of well deviation.

Modeling flow behavior also becomes necessary for many other flow geometry and pipe orientations. For example, transient testing of a sucker-rod pumping well requires holdup and pressure-drop estimates for multiphase fluid in the tubing/casing annulus of a well. Similarly, steam injection and the design of gas anchors often require understanding two-phase behavior, when flow occurs downward. Modeling of phase redistribution during shut-in tests might require understanding bubble migration in countercurrent two-phase flow. In addition, flow of oil/water is encountered in many mature oil reservoirs where production-logging diagnosis is required for water management.

In this chapter, we first present empirical correlations and mechanistic models for computing flow patterns and pressure drop in deviated wells. Multiphase flow in horizontal wells is discussed thereafter. We then present models for multiphase flow behavior in annuli, downward direction, and countercurrent flow. The last section discusses two-phase flow of oil and water in vertical and deviated wells.

4.2 Flow in Deviated Wells

Flow of multiphase fluids in vertical pipes is now reasonably well understood. As described in Chap. 3, a number of models are available, which allow delineation of flow patterns at any position in the well. Following the flow-pattern delineation, estimation of holdup and pressure drop becomes possible using models appropriate for the given flow regime. In contrast, understanding multiphase flow behavior in deviated wells has not matured to the level of its vertical counterpart. Correlations available to determine flow-pattern transitions and to estimate holdup and pressure gradient in inclined pipes are largely empirical. Recently, a few mechanistic models for computing flow regime, holdup, and pressure drop have emerged for multiphase flow in deviated wells. In Sec. 4.2.1, we discuss flow patterns and their determination, using both maps and modeling.

4.2.1 Flow Patterns in Upwardly Inclined Systems. Flow patterns observed in upward inclined flow are quite similar to those observed in vertical upward flow, especially for near-vertical systems. In other words, we observe bubbly and dispersed bubbly, slug, churn, and annular flow in inclined systems. These flow patterns are shown in **Fig. 4.1.** Slug and churn flows are often lumped together and are called intermittent flow because they behave in a similar manner and are difficult to distinguish. For systems deviated by more than 20° from vertical, churn flow is rarely observed. For near-horizontal systems, the bubbly flow pattern is sometimes absent. Indeed, Taitel et al.[1] contended that for systems deviated by more than 50° from vertical, bubbly flow never occurs. Additionally, for near-horizontal systems, stratified flow is observed.

One distinction between flow patterns in vertical and inclined systems becomes evident when we examine Fig. 4.1. Because of buoyancy, more of the gas phase tends to flow along the upper wall of the pipe than the lower wall. This gas segregation is particularly true for flow patterns in which phase velocities are generally small, as with bubbly and slug flow. In these two flow regimes, gravity effect dominates, and bubbles tend to favor the upper portion of the channel. For annular flow, and to some extent for churn and dispersed bubbly flow, strong fluid shear force counteracts gravity, and much of the gas phase tends to flow through the central portion of the channel, as in a vertical system.

Another distinction between vertical and inclined flow is the influence of channel inclination on the shape of the bubbles. The increased radial pressure on the bubbles tends to make them sharper than their counterpart in vertical systems. This observation is particularly true of Taylor bubbles in slug

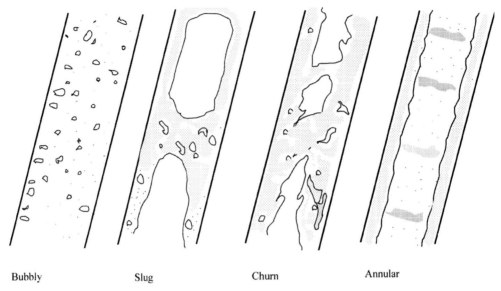

| Bubbly | Slug | Churn | Annular |

Fig. 4.1—Flow patterns for cocurrent gas/liquid flow in inclined pipes.

flow. In vertical flow, the Taylor bubbles have been shown, both theoretically and experimentally, to have a symmetrical, hemispherical top. In inclined flow, the top of the Taylor bubble is shaped much more like an ellipsoid than a hemisphere and is no longer symmetrical about the bubble axis. The effect of this shape change on the bubble's rise velocity and holdup is discussed later.

4.2.2 Pattern Transition Criteria. There are very few datasets or correlations available for flow pattern transition in inclined systems. Physical modeling of such systems is even scarcer. The empirical work by Weisman and Kang[2] on flow pattern transition is a major contribution in this area and is presented first. Modeling approach to pattern transition is then presented with data and analysis from various authors.[1-6]

Flow-Pattern Maps. The major premise of Weisman and Kang[2] is that the boundaries of flow patterns existing at very high flow rates are usually unaffected by well deviation. For instance, they found that the transitions to annular flow and dispersed bubbly flow are unaffected by a pipe's inclination angle. This observation, according to Weisman and Kang,[2] extends all the way from vertical to horizontal flow. Their simplified correlation for transition to annular flow, for all inclination angles, is given by

$$(\text{Fr}_{sg})(\text{Ku}_{sg}) = 25\left(\frac{v_{sg}}{v_{sL}}\right)^{0.625} , \quad \dots\dots\dots\dots (4.1)$$

where both the Froude number, $\text{Fr}_{sg} (=v_{sg}^2/gd)$, and the Kutadelaze number, Ku_{sg}, are based on superficial gas velocity, v_{sg}.

$$\text{Ku}_{sg} = \frac{v_{sg}\rho_g}{[g(\rho_L - \rho_g)\sigma]^{0.25}} . \quad \dots\dots\dots\dots (4.2)$$

We should note that, unlike Weisman and Kang,[2] Taitel *et al.*[1] found the transition to annular flow to be independent

of liquid velocity and pipe diameter. Otherwise, however, the two correlations generally indicate similar dependency of the gas velocity at transition on liquid and gas densities and surface tension.

Weisman and Kang[2] proposed that the following condition must prevail for transition to dispersed bubbly flow for all angles of inclination to occur.

$$\left[\frac{(-dp/dz)_L}{g(\rho_L - \rho_g)}\right]^{0.5}\left[\frac{g(\rho_L - \rho_g)d^2}{\sigma}\right]^{0.25} \geq 9.7 , \quad \dots\dots (4.3)$$

where $(dp/dz)_L$ is the frictional pressure gradient of liquid flowing alone through the pipe. Predictions of the Weisman-Kang correlation for the transition to dispersed bubbly flow are also similar to those of Taitel *et al.*[1] in vertical flow (Eq. 3.10). Both correlations suggest a mixture velocity of about 10 ft/sec (3.05 m/s) for air/water systems at standard conditions before transition to dispersed bubbly flow occurs. However, the Weisman-Kang correlation indicates independence of this transition to gas velocity; whereas, the Taitel *et al.*[1] model does not.

Following the Bornea *et al.*[3] approach for horizontal and slightly inclined systems, Weisman and Kang[2] did not distinguish churn from slug flow but lumped these two flow patterns together as intermittent flow. Their approach to delineate the transition between bubbly and intermittent flow uses Froude numbers, based on v_{sg} and v_m, as the correlating parameters. Their transition expression is given by

$$\frac{v_{sg}^2}{gd} = 0.2\left(\frac{v_m}{gd}\right)^{1.56}(1 - 0.65\cos\alpha)^2 . \quad \dots\dots\dots (4.4)$$

The last term, $(1 - 0.65\cos\alpha)^2$, accounts for the effect of inclination. Weisman and Kang[2] showed good agreement between the transition condition calculated with Eq. 4.4, and the bubbly-intermittent transition data for systems inclined at various angles from the horizontal, 2.75 to 90°.

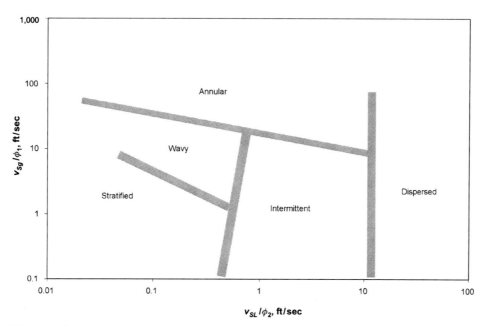

Fig. 4.2—Generalized flow pattern map of Weisman and Kang (from Ref. 2; reprinted with permission from Elsevier Science).

Fig. 4.2 presents the flow-pattern map of Weisman and Kang.[2] The basic map, with v_{sg} and v_{sL} as the axes, is for two-phase flow in a horizontal system with particular (standard) values of fluid properties and system dimensions. The parameters ϕ_1 and ϕ_2 are used to make the map general, not only for all fluids but also for inclination angles. The expressions for ϕ_1 and ϕ_2, as reported by Weisman and Kang[2], are reproduced in **Table 4.1.**

Individual Transition Criteria. Physical analysis for the transition from bubbly to slug flow, presented by Hasan[5] and Hasan and Kabir,[6] follows the approach discussed for vertical systems. Recall that for vertical systems, when the gas volume fraction exceeds 0.25, transition from bubbly flow generally occurs. However, in an inclined pipe, the gas phase tends to flow along the upper wall. This preferential flow increases the actual in-situ gas fraction near the upper wall. Therefore, near the upper wall the in-

situ gas fraction may exceed the value of 0.25, even when the cross-sectional average is much lower. As a result, collisions among the bubbles increase sharply, forming Taylor bubbles, and the transition to slug flow occurs at a cross-sectional average volume fraction lower than 0.25.

We can apply Eq. 3.3 for holdup in vertical systems to an inclined pipe, if the actual superficial velocity of the gas phase at the upper section of the pipe is used rather than the cross-sectional average. In an inclined pipe, we assume that the actual cross-sectional area available for the gas to flow is the projection of the area on a horizontal plane. Thus, if A is the pipe cross-sectional area, then the area available for gas flow through a pipe inclined at an angle, α, to the horizontal is $A\sin\alpha$. Therefore, the actual superficial velocity of the gas phase is

$$\left(v_{sg}\right)_a = \frac{q_g}{A\sin\alpha} = \frac{v_{sg}}{\sin\alpha} \cdot \quad\ldots\ldots\ldots\ldots\ldots\ldots(4.5)$$

By substituting $(v_{sg})_a$ in place of v_{sg} in Eq. 3.3, we obtain the local volume fraction, f_{gL}, near the upper wall.

$$f_{gL} = \frac{[v_{sg}/\sin\alpha]}{C_0[v_{sL} + v_{sg}/\sin\alpha] + v_\infty} \cdot \quad\ldots\ldots\ldots\ldots(4.6)$$

By rearranging and using $f_{gL}=0.25$ at transition,

$$v_{sg} = \left[\frac{C_0 f_g}{1-C_0 f_g}v_{sL} + \frac{C_0 f_g}{1-C_0 f_g}v_\infty\right]\sin\alpha$$

$$= [0.43v_{sL} + 0.357v_\infty]\sin\alpha \cdot \quad\ldots\ldots\ldots\ldots(4.7)$$

The bubble rise velocity, v_∞, determined by the balance of the buoyancy and drag forces, can be different for an inclined system from that for a vertical system. The buoyancy force obviously decreases as the pipe is deviated from the vertical

TABLE 4.1—PARAMETERS FOR THE WEISMAN AND KANG FLOW-PATTERN MAP			
Flow Orientation	Transition To	ϕ_1	ϕ_2
Horizontal, Vertical, and Inclined	Dispersed flow	1.0	$(\rho_L/\rho_{sL})^{-0.33}$ $(d/d_s)^{0.16}$ $(\mu_{sL}/\mu_L)^{0.09}$ $(\sigma/\sigma s)^{0.24}$
	Annular flow	$(\rho_{sg}/\rho_g)^{0.23}$ $(\Delta\rho/\Delta\rho_s)^{0.11}$ $(\sigma/\sigma_s)^{0.11}$ $(d/d_s)^{0.415}$	1.0
Vertical and Inclined	Bubbly	$(d/d_s)^n$ $(1-0.65\cos a)$	1.0
	Intermittent	$n = 0.26e^{-0.17\,v_{sL}/v_{ssL}}$	

s denotes standard condtions, d_s=1.0 in., r_{sg}=0.0013 kg/L, r_{sL}=1 kg/L, s_s=70 dynes/cm, v_{ssL}=1.0 ft/sec

system, which tends to reduce the bubble rise velocity. However, as mentioned earlier, deviation from the vertical system also causes a shape change, generally making the bubble-nose sharper. A sharper bubble-nose causes a decrease in the drag force on it. Therefore, the overall effect of pipe inclination on these two forces can cancel out, and the influence of pipe inclination on the terminal rise velocity of the bubble can be negligible. Limited data of Hasan and Kabir[6] indicate that the terminal rise velocity of small bubbles is not appreciably affected by the inclination angle. Therefore, the Harmathy correlation[7] for v_∞ (Eq. 3.6) can be used in Eq. 4.7. Patel's[8] data corroborate this contention.

Bornea *et al.*[3] also extended their analysis for transition in vertical systems, presented in Chap. 3, to inclined systems by replacing the terminal rise velocity of the bubble with $v_\infty \sin\alpha$. For example, they suggested that transition from bubbly flow occurs when v_{sg} is greater than $0.33v_{sL}+0.25\sin\alpha v_\infty$. This criterion is doubtful because, as we indicated earlier, the rise velocity of small bubbles does not appear to decrease with deviation from vertical systems. However, for most systems with low superficial liquid velocity, the difference is negligible. Hasan and Kabir[6] showed excellent agreement of Eq. 4.7 with the data of Bornea *et al.*[3] and those of Weisman and Kang.[2]

Bornea *et al.*[3] also pointed out that preferential migration of bubbles to the upper part of a deviated pipe leads to a limiting inclination angle beyond which bubbly flow cannot exist. By equating buoyancy to lift forces, they proposed that when well inclination (from horizontal) is less than that given by the expression,

$$\frac{\cos\alpha}{\sin^2\alpha} = \frac{3}{4}\cos 45°\frac{v_\infty}{g}\left(\frac{C_L\gamma^2}{d}\right), \quad \ldots\ldots\ldots\ldots (4.8)$$

bubbly flow cannot exist. For the lift coefficient, C_L, in Eq. 4.8, Bornea *et al.*[3] recommended a value of 0.8, while the distortion coefficient, γ, varies between 1.1 and 1.5. For air/water flow through a 2-in. ID pipe at standard conditions, Eq. 4.8 suggests that the maximum well inclination for bubbly flow is about 55 to 70°.

In addition to deviation, well diameter also imposes a restriction on the occurrence of bubbly flow. The diameter of the well must be large enough to satisfy the condition that the Taylor-bubble rise velocity is greater than that for the small bubbles, i.e., $v_{\infty T} > v_\infty$. For vertical flow, this condition results in a well diameter that must exceed the value given by Eq. 3.8. Bornea *et al.*[3] and Kaya *et al.*[9] suggested the same expression for deviated wells. However, the differences in Taylor-bubble rise velocity in deviated wells might need to be taken into account.

Transition to Churn Flow. As mentioned earlier, the chaotic nature of churn flow pattern makes modeling the dynamics of this flow regime very difficult. The analysis presented in Chap. 3 for vertical systems might apply. Kaya *et al.*[9] presented an analysis that appears promising and is well supported by data. They noted that the transition to churn flow occurs when the gas volume fraction exceeds 0.78. They also argued that the average f_g in this flow regime may be approximated, following the drift-flux approach, as given by

$$f_g = \frac{v_{sg}}{C_o v_m + v_{\infty T_o}}. \quad \ldots\ldots\ldots\ldots\ldots (4.9)$$

With the transition f_g of 0.78 and $C_o = 1.2$, they arrived at the expression for v_{sg}, in which churn flow will occur,

$$v_{sg} = 12.19\left(1.2v_{sL} + v_{\infty T_o}\right). \quad \ldots\ldots\ldots\ldots (4.10)$$

Note that if we followed the Hasan-Kabir suggestion that the value of C_o is 1.15 for churn flow, the required gas velocity for the transition will be much smaller; that is, $v_{sg} = 7.57(1.2v_m + v_{\infty T\alpha})$. However, Kaya *et al.*[9] showed data from a number of sources in support of Eq. 4.10. Note that Eq. 4.10 indicates dependence of this transition on the Taylor-bubble rise velocity, which, in turn, depends on well deviation.

Transition to Dispersed Bubbly Flow. Bornea *et al.*[3] recommended the same criteria developed for vertical systems in deviated wells.

Transition to Annular Flow. Following the approach of Taitel *et al.*,[4] Bornea *et al.*[3] presented an analysis that results in the expression for transition to annular flow, which is written as

$$v_{sg} = 3.1(\sin\alpha)^{1/4}\left(g\sigma(\rho_L - \rho_g)/\rho_g^2\right). \quad \ldots\ldots\ldots (4.11)$$

Eq. 4.11 shows that superficial gas velocity, needed for transition to annular flow, depends on the one-fourth power of the sine of the inclination angle.

The work of Weisman and Kang[2] shows that, with the exception of bubbly slug flow transition, the transition criteria established for vertical systems are apparently applicable to inclined systems. Because the criteria established in Chap. 3 are based on sound physical modeling, they are preferable to the ones proposed by Weisman and Kang.[2] However, the criterion proposed by Kaya *et al.*[9] for transition to churn flow indicates slight dependence of this transition on well deviation. The work of Bornea *et al.*[3] also shows that the transition to annular flow is mildly affected by the channel inclination angle. However, because of the support provided by the Weisman-Kang work and for the sake of simplicity, one may ignore the influence of channel inclination angle on flow pattern transition in any regime other than the bubbly flow.

4.2.3 Holdup and Pressure Drop in Deviated Wells: Empirical Correlations.

We now present empirical methods available for computing holdup and pressure drop in inclined two-phase flow. The most extensive experimental study on inclined two-phase flow was reported by Beggs,[10] and by Beggs and Brill.[11] While a number of other significant works have since been performed, most notably by Mukherjee and Brill,[12] the Beggs and Brill[11] method remains perhaps the most accurate and certainly the best known.

The Beggs and Brill Correlation. The Beggs and Brill[11] correlation is based on the data they gathered in 90-ft pipes with pipe ID's of 1 and 1.5 in. These pipes were inclined at various angles between zero and 90 degrees in both upward and downward directions.

We first briefly describe the Beggs and Brill[11] method for horizontal systems because their correlation for inclined systems is based on its modification. They divided the flow patterns observed in horizontal systems into four categories. The first is segregated flow, which includes smooth and wavy stratified flow and annular flow. The intermittent flow pattern encompasses slug and plug flow. The transition flow regime includes regions between intermittent and stratified flow patterns, and the distributed flow pattern comprises bubbly and mist flows.

Beggs and Brill based their horizontal flow-pattern map on the input liquid volume fraction C_L ($=v_{sL}/v_m$) and the mixture Froude number ($\mathrm{Fr}_m=v_m^2/gd$). They defined the four transition parameters as

$$L_1 = 316\,C_L^{0.302}, \quad L_2 = 0.0009252\,C_L^{-2.4684},$$

$$L_3 = 0.1\,C_L^{-1.4516}, \text{ and } L_2 = 0.5\,C_L^{-6.738} \quad \ldots\ldots (4.12)$$

The flow patterns are determined by the following conditions:

Segregated: $C_L < 0.01$ and $\mathrm{Fr} < L_1$,
      or $C_L > 0.01$ and $\mathrm{Fr} < L_2$;

Transition: $C_L < 0.01$ and $L_2 < \mathrm{Fr} < L_3$;

Intermittent: $0.01 < C_L > 0.4$ and $L_3 < \mathrm{Fr} < L_1$,
      or $C_L > 0.4$ and $L_3 < \mathrm{Fr} < L_4$; and

Distributed: $C_L < 0.4$ and $\mathrm{Fr} > L_1$,
      or $C_L > 0.4$ and $\mathrm{Fr} > L_4$.

The flow pattern map with the transition parameters, which are linear on log/log coordinates, is shown in **Fig. 4.3**.

They proposed the correlation for liquid holdup, f_L ($=1-f_g$), for horizontal (0-degree inclination) systems as

$$f_{L(0)} = a\,C_L^b / \mathrm{Fr}^c \quad \cdots\cdots\cdots\cdots\cdots (4.13)$$

The following are the values of parameters a, b, and c, which depend on specific flow patterns.

	a	b	c
Segregated	0.980	0.4846	0.0868
Intermittent	0.845	0.5351	0.0173
Distributed	1.065	0.5824	0.0609

When the flow regime falls in the transition zone, they suggested that f_L be estimated from a linear interpolation of f_L values calculated for the segregated and intermittent flow regimes. Thus,

$$f_{L,\mathrm{tran}} = \left[\frac{(L_3 - \mathrm{Fr})}{(L_3 - L_2)}\right] f_{L,\mathrm{seg}} + \left[\frac{(\mathrm{Fr} - L_2)}{(L_3 - L_2)}\right] f_{L,\mathrm{int}} \quad \cdots\cdots (4.14)$$

The frictional pressure gradient is calculated with equation

$$\left(-\frac{dp}{dz}\right)_F = \frac{2 f_m \rho_n v_m^2}{g_c d} \quad \cdots\cdots\cdots\cdots\cdots\cdots (4.15)$$

In Eq. 4.15, ρ_n is the no-slip mixture density, $\rho_n = \rho_L C_L + \rho_g C_g$. The mixture friction factor, f_m, is related to the no-slip, two-phase friction factor, f_n, by

$$f_m = f_n e^s, \quad \cdots\cdots\cdots\cdots\cdots\cdots\cdots\cdots (4.16)$$

where f_n is the no-slip friction factor based on the no-slip Reynolds number, $\mathrm{Re}_n = d v_m \rho_n / \mu_n$, and μ_n is the no-slip mixture viscosity, $\mu_n = \mu_L C_L + \mu_g C_g$. To calculate the exponent, s, needed to determine the two-phase friction factor, Beggs and Brill[10] defined a parameter, y, in terms of C_L, and holdup as

$$y \equiv C_L / f_{L(0)}^2 \quad \cdots\cdots\cdots\cdots\cdots\cdots\cdots\cdots (4.17)$$

The exponent, s, is empirically related to the parameter, y, when $y > 1.2$, and is written as

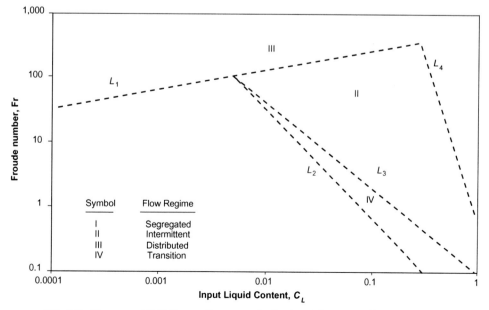

Fig. 4.3—Beggs and Brill flow-pattern map for horizontal systems (from Ref. 11).

$$s = \frac{\ln y}{-0.0523 + 3.182(\ln y) - 0.8725(\ln y)^2 + 0.01853(\ln y)^4} .$$
$$\dotfill (4.18)$$

For a value of y between 1.0 and 1.2, s is given by

$$s = (\ln 2.2y - 1.2) \quad 1 < y < 1.2 . \dotfill (4.19)$$

Thus, frictional pressure gradient is dependent on the flow regime because y depends on $f_{L(\alpha)}$, which, in turn, depends on the flow regime, as well as on the inclination angle.

For inclined multiphase systems, Beggs and Brill[11] suggested the following calculation procedure. The flow regime that would exist, if the system was horizontal, is first determined using the criteria previously discussed. Holdup is then calculated with Eq. 4.13. Thereafter, it is multiplied by the correction factor, $F(\alpha)$, to estimate the holdup for the actual inclined system. In other words,

$$f_{L(\alpha)} = f_{L(0)} F(\alpha) , \dotfill (4.20)$$

$$F(\alpha) = 1 + Z\left[\sin(1.8\alpha) - \sin^3(1.8\alpha)\right] , \dotfill (4.21)$$

$$Z = (1 - C_L)\ln\left[dC_L^e v_{dL}^f \text{Fr}_g\right] , \dotfill (4.22)$$

and $v_{Ld} = v_{sL}\sqrt[4]{\rho_L / g\sigma} . \dotfill (4.23)$

Parameters d, e, f, and g depend on the flow pattern that was determined with an equivalent horizontal system. The following are the specific flow patterns with parameter values.

	d	e	f	g
Segregated uphill	0.011	−3.768	3.539	−1.614
Intermittent uphill	2.96	0.305	−0.4473	0.0978
Distributed uphill	No correction, $F(\alpha) = 1.0$			
All flow regimes downhill	4.70	−0.3692	0.1244	−0.5056

Beggs and Brill[11] did not suggest any specific method for calculating the accelerational component. Where it is significant, the accelerational gradient can be calculated with either the separated or the homogeneous flow approach, and ρ_m can be estimated with the Beggs and Brill method. The total pressure gradient is given by

$$-\frac{dp}{dz} = \frac{g\sin\alpha}{g_c}\left(\rho_L f_L + \rho_g f_g\right) + \frac{f_m v_m^2 \rho_n}{2g_c d} + \frac{\rho_m v_m}{g_c}\frac{dv_m}{dz} .$$
$$\dotfill (4.24)$$

Other Correlations. A few other methods have been proposed for computing flow behavior using a flow-pattern approach. For instance, Singh and Griffith,[13] Bonnecaze et al.,[14] Mattar and Gregory,[15] and Asheim[16] have proposed correlations for estimating holdup in slug flow, which are very similar to the expression for f_{gT}, given by Eq. 4.14. In fact, based on data from pipes inclined at 5, 10, and 15 degrees

from horizontal, Singh and Griffith suggested that holdup in inclined slug flow can be represented by $f_g = v_{sg}/(0.95v_m + 1.15)$. The correlation makes the simplifying assumption that the Taylor bubble may represent the drift-flux for the entire gas flow. In addition, comparison of this equation, with its counterpart for vertical systems, indicates that Singh and Griffith found the Taylor-bubble rise velocity, in inclined pipes, to be independent of not only pipe diameter but also of inclination angle. As we discussed, Beggs and Brill[11] found holdup to be a strong function of pipe deviation. The data reported by Wallis[17] also show holdup, during inclined slug flow, to be a strong function of inclination angle. Therefore, the procedure presented in this text is preferred to correlations similar to those proposed by Singh and Griffith.[13]

Most of these works, however, appear to agree that the liquid holdup for intermittent flow in a well slightly deviated from vertical is usually higher than that calculated under conditions similar to vertical flow. Indeed, the data of Beggs and Brill[11] suggest that liquid holdup becomes a maximum at an angle of +50° from the horizontal.

4.2.4 Holdup and Pressure Drop in Deviated Wells: Mechanistic Models.
There are very few mechanistic models for computing holdup and pressure drop in deviated systems. Hasan,[5] Hasan and Kabir,[6] Kaya et al.,[9] and Gomez et al.[18] have proposed comprehensive models for deviated wells. We present the major developments of these models, with some modifications.

The Hasan-Kabir model uses the flow-pattern approach for vertical systems, discussed in Chap. 3, with modifications for the system's deviation from vertical orientation. Hasan and Kabir,[6] as well as Kaya et al.[9] noted that for annular and dispersed bubbly flow, the flow rates are very high. Consequently, the influence of buoyancy is small, and the effect of pipe inclination is negligible. Therefore, for these flow regimes, the relationships developed for vertical systems can be used without any modifications. Therefore, we address only the bubbly and intermittent flow patterns.

Bubbly Flow. For vertical systems, Hasan and Kabir[6] postulated that the in-situ velocity, v_g, of the gas phase, is the sum of the terminal rise velocity, v_∞, and the mixture velocity, v_m, multiplied by the flow parameter, C_o. Hence, $v_g = v_{sg}/f_g = C_o v_m + v_\infty$. The analysis should also hold for deviated wells. Therefore, as in Eq. 3.21, holdup is given by

$$f_L \equiv 1 - f_g = 1 - \frac{v_{sg}}{C_o v_m + v_\infty} . \dotfill (4.25)$$

Kaya et al.[9] and Gomez et al.,[18] following the approach of Ansari et al.[19] for vertical systems, arrived at a slightly different expression.

$$f_L \equiv 1 - f_g = 1 - \frac{v_{sg}}{C_o v_m + v_\infty \sqrt{f_L \sin\alpha}} . \dotfill (4.26)$$

Therefore, the procedure for estimating holdup and pressure drop in deviated wells will be similar to those discussed for vertical systems. One, however, will need values for the flow parameter, C_o, and the bubble rise velocity, v_∞, in an inclined system.

Flow Parameter and Bubble Rise Velocity. For vertical systems, we were able to reason that the value of the flow parameter, C_o, should be 1.2 because the flow is turbulent, and the bubbles ride the central portion of the channel, where the mixture velocity is 1.2 times the cross-sectional average value. The bubble concentration profile is likely to be affected by the pipe's deviation. Intuitively then, one can expect C_o to be influenced by well deviation, which has led Gomez et al.[18] to use $C_o=1.15$.

However, the effect of pipe inclination on C_o appears negligible. This trend is observed in the data of Patel[8] for pipes deviated up to 32° from vertical. Even for the case of elongated bubble flow through horizontal pipes, the value of C_o has been generally found to be 1.2.[20-21] Consequently, Hasan and Kabir[6] and Kaya et al.[9] proposed a value of 1.2 for C_o in Eqs. 4.25 or 4.26. As discussed earlier, the bubble rise velocity may be assumed to remain unchanged with pipe inclination. Therefore, the same expression, with the identical values of parameters, used in vertical flow, can be used to estimate holdup in deviated wells. The only difference between bubbly flow in deviated wells and that in vertical wells is the transition to slug flow.

Once holdup is estimated, the total pressure gradient may be calculated by adding the frictional and accelerational components to the static head. The contribution of these components, which are very small, may be estimated with the method applicable to vertical systems (Eq. 3.17). The static head for an inclined system, of course, equals $\rho_m \sin\alpha$. Therefore,

$$-\frac{dp}{dz} = \frac{g\sin\alpha}{g_c}\left(\rho_L f_L + \rho_g f_g\right) + \frac{f_m v_m^2 \rho_m}{2g_c d} + \frac{\rho_m v_m}{g_c}\frac{dv_m}{dz}.$$
$$\dots\dots\dots\dots\dots\dots\dots (4.27)$$

Slug Flow. Application of the simple drift-flux model, developed for bubbly flow, to slug flow becomes difficult. This difficulty stems from the difference in drift velocities between the small and the Taylor bubbles and the asymmetric nature of the distribution and shape of the bubbles. As discussed in Chap. 3, one simple way to account for different drift velocities in slug flow is to use some type of an average rise velocity for all gas bubbles—large and small—in the system. Therefore, for estimating in-situ gas volume fraction during slug flow, we use Eq. 3.26, reproduced here for convenience.

$$f_L \equiv 1 - f_g = 1 - \frac{v_{sg}}{C_o v_m + \bar{v}_{\infty\alpha}}.\quad \dots\dots\dots\dots (4.28)$$

As in the case of vertical flow, the average rise velocity is expressed in terms of the Taylor-bubble rise velocity in a deviated well, small-bubble rise velocity, and bubbly-slug transition velocity as

$$\bar{v}_{\infty\alpha} = v_{\infty T\alpha}(1 - e^{-v_t/v_{sg}}) + v_\infty e^{-v_t/v_{sg}},\quad \dots\dots\dots (4.29)$$

where v_t, the superficial gas velocity for transition to intermittent flow, is given by Eq. 4.7.

If further rigor is desired, one can take the cellular approach, as done in Chap. 3 for vertical systems, and model the dynamics of the Taylor bubble and liquid slug portions of the cell. Unfortunately, for deviated systems, the asymmetric nature of the Taylor bubble, the liquid film, and bubble distribution in the channel makes such an analysis extremely difficult. The effort of Kaya et al.[9] and Gomez et al.[18] to adapt the Ansari[19] vertical flow model for this regime, with modifications for well deviation, is an auspicious beginning. These adaptations[9,18] are presented in the next section for flow in near-horizontal systems.

Flow Parameter C_o. As discussed in bubbly flow, the flow parameter might be affected by channel inclination. However, data, gathered by Lau[22] and Patel,[8] show that the value of the flow parameter remains constant at 1.2, irrespective of the channel inclination. This finding makes the estimation procedure simple. Both Hasan and Kabir[6] and Kaya et al.[9] used this value of the flow parameter. However, we note that data supporting a constant value of $C_o=1.2$ for all inclinations are limited and are derived from small-diameter pipes.

Taylor-Bubble Rise Velocity, $v_{\infty T\alpha}$. Unlike the flow parameter in inclined flow, the terminal rise velocity of a Taylor bubble is strongly influenced by pipe inclination. The high Eotvos number data from Wallis[17] clearly show strong variation in Taylor-bubble rise velocity with pipe inclination. Note that for most practical systems, the inverse viscosity number is very high (>30,000; refer to material on slug flow in Chap. 3). In such cases, the Wallis[17] data indicate that the Taylor-bubble rise velocity increases with increasing deviation of the pipe from the vertical system, until a maximum is reached for a deviation angle of about 50°. The rise velocity then gradually decreases with increasing deviations and finally becomes zero for horizontal systems. The data of Patel,[8] among others, also lead to a similar conclusion. Because for most practical systems the Eotvos number is large, this observation is of great significance.

Balancing the buoyancy force against the drag force, experienced by a rising bubble, leads to the expression for the rise velocity of a bubble of volume V_B and projected area A_P,

$$V_B g\sin\alpha\left(\rho_L - \rho_g\right) = \frac{1}{2}C_{D\alpha}v_{\infty T\alpha}^2\rho_L A_{P\alpha}\quad \dots\dots\dots (4.30)$$

In Eq. 4.30, $C_{D\alpha}$ is the drag coefficient for the bubble and $v_{\infty T\alpha}$ is its rise velocity in a pipe, inclined to the horizontal by an angle, α. A similar expression can be written for a vertical system. Taking the ratio of these two expressions,

$$\frac{v_{\infty T\alpha}}{v_{\infty T}} = \sqrt{\sin\alpha\frac{(C_D A_P)_{90}}{C_{D\alpha}A_{P\alpha}}}.\quad \dots\dots\dots\dots (4.31)$$

If the product of the drag coefficient and projected area of the bubble were the same for vertical and inclined systems; that is, if $(C_D A_P)_{90}/(C_{D\alpha}A_{P\alpha})=1$, then Eq. 4.31 suggests that the rise velocity of the bubble will gradually decrease, as the deviation of the pipe increases. However, in inclined flow, the Taylor bubble has a sharper nose, compared to that in vertical

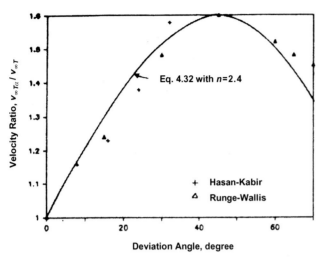

Fig. 4.4—Correlating Taylor-bubble rise velocity ratio with well deviation angle, Eq. 4.32 (from Ref. 6).

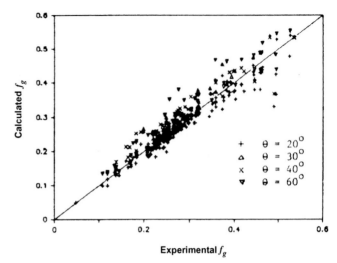

Fig. 4.5—Laboratory data support slug flow model, Eq. 4.28 (from Ref. 6).

systems, with a consequent lower drag coefficient. This lowering of the drag coefficient increases, as the pipe deviates from the vertical. In addition, the projected area in a deviated well is also smaller. The net effect is that the ratio, $(C_D A_P)_{90}/(C_{D\alpha} A_{P\alpha})$, becomes greater than 1.0. Consequently, an increase in the terminal rise velocity with pipe deviation occurs when the deviation is small, with a consequent increase in liquid holdup, compared to that for a vertical system.

At large deviations from vertical, the buoyancy force begins to decrease much faster than the drag force and the bubble rise velocity begins to decrease with further deviation from the vertical. The variation in the $C_D A_{P\alpha}$ product with inclination angle may be approximated by $(C_D A_P)_{90}(1+\cos\alpha)^n$.

$$v_{\infty T\alpha} = v_{\infty T}\sqrt{\sin\alpha(1+\cos\alpha)^n} \quad \cdots \cdots \cdots \cdots (4.32)$$

The data of Runge and Wallis, as reported by Wallis,[17] is well represented by Eq. 4.32, if $n=2.4$ is used, as shown in **Fig. 4.4.** With this value of n, the bubble's terminal rise velocity in intermittent flow becomes (using the Taylor-bubble rise velocity for vertical flow, Eq. 3.30)

$$v_{\infty T\alpha} = 0.345\sqrt{gd(\rho_L - \rho_g)/\rho_L}(1+\cos\alpha)^{1.2}\sqrt{\sin\alpha} \quad \cdot$$
$$\cdots \cdots \cdots \cdots \cdots \cdots (4.33)$$

Combining Eq. 4.33 with Eqs. 4.28 and 4.29 will yield liquid holdup and, therefore, the mixture density. The total pressure gradient can then be evaluated with the method developed for vertical flow (Eqs. 3.56 or 4.22). Eq. 4.28 shows that at small deviation angles, liquid holdup increases with increasing deviation of the pipe from the vertical system, reaching a maximum value at deviation angles of about 50°. This observation is consistent with the findings of Beggs and Brill.[11]

A different approach was adapted by Bendiksen,[23] who proposed the expression for $v_{\infty T\alpha}$.

$$v_{\infty T\alpha} = (0.35\sin\alpha + 0.54\cos\alpha)\sqrt{gd(\rho_L - \rho_g)/\rho_L} \quad \cdot$$
$$\cdots \cdots \cdots \cdots \cdots \cdots (4.34)$$

Eq. 4.34, which has been adapted by many researchers, including Kaya et al.[9] and Gomez et al.,[18] calculates nonzero rise velocity for a Taylor bubble in a horizontal system.

The goodness of the simplified slug-flow model's performance, which we discussed, can be observed by inspecting both **Figs. 4.5** and **4.6,** which display in-situ gas volume fraction and pressure-gradient data, respectively. We presented these figures earlier in Ref. 6. In the same study, we showed that the simplified mechanistic model performs satisfactorily in representing the Beggs-Brill data,[11] encompassing all four flow regimes. **Figs. 4.7** and **4.8** compare the gas volume fraction and pressure-gradient data, respectively.

Field Example 4.1. Problem. A 17.5° deviated well (inclined at 72.5° from horizontal) has a measured depth of 6,241 ft. The well produces 33° (API) oil at 2,922 STB/D with 20.02% water cut through a 2.43-in. (0.202-ft) ID tube. The gas/oil ratio (GOR) is 447 scf/STB, and the gas gravity is 0.6. The following property values and com-

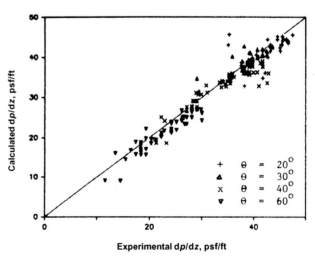

Fig. 4.6—Laboratory data lend support to pressure gradient calculations in slug flow (from Ref. 6).

FLUID FLOW AND HEAT TRANSFER IN WELLBORES

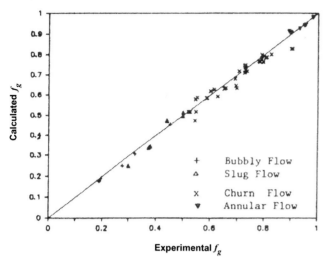

Fig. 4.7—Laboratory data lend support to f_g calculations in all flow regimes (from Ref. 10).

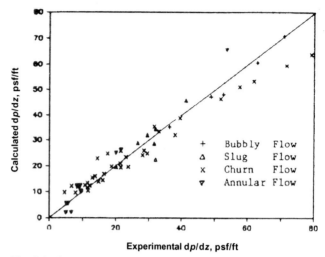

Fig. 4.8—Laboratory data lend support to pressure gradient calculations in all flow regimes (from Ref. 10).

puted fluid parameters are available at the wellhead, where the pressure is 361 psig.

$$v_{sL} = 6.153 \text{ ft/sec}$$
$$v_{sg} = 14.8 \text{ ft/sec}$$
$$\rho_L = 53.36 \text{ lbm/ft}^3$$
$$\rho_g = 1.03 \text{ lbm/ft}^3$$
$$\mu_L = 2.25 \text{ cp}$$
$$\mu_g = 0.018 \text{ cp}$$
$$\sigma = 29 \text{ dynes/cm} = 0.064 \text{ lbm/sec}^2$$

Calculate the pressure gradient at this point.

Solution. *Flow Pattern and Transition Criteria.*

Eq. 3.6: $v_\infty = 1.53 [g\sigma(\rho_L - \rho_g)/\rho_L^2]^{0.25}$
$= 1.53 [(32.2)(0.064)(52.33)/53.36^2]^{0.25} = 0.675 \text{ ft/sec}.$

Eq. 4.33: $v_{\infty T\alpha} = 0.345 [gd (\rho_L - \rho_g)/\rho_L]^{0.5} [(\sin\alpha)^{1/2}$
$(1+\cos\alpha)^{1.2}] = 0.345 [(32.2)(0.202)(52.33)/53.36]^{0.5} (1.339)$
$= 1.169 \text{ ft/sec}.$

Because $v_{\infty T} > v_\infty$, Eq. 4.7 would apply for transition from bubbly to slug flow.

Eq. 4.7: $v_t = (0.429 v_{sL} + 0.357 v_\infty)(\sin 72.5)$
$= [(0.429)(6.211) + (0.357)(0.769)](0.9537)$
$= 2.747 \text{ ft/sec}.$

Because the actual $v_{sg} > 2.75$ ft/sec, the pattern is not bubbly. Test each flow regime before moving forward with any calculations. First, use Eq. 3.10 to compute the minimum mixture velocity needed for the dispersed bubbly flow to exist. Note that the actual mixture velocity is $v_{sg} + v_{sL} = 20.95$ ft/sec. Eq. 3.10 requires an estimate of the friction factor. Use a value of $f = 0.0199$, whose computation will be shown later.

The left-hand side (LHS) of Eq. 3.10 is: $2(20.95)^{1.2}$
$(0.0199/0.4)^{0.4} (53.36/0.064)^{0.6} [0.4(0.064)/\{(32.2)$
$(52.33)\}]^{0.5} = 5.088.$

The right-hand-side (RHS) of Eq. 3.9 is: $0.725 + 4.15$
$(14.68/20.9)^{0.5} = 4.21.$

Therefore, the mixture velocity (LHS) is high enough (compared to the RHS) to support either dispersed bubbly or churn flow. Using Eq. 3.11 ($v_{sg} = 1.08 v_{sL}$) we conclude that because actual v_{sg} is greater than $(1.08 v_{sL} =)6.645$ ft/sec, dispersed bubbly flow cannot be sustained, so churn flow is a likely pattern. However, we have to check if this high gas velocity could cause annular flow to exist.

Transition to Annular Flow. We use Eq. 3.12 to estimate the minimum gas velocity needed to sustain annular flow. In Eq. 3.12, $v_{sg} = 3.1[(32.2)(0.064)(52.33)/1.03^2]^{1/4}$
$= 9.85$ ft/sec. Although the actual superficial gas velocity is higher than that estimated with Eq. 3.12 for annular flow, the calculated in-situ gas volume fraction, f_g of 0.586, as shown later, is too low to sustain annular flow. Bornea *et al.* indicated that when f_g is less than 0.85, the liquid phase often bridges the entire flow channel, causing the pattern to be either slug or churn. Therefore, the flow pattern at the wellhead in this example is deemed to be churn flow.

Gas Volume Fraction and Pressure Gradient—The Hasan-Kabir Model. *Gas Volume Fraction.*

$x = v_{sg} \rho_g /(v_{sg} \rho_g + v_{sL} \rho_L) = (14.8)(1.03)/[(14.8 \times 1.03) + (6.153)(53.36)] = 0.044.$

Eq. 3.28: $\bar{v}_\infty = 0.675[1 - e^{-2.747 \times 14.8}] + 1.169 e^{-2.747 \times 14.8}$
$= 1.085 \text{ ft/sec}.$

Eq. 3.27: $f_g = 14.8/[1.15(20.953) + 1.085] = 0.586.$ Holdup: $f_L = 0.414.$

Pressure Gradient.

Eq. 2.18: $\rho_m = 53.36(0.414) + 1.03(0.586)$
$= 22.71 \text{ lbm/ft}^3.$

Eq. 2.15: $(dp/dz)_H = \rho_m g\sin\alpha/g_c = 21.66 \text{ psf/ft}$
$= 0.150 \text{ psi/ft}.$

Eq. 2.23: $\mu_m = 0.956(2.25) + 0.044(0.018) = 2.15 \text{ cp}.$
$Re_m = (0.20)(20.89)(22.71)/(2.15 \times 0.000672) = 66,792.$

Eq. 1.11: $f = 0.32(66,792)^{-0.25} = 0.02$.

Eq. 2.14: $(dp/dz)_F = (0.02)(20.95)^2(22.71)/[2(32.2)(0.2)]$
$= 15.21$ psf/ft $= 0.1057$ psi/ft.

Eq. 2.17: $dp/dz = 0.150 + 0.1057 = 0.256$ psi/ft $=$ total pressure gradient at wellhead.

Gas Volume Fraction and Pressure Gradient—The Ansari et al. Model. *Gas Volume Fraction.*

Eq. 3.37: $f_{gLS} = 14.68/[2.65(20.95) + 0.425] = 0.259$,
and $f_{LLS} = 1 - 0.259 = 0.741$.

Eq. 3.35: $v_{gLS} = 1.2(20.89) + (0.769)(0.741)^{0.5} = 25.73$
ft/sec. $v_{TB} = 1.2(20.89) + 0.97 = 26.0$ ft/sec.

Eq. 3.39: $\bar{A} = (26)(0.259) + (0.741)\{20.95 - 0.259$
$[0.769(0.741)^{0.5}]\} = 22.1$ ft/sec.

Eq. 3.36: $v_{LTB} = 9.916\{32.2(0.20)[1 - \sqrt{f_{gTB}}]\}^{0.5}$
$= 25.16(1 - \sqrt{f_{gTB}})^{0.5}$.

Eq. 3.40: $f_{LTB} = (26 - 25.16)/(26 + v_{LTB})$. However, f_{LTB}
$= 1 - f_{gTB}$, requiring simultaneous solutions of Eqs. 3.36
and 3.40. Trial-and-error gives $f_{LTB} = 0.12$, and $v_{LTB} = 6.278$
ft/sec.

Eq. 3.33: $(26 + 6.278)(0.12) = (26 - v_{LLS})(0.741)$, and v_{LLS}
$= 20.8$ ft/sec.

Eq. 3.34: $(26 - v_{gTB})(1 - 0.12) = (26 - 7.8)(0.259)$, and v_{gTB}
$= 25.8$ ft/sec.

Eq. 3.30: $14.68 = \beta(25.8)(1 - 0.12) + (1 - \beta)(7.8)(1 - 0.741)$,
and $\beta = 0.499$.

Pressure Gradient.

Eq. 3.47: $\rho_{LS} = 53.33(0.741) + 1.03(0.259) = 39.8$ lbm/ft³.

Eq. 3.48: $(dp/dz)_H = [\rho_{LS}(1 - \beta) + \rho_g\beta]g\sin\alpha/g_c = 19.35$ psf/ft
$= 0.1345$ psi/ft, $\mu_{LS} = \mu_g f_{gLS} + \mu_L(1 - f_{gLS}) = 1.67$ cp,
$Re_{LS} = dv_m\rho_{LS}/\mu_{LS} = 150,481$, and $f_{LS} = 0.0169$.

Eq. 3.49: $(dp/dz)_F = (0.0169)(20.95)^2(39.8)(1 - 0.499)/$
$[2(32.2)(0.2)] = 11.23$ psf/ft $= 0.078$ psi/ft.

Eq. 2.17: $dp/dz = 0.135 + 0.078 = 0.213$ psi/ft $=$ total pressure
gradient at wellhead.

The Beggs and Brill Correlation.

$C_L = v_{sL}/v_m = 6.153/20.95 = 0.294$, and $Fr = v_m^2/gd = 67.2$.

$L_1 = 316C_L^{0.302} = 218.1$, and $L_2 = 0.0009252C_L^{-2.4684} = 0.019$.

$L_3 = 0.1C_L^{-1.4516} = 0.592$, and $L_4 = 0.5C_L^{-6.738} = 1,926$.

Fr is less than both L_1 and L_4 but greater than L_3. Therefore,
the flow pattern is intermittent, and the following are the
applicable parameter values.

$\quad a = 0.845$.
$\quad b = 0.5351$.
$\quad c = 0.0173$.
$\quad d = 2.96$.
$\quad e = 0.305$.

$\quad f = -0.4473$.
$\quad g = 0.0978$.

Liquid Holdup.

Eq. 4.13: $f_{L(0)} = aC_L^b/Fr^c = 0.845(0.294)^{0.5351}/(67.2)^{0.0173}$
$= 0.408$.

Eq. 4.22: $Z = (1 - C_L)\ln[d(C_L)^e(v_{Ld})^f(Fr)^g] = -0.038$.

Eq. 4.21: $F(\alpha) = 1 + Z[\sin(1.8\alpha) - \sin^3(1.8\alpha)] = 0.982$.

Eq. 4.20: $f_L = f_{L(0)} \times F(\alpha) = 0.40$.

Pressure Gradient.

Eq. 2.18: $\rho_m = 53.33(0.40) + 1.03(0.60) = 21.99$ lbm/ft³.

Eq. 2.15: $(dp/dz)_H = \rho_m g\sin\alpha/g_c = 22.14$ psf/ft $= 0.1467$
psi/ft.

$\mu_n = \mu_L C_L + \mu_g(1 - C_L) = 0.674$ cp, $\rho_n = \rho_L C_L + \rho_g$
$(1 - C_L) = 16.58$ lbm/ft³, and $Re_n = dv_m\rho_n/\mu_n$
$= (0.20)(20.89)(16.58)/(0.674 \times 0.00672) = 153,944$.

Eq. 1.11: $f_n = 0.184(153,944)^{-0.2} = 0.167$.

Eq. 4.17: $y = C_L/f_L^2 = 1.83$.

Eq. 4.18: $s = \ln(y)/[-0.0523 + 3.182(\ln y) - 0.8725(\ln y)^2$
$+ 0.01853(\ln y)^3] = 0.3894$.

Eq. 4.16: $f_m = f_n e^s = 0.025$.

Eq. 4.15: $(dp/dz)_F = (0.025)(20.95)^2(16.40)/$
$[2(32.2)(0.2)] = 13.8$ psf/ft $= 0.096$ psi/ft.

Eq. 2.17: $dp/dz = 0.1467 + 0.096 = 0.2426$ psi/ft $=$ total pressure gradient at wellhead.

We note that Ansari *et al.* did not suggest applicability of
their model for deviated wells. Nonetheless, we showed calculations for the Ansari model using Eq. 4.33 for the Taylor-bubble rise velocity. One can also use Eq. 4.34 with
minute changes in estimated holdup and pressure gradient
for this example.

Calculations presented above are for the wellhead condition of an actual well. The computed values show that our
model estimated somewhat higher values for liquid holdup
and pressure gradient than the other two methods. However,
the differences in the computed values diminish as the bottomhole is approached.

An interesting point to note is that $F(\alpha)$ for the Beggs
and Brill method is less than one for this case, suggesting that
liquid holdup for this slightly deviated well is about 4% lower
than for flow in a vertical well under similar conditions. In
practice, liquid holdup is rarely lower for wells deviated by
less than 50° than that in vertical wells. Therefore, this particular example shows that computations using even the most
robust of empirical correlations can sometimes lead to non-
physical results.

Note that in this example, as well as the one in Chap. 3,
we ignored kinetic energy losses. That is because rigorous
calculations showed that the pressure drop owing to kinetic
energy losses amounted to less than 0.07% of the total pres-

TABLE 4.2—PRESSURE TRAVERSE CALCULATIONS				
Depth, ft	Pressure, psig			
Measured	Measured Data	Hasan-Kabir	Ansari	Beggs-Brill
0	361	361	361	361
1,000	611	615	580	609
2,000	876	884	810	861
3,000	1,161	1,174	1,064	1,144
4,000	1,473	1,482	1,352	1,447
5,250	1,875	1,886	1,717	1,845
5,750	2,084	2,053	1,867	2,009
6,000	2,189	2,137	1,947	2,091
6,250	2,238	2,222	2,025	2,173

sure drop. **Table 4.2** presents the results of pressure traverse calculations, and **Fig. 4.9** compares the same information with measured data. Calculations showed that bubbly flow exists at the bottomhole. Because the computation was done top-down, so results could be compared directly at the wellhead condition, discrepancy occurs at the well bottom. As mentioned in the example in Chap. 3, experience shows that when computations are done along the direction of flow—bottom-up—errors decrease.

4.3 Flow in Horizontal Pipes and Wells

Over the last decade the tremendous importance and interest in horizontal and multilateral wells has presented a challenge for superior understanding of two-phase flow behavior in horizontal systems. Analysis of horizontal multiphase flow behavior can be adapted for slightly inclined systems. Besides wellbores, transportation of petroleum fluids demand modeling multiphase flow in horizontal and slightly inclined systems, leading to pipeline design over flat or hilly terrain.

4.3.1 Flow Patterns in Horizontal Flow. Flow patterns that occur during two-phase flow through horizontal pipes are in many ways similar to those observed during vertical flow. However, there are some important differences, arising mainly from the differential effects of gravity on lighter and heavier phases. Except at high flow rates, distribution of the phases tends to be asymmetrical, with the gas phase concentrating toward the upper wall. As in vertical flow, subjective judgement in designating flow patterns causes difficulty in presenting a general discussion on various flow regimes and transition from one regime to another. Here, we will follow the discussion of Taitel *et al.*,[1] which is in general agreement with most of the other works in the area.[24,25] Taitel *et al.* described six distinct flow regimes in horizontal two-phase flow, which are shown in **Fig. 4.10.**

Stratified Smooth Flow (SSF). At very low flow rates of the phases, the liquid flows through the bottom portion of the pipe, while the gas flows at the top. The two phases, thus, are stratified, and the interface between them is smooth.

Stratified Wavy Flow (SWF). At somewhat higher gas flow rates than is needed for SSF, the liquid and the gas phases are still separated, as before, but the interface becomes wavy.

Plug (or Elongated Bubble) Flow (PF). At somewhat lower gas flow rates but higher liquid rates than is needed

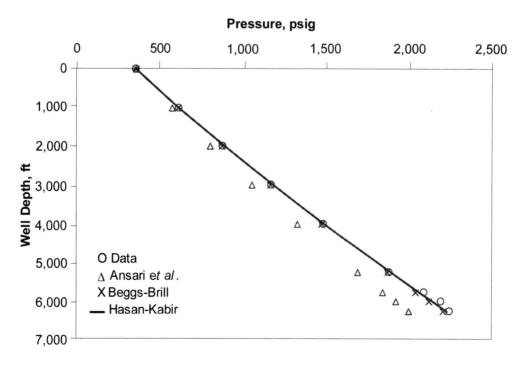

Fig. 4.9—Comparison of model performance with field data.

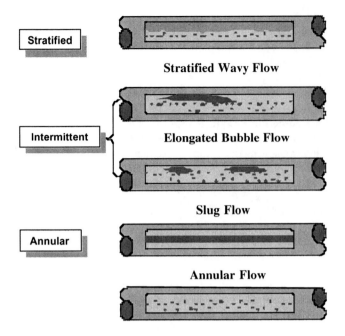

Stratified

Stratified Wavy Flow

Intermittent

Elongated Bubble Flow

Slug Flow

Annular

Annular Flow

Dispersed Bubble Flow

Fig. 4.10—Flow patterns in horizontal systems (from Ref. 1; used with permission of the American Institute of Chemical Engineers).

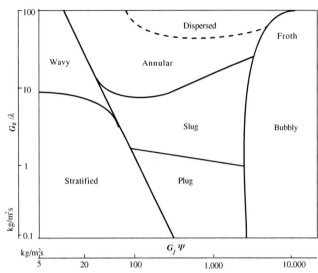

Fig. 4.11—Horizontal flow pattern map of Baker (from Ref. 25; courtesy of *Oil & Gas J.*).

for SWF, the liquid could fill the entire pipe and flow as plugs. In that case, the gas flows as elongated bubbles near the top of the pipe.

Slug Flow (SF). At higher gas flow rates the bubbles become large, filling up a substantial portion (but not entirely, as in vertical slug flow) of the flow cross section. The liquid slugs in between move violently downstream and are usually aerated by small bubbles. The distinction between plug and slug flow is difficult and becomes subjective because of similar appearances. Indeed, Taitel *et al.*[1] combined these two patterns into one and called it intermittent flow.

Annular Flow (AF). At high rates, the gas flows through the center of the pipe and the liquid flows along the tube wall, forming an annulus. This flow pattern is very similar to its counterpart in vertical flow, except that the liquid film is thicker at the bottom than at the top because of gravity in horizontal flow. Annular flow may be visualized to form from slug flow when the aeration in the slug becomes sufficient to form a continuous phase. It forms from stratified flow when the liquid flow rate is low and the gas flow rate is high enough to spread the liquid around the tube.

Dispersed Bubbly Flow (DBF). At very high liquid-rates, the gas phase may become dispersed as small bubbles in a continuous liquid phase. Similar to its counterpart in vertical flow, the shear energy of the turbulent liquid phase reduces the effect of gravity causing the gas bubbles to be distributed more or less uniformly across the flow channel. The bubble concentration profile is still asymmetrical, with the peak occurring at some point above the pipe axis.

4.3.2 Flow-Pattern Maps and Transition Criteria. As in vertical flow, a number of flow-pattern maps in two-dimensional (2D) coordinates have appeared to represent flow regime transitions in horizontal systems. In some cases, attempts have been made to make the maps general by incorporating dimensionless groups (usually property groups) in the axes of the maps. One of the very durable maps is that of Baker,[25] which is often used in the petrochemical industry and is shown in **Fig. 4.11**. Along with the gas and liquid mass fluxes, the map uses the dimensionless parameters, λ and ψ, which are defined in Eqs. 4.35 and 4.36.

$$\lambda = \sqrt{(\rho_g / \rho_A)/(\rho_L / \rho_w)} \quad \cdots\cdots\cdots\cdots\cdots (4.35)$$

$$\psi = (\sigma_w / \sigma)\sqrt[3]{(\mu_L / \mu_w)/(\rho_w / \rho_L)^2} \quad \cdots\cdots\cdots (4.36)$$

The subscripts A and w refer to values of the physical properties of air and water at standard conditions (atmospheric pressure and 60°F).

As pointed out for the case of vertical flow, representation of the effect of secondary variables in a 2D map is impossible. However, we cannot expect one pair of dimensionless variables to generalize the transitions for all the flow regimes. Analysis of transitions for the individual patterns, based on a sound physical model and verified by experimental data is, therefore, likely to be more accurate. We now present such an analysis for a near-horizontal system.

Transition Between Stratified and Intermittent or Annular Flow. We follow the analysis presented by Taitel *et al.*[1] for the transition between stratified (both smooth and wavy) and intermittent (slug and plug) flows and between stratified and annular flows in a system inclined by an angle, α, from a horizontal plane. **Fig. 4.12** schematically represents smooth stratified flow in a circular channel. The liquid film occupies an area, A_L, with a depth, h, and in-situ velocity of v_L. The gas phase has an in-situ velocity of v_g and occupies an area, A_g; hence, $f_L = A_L/A$. The equilib-

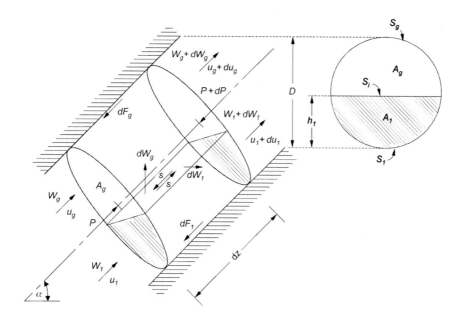

Fig. 4.12—Stratified two-phase flow in a slightly inclined system (from Ref. 1; used with permission of the American Institute of Chemical Engineers).

rium in stratified flow will be disturbed if the gas flow rate is high enough to create an unstable wave. By analyzing the stability of a finite wave, Taitel et al.[1] derived a relationship for the gas velocity at which the transition from stratified to either intermittent or annular flow takes place.

$$v_g > [1-(h/d)]\left[\frac{g\cos\alpha(\rho_L - \rho_g)A_g}{\rho_g(dA_L/dh)}\right]^{0.5} \quad \dots\dots\dots (4.37)$$

To estimate the important parameter, h/d, the momentum balance, for the gas and liquid phases, yields

$$-A_g dP - \tau_{wg}dzS_g - \tau_i dzS_i - \rho_g A_g gdz\sin\alpha$$
$$= w_g dv_g + v_g dw_g + dw_l v_l , \quad \dots\dots\dots\dots (4.38)$$

and $-A_L dP - \tau_{wL}dzS_L - \tau_i dzS_i - \rho_L A_L gdz\sin\alpha = w_L dv_L .$
$$\dots\dots\dots\dots\dots (4.39)$$

Neglecting the accelerational component (RHS of Eqs. 4.38 and 4.39) and equating the pressure gradient in each phase,

$$\tau_{wg}\frac{S_g}{A_g} - \tau_{wL}\frac{S_L}{A_L} + \tau_i S_i\left(\frac{1}{A_L} + \frac{1}{A_g}\right) - \left(\rho_L - \rho_g\right)g\sin\alpha = 0 .$$
$$\dots\dots\dots\dots\dots (4.40)$$

We evaluate shear stress in the usual manner, $\tau_{wg} = f_g\rho_g v_g^2/8$, $\tau_{wL} = f_l\rho_L v_L^2/8$, etc., where friction factors for both phases are estimated with a Blasius-type equation, $f = C(Dv\rho/\mu)^{-m}$. To transform this equation into a dimensionless form, divide the length dimension (e.g., h) by the pipe diameter, d, and the areas (e.g., A_L) by d^2 to obtain dimensionless variables denoted by overbars (e.g., $\bar{h} = h/d$). Superficial velocities

$v_{sg}(=w_g/\rho_g A)$ and $v_{sL}(=w_L/\rho_L A)$ are used to render velocities (e.g., v_L) dimensionless (e.g. $\bar{v}_L = v_L/v_{sL}$). Thus, Eq. 4.40 becomes

$$X^2\left[\left(\bar{v}_L\bar{d}_L\right)^{-n}\bar{v}_L^2\frac{\bar{S}_L}{\bar{A}_L}\right] - \left[\left(\bar{v}_g\bar{d}_g\right)^{-m}\bar{v}_g^2\left(\frac{\bar{S}_g}{\bar{A}_g} + \frac{\bar{S}_i}{\bar{A}_L} + \frac{\bar{S}_i}{\bar{A}_g}\right)\right] = 4Y ,$$
$$\dots\dots\dots\dots\dots (4.41)$$

where X is the Lockhart-Martinelli parameter discussed earlier in Chap. 2, which is given by

$$X^2 = \left[\left(\frac{dp}{dz}\right)_F\right]_L \Big/ \left[\left(\frac{dp}{dz}\right)_F\right]_g . \quad \dots\dots\dots\dots (2.27)$$

In Eq. 4.41, Y represents the ratio of gravitational to gas-phase frictional gradient and is given by

$$Y = \frac{(\rho_l - \rho_g)g\sin\alpha}{2(C/d)(v_{sg}d\rho_g/\mu_g)^{-m}\rho_g v_{sg}^2} = \frac{(\rho_l - \rho_g)g\sin\alpha}{\left|(dp/dz)_{sg}\right|} .$$
$$\dots\dots\dots\dots\dots (4.42)$$

The X-Y relationship is shown in graphical form in **Fig. 4.13.** Note that when α equals zero, $Y=0$, and Eq. 4.42 represents the relationship between X and Y for a horizontal system.

Application of Eq. 4.41 requires expressions for various dimensions, such as S_L, S_i, A_L, in terms of the single variable, h. For a circular geometry, the cross-sectional area for liquid flow, A_L, and its variation, dA_L/dh, is related to the liquid height, h, by

$$A_L = \left(d^2/4\right)[\pi - \cos^{-1}\xi + \xi\sqrt{(1-\xi^2)}] , \quad \dots\dots\dots (4.43)$$

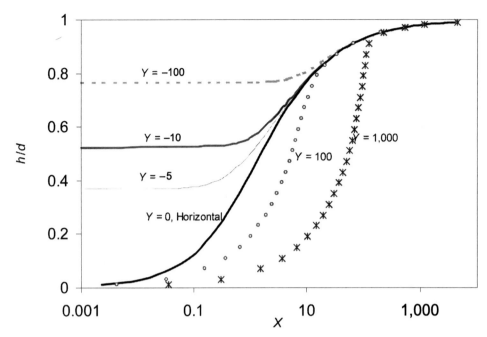

Fig. 4.13—Dimensionless liquid level as a function of *X* and *Y* (from Ref. 1; used with permission of the American Institute of Chemical Engineers).

and $\dfrac{dA_L}{dh} = d\sqrt{1-\xi^2}$, $\quad\ldots\ldots\ldots\ldots\ldots\ldots$ (4.44)

where $\xi = 2(h/d)-1$. Similarly, the wetted liquid perimeter, S_L, and the interface perimeter, S_i, are

$$S_L = d(\pi - \cos^{-1}\xi), \text{ and } S_i = d\sqrt{(1-\xi^2)} \quad \ldots\ldots (4.45)$$

Note that the in-situ velocities needed in Eq. 4.41 can be calculated from the superficial velocities once A_L and A_g (=1– A_L) are known.

Therefore, the transition from stratified flow to intermittent or annular flow is determined by the liquid level, *h*, for a given gas velocity, v_g, as represented by Eq. 4.37. However, although Eq. 4.37 gives the gas velocity at which stratified flow changes, it does not indicate whether this change is to the annular or the intermittent flow pattern. When the liquid level is high enough to maintain a liquid slug (i.e., a complete bridge), a stable slug can form, which will transition to intermittent flow. However, if the liquid level is below the center line, $h/d<0.5$, a complete bridge of liquid between the top and the bottom of the pipe cannot be maintained. In such a case, the waves formed on the liquid surface will be swept around the tube, resulting in annular flow. Note that this reasoning also applies to the transition from dispersed bubbly to annular flow.

Transition to annular flow takes place when the gas velocity exceeds that given by Eq. 4.37 and *h/d* is less than 0.5. For horizontal flow, this value of *h/d* corresponds to 1.6 for the Lockhart-Martinelli parameter, *X*, as shown in Fig. 4.13. When v_g exceeds that given by Eq. 4.37 and $h/d>0.5$, transition to intermittent flow occurs.

Bornea *et al.*[3] pointed out that a value of *h/d*<0.5 is probably not sufficient for transition to annular flow because the liquid slugs always carry some gas bubbles. Therefore, even when the calculated liquid level in the pipe is below the midpoint, a complete liquid bridge may be possible. If a gas holdup of about 35% is assumed in the liquid slugs, then transition to annular flow will occur when *h/d*<0.35. However, all the liquid being available to form the slugs is an improbable scenario because the gas bubbles are not likely to fill up the entire pipe cross section. Therefore, the transition to annular flow probably occurs when the *h/d* ratio falls below 0.40 to 0.45. For horizontal flow, this *h/d* ratio corresponds to a value of about 1.0 for the Lockhart-Martinelli parameter, *X*.

Transition Between Smooth and Wavy Stratified Flows. Transition between smooth and wavy stratified flows is difficult to determine because it depends on the judgement as to when waves have formed. Taitel *et al.*[1] offered an analysis based on the phenomenon of wave formation and some simplifying assumptions, such as wave propagation velocity is much smaller than the gas in-situ velocity and that the sheltering coefficient is 0.01. Their analysis suggests that the flow pattern changes from smooth to wavy stratified flow, when the in-situ gas velocity exceeds that given by

$$v_g > \sqrt{\frac{400\mu_L(\rho_L - \rho_g)g\cos\alpha}{\rho_L\rho_g v_L}} \quad \ldots\ldots\ldots\ldots (4.46)$$

Transition Between Intermittent and Dispersed Bubbly Flow. At high liquid and low gas velocities, the turbulent fluctuations of the liquid cause the gas to disperse as bubbles throughout the channel, resulting in bubbly flow. As the liquid velocity decreases, buoyant forces tend to push the gas bubbles upward, allowing agglomeration and,

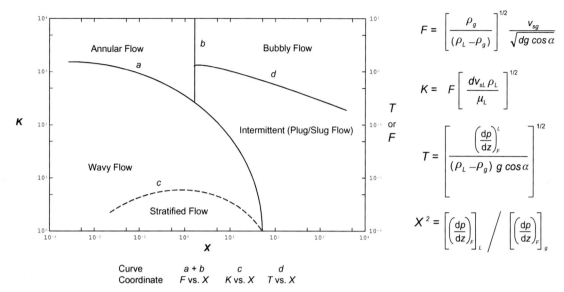

$$F = \left[\frac{\rho_g}{(\rho_L - \rho_g)} \right]^{1/2} \frac{v_{sg}}{\sqrt{dg \cos \alpha}}$$

$$K = F \left[\frac{dv_{sL} \rho_L}{\mu_L} \right]^{1/2}$$

$$T = \left[\frac{\left(\frac{dp}{dz} \right)_F^L}{(\rho_L - \rho_g) g \cos \alpha} \right]^{1/2}$$

$$X^2 = \left[\left(\frac{dp}{dz} \right)_F \right]_L \Bigg/ \left[\left(\frac{dp}{dz} \right)_F \right]_g$$

Curve	a + b	c	d
Coordinate	F vs. X	K vs. X	T vs. X

Fig. 4.14—Horizontal flow-pattern map of Taitel and Dukler; used with permission of the American Institute of Chemical Engineers.

finally, transition to slug or plug flow. Thus, a balance between the buoyant forces is expressed as

$$F_B = g \cos \alpha (\rho_L - \rho_g) A_g , \qquad (4.47)$$

and the force owing to turbulent fluctuation, expressed as

$$F_t = 0.25 \rho_L v_L^2 f_L S_i / 4 , \qquad (4.48)$$

should establish the transition between bubbly and intermittent flow. Taitel et al.[1] took this approach and arrived at the criterion for the transition from intermittent to bubbly flow, which is written as

$$v_L = \sqrt{\frac{4 A_g g \cos \alpha}{S_i f_L} \left(\frac{\rho_L - \rho_g}{\rho_L} \right)} . \qquad (4.49)$$

The liquid-friction factor f_L can be determined from the Blassius equation where the Reynolds number is calculated using the hydraulic diameter $(= 4A_L/S_L)$, liquid viscosity, liquid density, and the in-situ liquid velocity. The terms in Eq. 4.49 depend only on h/d, which can be evaluated form the Lockhart-Martinelli parameter, X, and the inclination angle, α, using Fig 4.13.

Taitel and Dukler expressed these transition equations in terms of Lockhart-Martinelli parameter, X, and three other dimensionless parameters, such as F, K, and T. These parameters are shown on the flow-pattern map (**Fig. 4.14**). Note that α is zero for horizontal flow.

Taitel and Dukler also converted this horizontal flow-pattern map for air/water systems at standard conditions and showed its excellent agreement with the map of Mandhane et al.[27] This is especially true when the differences in definitions for bubbly and annular flow by Mandhane et al. and Taitel et al. are taken into account. If the transition to annular flow is assumed to take place for $X < 1.0$ and the gas velocity is high enough so that Eq. 4.37 is satisfied, the agreement between

the Mandhane data and the Taitel et al. map becomes slightly better at low flow rates and somewhat worse at high flow rates. The Taitel et al. transition equations or the horizontal flow map derived from it, shown in Fig. 4.8, appear to be based on a sound physical model and are supported by experimental data. Another attractive feature of the model is that it appears to be applicable in a somewhat modified form for slightly inclined flow as well.

4.3.3 Holdup and Pressure Drop in Near-Horizontal Flow. The static pressure gradient is absent in horizontal two-phase flow and is small for near-horizontal systems. In addition, the contribution of the accelerational component also tends to be small because the total pressure change, causing variation in ρ_g, is usually small. The estimation of the frictional pressure gradient, therefore, becomes very important. This reasoning obviously reduces the importance of slip between phases. Therefore, in this section, we will not concern ourselves with an accurate correlation for holdup in any flow regime. We recommend the Lockhart-Martinelli correlation for calculating holdup in all flow regimes, unless a simpler and more accurate correlation is available in any given regime.

Estimating friction factor and, hence, the frictional pressure gradient is usually entirely empirical in nature. In other words, useful models for near-horizontal systems are few. Nonetheless, a number of recent modeling efforts appear very promising.[18,26]

Stratified Wavy/Smooth Flow. The stratified wavy flow regime is difficult to analyze because of waves on the liquid surface. The characteristics of these waves vary with varying gas and liquid properties and flow rates, making it difficult to predict the frictional resistance offered by the waves. The Lockhart-Martinelli method is probably as good (and simpler) as any of the few other methods available for pressure-drop computation in this flow regime. Govier and Aziz[28] also suggested a simple method, which requires estimating the gas flow rates at which transitions from wavy flow to smooth flow and annular flow take place at the given liquid flow rate. The pressure gradients at those two flow rates are then calculated using correlations specific to the smooth stratified flow and annular flow regimes. A log/linear interpolation for the given gas flow rate is then made by making a log/log plot of pressure gradient vs. gas flow rate. The holdup can also be estimated in a similar manner by log/linear interpolation. Of course, the Lockhart-Martinelli method can also be applied.

The stratified smooth flow regime is the simplest to analyze theoretically because of the simple geometry of the interface. However, this flow pattern is also the least likely to occur in practice. There are, therefore, very few field or experimental data available for this flow regime. The Lockhart-Martinelli method is probably accurate enough for predicting the pressure gradient. However, for liquid/liquid flow, the Lockhart-Martinelli method significantly overestimates the frictional pressure gradient. Baker[25] also indicated significant differences between Lockhart-Martinelli predictions and his data. Baker's empirical correlation for ϕ_g, the gas phase friction multiplier (see Chap. 2, Sec. 2.5.1, Eq. 2.23) for a smooth stratified flow regime, is

$$\phi_g = \frac{15,400X}{[\rho_L v_{sL}]^{0.8}} \cdot \quad \dots \dots \dots \dots \dots (4.50)$$

Note that this expression is another way of accounting for the effect of mass flux on a friction multiplier, as discussed in Chap. 2. One can also calculate a liquid-phase friction factor with the Blassius equation. The hydraulic diameter needed to calculate the Reynolds number can be determined from $4 A_l / S_l$, as described in the discussion of Eq. 4.43.

The liquid holdup and pressure gradient in stratified smooth and stratified wavy regions can be calculated in the manner suggested by Taitel and Dukler[1] and discussed in the last section. Both Gomez et al.[18] and Xiao et al.[26] have adapted this approach and suggested using Eq. 4.40 for estimating pressure gradient in both smooth and wavy stratified flows. Xiao et al.[26] proposed using the Moody friction factor chart (or Eq. 1.12) for f_L and f_g, although they noted that f_L, calculated in this manner, is often inaccurate because of the presence of interfacial waves. For interfacial friction factor, f_i, in small diameter pipes (d $\leq$ ½-in.), they recommended using $f_i = f_g$ when

$$v_{sg} \leq v_{sgt}, \quad \dots \dots \dots \dots \dots (4.51)$$

where $v_{sgt} = 5(p_s / p)^{0.5}, \quad \dots \dots \dots \dots (4.52)$

where p_s is standard atmospheric pressure (14.7 psi) expressed in the same units as p. When d$\leq$0.5-in., and $v_{sg} \geq v_{sgt}$, they suggested

$$f_i = f_g \left(1 + 15 v_{sgt}(v_{sg} - v_{sgt})\sqrt{h/d}\right) \cdot \quad \dots \dots (4.53)$$

For pipes with diameters larger than ½-in., they recommended using equivalent roughness factors for use with the Moody friction factor chart or equations.

$$\varepsilon = \frac{34\sigma}{\rho_g v_L^2}, \quad \dots \dots \dots \dots \dots (4.54)$$

$$\text{when } \frac{\rho_g v_L^2 \varepsilon}{\sigma} \frac{\mu_L^2}{\sigma \rho_L \varepsilon} \succ 0.005 \cdot \quad \dots \dots \dots (4.55)$$

Otherwise, for $d \geq$ ½-in., they recommended

$$\varepsilon = \frac{170\sigma}{\rho_g v_L^2}\left(\frac{\rho_g v_L^2 \varepsilon}{\sigma} \frac{\mu_L^2}{\sigma \rho_L \varepsilon}\right)^{0.3} \cdot \quad \dots \dots (4.56)$$

Gomez et al.[18] followed Xiao et al.'s method for calculating f_i and agreed with their suggestion that f_g be calculated with the Moody friction factor chart (or Eq. 1.12). However, for f_L, they suggested the correlation,

$$f_L = \frac{1.629}{Re_L^{0.5161}}(v_{sg} / v_{sL})^{0.0926} \cdot \quad \dots \dots \dots (4.57)$$

Intermittent Flow. For the intermittent (slug and plug) flow pattern, the drift flux approach to flow modeling may be taken. In horizontal and near-horizontal systems, the drift velocity of the bubbles is low and the single drift velocity, that of the Taylor bubble, may be used for the entire cell. Therefore, the holdup is given by

$$f_L \equiv 1 - f_g = 1 - \frac{v_{sg}}{C_o v_m + v_{\infty To}} \cdot \quad \dots \dots \dots (4.58)$$

Taylor-bubble rise velocity may be estimated with either Eqs. 4.33 or 4.34. The value of the parameter, C_o, depends on the velocity profile and the distribution of the bubbles across the flow channel. For laminar flow ($dv_m\rho_L/\mu_L < 1000$), the value of C_o has been found to be 2.0. The local velocity at the pipe axis during laminar flow is twice that of the average velocity in the pipe, which suggests that the bubbles occupy the central portion of the flow channel. While this conclusion is obviously not true for horizontal flow, it is safe to use a value of 2.0 for C_o. For highly turbulent flow ($dv_m\rho_L/\mu_L > 200,000$), C_o is found to be between 1.2 and 1.35, as shown by Hughmark,[20] and Gregory and Scott.[21] Their work suggests that the bubbles occupy the pipe center, which is likely to occur during highly turbulent flow. For the intermediate region, the data of Hughmark may be approximated by $C_o = 3.04 - 0.151 \ln (dv_m\rho_L/\mu_L)$.

Gomez et al.[18] and Kaya et al.[9] extended the Ansari et al.[17] vertical slug flow model (see Chap. 3, Sec. 3.3.2) for inclined and horizontal systems. They assumed that the liquid film surrounding the Taylor bubble has a uniform thickness. Using an approach similar to that for stratified flow, they suggested that an equivalent form of Eq. 4.40 can be solved iteratively for the area occupied by the Taylor bubble, A_g, and the area for the liquid film, A_L, thereby allowing the computation of the liquid-film thickness.

Gomez et al. used the following correlation for liquid holdup in the slug body, f_{LLS}.

$$f_{LLS} = e^{-(0.45\alpha_R + 2.48*10^{-6} \mathrm{Re}_{LS})} \cdot \quad\ldots\ldots\ldots\ldots\ldots\ldots (4.59)$$

Gomez *et al.* claimed that α_R, the well inclination from horizontal in radians, makes the method applicable to all inclination angles. In Eq. 4.59, the slug body Reynolds number, Re_{LS}, is

$$\mathrm{Re}_{LS} = \rho_L v_m d / \mu_L \cdot \quad\ldots\ldots\ldots\ldots\ldots\ldots (4.60)$$

For calculating frictional gradient during slug flow, Hughmark[20] suggested that the corresponding single-phase equation can be used with in-situ liquid velocity and liquid properties; that is,

$$\left(\frac{dp}{dz}\right)_F = \frac{2 f_{fL} \rho_L v_L^2}{g_c d} \cdot \quad\ldots\ldots\ldots\ldots\ldots (4.61)$$

In Eq. 4.61, f_{fL} is the single-phase friction factor calculated with the liquid-phase Reynolds number, $d v_L \rho_L / \mu_L$. Gregory and Scott[21] found the Hughmark[20] correlation to be quite satisfactory. Gomez *et al.*[18] recommended calculating frictional losses for the various parts of the cell unit, the liquid slug, the liquid film, and the interface between the liquid film and the Taylor bubble. This calculation procedure for slug flow should be applicable for the entire intermittent flow regime. As indicated earlier, Taitel and Dukler[1] did not think that it was necessary to treat the slug and plug flows as two distinct flow patterns.

Dispersed Bubbly Flow. The dispersed-bubbly flow pattern is particularly amenable to modeling by the drift flux approach. As in the case of intermittent flow, the drift velocity between the phases may be neglected. Because of the high liquid flow rate the bubble concentration profile is more symmetrical around the tube axis, and a value of 1.2 for C_o may give good results. Therefore, holdup can be correlated with the equation,

$$f_L \equiv 1 - f_g = 1 - \frac{v_{sg}}{1.2 v_m} \cdot \quad\ldots\ldots\ldots\ldots\ldots (4.62)$$

The frictional pressure gradient may be estimated from

$$\left(\frac{dp}{dz}\right)_F = \frac{2 f_m \rho_m v_m^2}{g_c d}, \quad\ldots\ldots\ldots\ldots\ldots\ldots (4.63)$$

where f_{fm} is estimated from the single-phase correlation using mixture density $\rho_m = f_L \rho_L + f_g \rho_g$ and mixture viscosity $\mu_m = f_L \mu_L + f_g \mu_g$.

Annular Flow. This flow pattern is similar to its counterpart in vertical flow because the high flow rates make the effect of gravity small. Therefore, the methods for computing holdup and pressure drop valid for vertical flow may also be applied to horizontal flow. Following the approach used in stratified flow, Gomez *et al.*[18] presented a rigorous method to write separate momentum balances for the liquid film and the gas core. The resulting expression is similar to Eq. 4.40, except that the term involving gas-wall shear stress is absent.

$$-\tau_{wL} \frac{S_L}{A_L} + \tau_i S_i \left(\frac{1}{A_L} + \frac{1}{A_g} \right) - \left(\rho_L - \rho_g \right) g \sin \alpha = 0 \cdot$$
$$\quad\ldots\ldots\ldots\ldots\ldots (4.64)$$

Note that neglecting kinetic energy losses, which was done to arrive at Eq. 4.62, could lead to inaccuracy. Gomez *et al.*[18] extended the approach they used for vertical systems (see Chap. 3, Sec. 3.3.4) to express the interfacial friction factor, f_{fi}, in terms of the friction factor that the core fluid would experience when flowing alone in the channel, f, and the inclination factor, I. Therefore,

$$f_{fi} = If \cdot \quad\ldots\ldots\ldots\ldots\ldots\ldots\ldots (4.65)$$

where for vertical systems,[18] the inclination factor, I_v, is given by

$$I_V = (1 + 300 \delta / d) \cdot \quad\ldots\ldots\ldots\ldots\ldots (4.66)$$

For horizontal systems, they adopted the correlation, proposed by Henstock and Hanratty,[29] to represent the inclination factor, I_H.

$$I_H = (1 + 800) \frac{\left[(0.707 \mathrm{Re}_{sL}^{0.5})^{2.5} + \left(0.0379 \mathrm{Re}_{sL}^{0.9} \right)^{2.5} \right]^{0.4}}{\mathrm{Re}_{sg}^{0.9}}$$
$$\frac{v_L}{v_g} \sqrt{\rho_L / \rho_g} \cdot \quad\ldots\ldots\ldots\ldots\ldots\ldots (4.67)$$

For an inclined system, Gomez *et al.* proposed the relation as

$$I_a = I_H \cos^2 \alpha + \sin^2 \alpha \cdot \quad\ldots\ldots\ldots\ldots (4.68)$$

Gomez *et al.* used Eq. 3.53 for estimating entrainment in annular flow for all angles of inclination.

4.3.4 Flow in Horizontal Wells. An important aspect of horizontal wells is that fluid influx may occur through almost the entire horizontal section of the well. This continual fluid influx means that the mass flow rate increases in the direction of flow during production and decreases in the flow direction during injection. The continual entry of fluid along the wellbore inhibits the full development of classical flow patterns. In addition, perforations in the well modify the pipe roughness characteristics and may change pipe friction factor. Furthermore, fluid inlet/exit through a perforation may cause significant changes in its kinetic energy. In openhole completions, the uneven formation surface and hole diameter presents further complications. Modeling two-phase flow in such wells, to account for all these factors, presents a serious challenge.

Ihara *et al.*[30] conducted experimental research and found that flow through perforations increases the apparent friction factor. Dikken[31] presented an interesting model for predicting pressure drop in horizontal wells. He ignored the effect of changes in kinetic energy and extra friction caused by flow through perforations. Results from his analysis, shown in **Fig. 4.15,** present dimensionless production as a function of

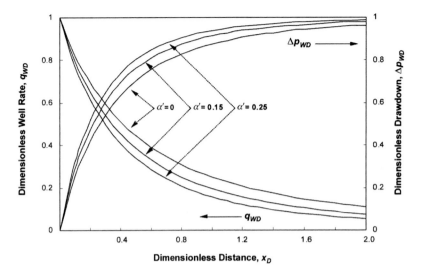

Fig. 4.15—Diminishing influx with increasing well length (from Ref. 31).

dimensionless distance and the exponent of the Blassius friction factor, α'. Note that $\alpha'=0$ for a completely rough pipe, and $\alpha'=0\ 0.25$ for a fully smooth pipe. His analysis showed that increasing turbulence limits production gains from lengthening a well beyond a certain critical length.

The most comprehensive work in this area was performed by Ouyang and Aziz.[32] They gathered data from 100-ft long pipes of various diameters with perforations at various positions. They noted that all available models underestimated the pressure-drop data. They postulated that kinetic energy loss owing to flow through perforations is very significant in such systems and that ignoring it causes the present models to underestimate pressure loss. Ouyang and Aziz[32] proposed a homogeneous model with an extra accelerational pressure loss term, $(dp/dz)_{AW}$, to account for fluid influx through perforations. Thus, similar to Eq. 1.5, they proposed that the total pressure gradient is given by

$$(dp\,/\,dz) = (dp\,/\,dz)_F + (dp\,/\,dz)_A + (dp\,/\,dz)_{AW}\;.$$
$$\cdots\cdots\cdots\cdots\cdots (4.69)$$

The first two terms on the right side of Eq. 4.67 are the same as those for the homogeneous models discussed in Chap. 2, Sec. 2.4. They expressed the acceleration terms, $(dp/dz)_A$ and $(dp/dz)_{AW}$, as

$$\left(\frac{dp}{dz}\right)_A = \frac{\beta}{1-\beta}\left[-(\tau_w S\,/\,A) - \rho_{tp}g\sin\alpha + (dp\,/\,dz)_{AW}\right],$$
$$\cdots\cdots\cdots\cdots\cdots (4.70)$$

and
$$\left(\frac{dp}{dz}\right)_{AW} = -\frac{\rho_m}{A}\left[\omega\left(v_m q_{ltp} + v_{tp}q_{lm}\right) + 2(1-\omega)v_{tp}q_{ltp}\right].$$
$$\cdots\cdots\cdots\cdots\cdots (4.71)$$

Ouyang and Aziz[32] used two types of velocities, v_m and v_{tp}. The mixture velocity, v_m, is the same one used in this book, i.e., $v_m = v_{sL} + v_{sg}$. The two-phase flow velocity, v_{tp}, is defined as

$$v_{tp} = v_{sL}(\rho_L\,/\,\rho_m) + v_{sg}(\rho_g\,/\,\rho_m)\,, \quad\cdots\cdots\cdots\cdots (4.72)$$

where ρ_m is the usual two-phase homogeneous mixture density, $\rho_m = (v_{sL}/v_m)\rho_L + (v_{sg}/v_m)\rho_g$. In a similar manner, they defined two volumetric influx rates.

$$q_{lm} = q_{lL} + q_{lg}\,, \quad\cdots\cdots\cdots\cdots\cdots (4.73)$$

$$\text{and } q_{ltp} = q_{lL}(\rho_L\,/\,\rho_m) + q_{lg}(\rho_g\,/\,\rho_m)\cdot \quad\cdots\cdots\cdots (4.74)$$

q_{lL} and q_{lg} are the liquid and gas inflow (or outflow) rates per unit wellbore length. The volumetric expansion coefficient, β, is given by $(\rho_m v_m v_{sg})/p$, and the weighting factor, ω, has an empirically-determined value of 0.8.

Ouyang and Aziz[32] proposed two correlations for the two-phase mixture friction factor for injection wells and three for producing wells, depending on the laminar or turbulent nature of flow. Their laboratory data lend credence to the correlations. The reader is advised to consult the original paper for details of the experiments and the model.

Discussion. The mechanistic approach to modeling flow in deviated wells, presented in Sec. 4.2.4, appears promising because of its theoretical basis. The models, however, are still being improved. There are disagreements, especially regarding the expression for bubble terminal-rise velocity in both bubbly and slug flows. Our data suggest that inclination angles have an insignificant influence on v_∞, but others have assumed that it varies with $\sin\alpha$. Similarly, the Taylor-bubble rise velocity data of Lau[22] is better represented by $n=4$ rather than $n=2.4$, as we[6] proposed originally. In addition, $v_{\infty Ta}$ values, evaluated using our model, are quite different from that proposed by Bendiksen[23] for near-horizontal systems. Another difficulty arises from the use of a constant value of the flow parameter, C_o, for all inclination angles, proposed by both Hasan and Kabir[6] and Kaya *et al.*[9] Further data, especially from large diameter pipes, are needed to fully establish the value of the flow parameter. The churn-flow regime, which has been lumped with the slug-flow regime, may require separate values of the parameters (e.g., $C_o = 1.15$). Unfortunately, no reliable method exists for delineating churn from slug flow at present.

In spite of these difficulties, the models advanced by Hasan and Kabir,[6] Kaya et al.,[9] and Gomez et al.[18] appear sound. They presented good agreement of their models with holdup and pressure-drop data from several sources. In particular, the recent model of Gomez et al.[18] appears to perform very well for both vertical and deviated wells. Nonetheless, much of the data[10-12] against which these models were validated are from 1- to 2-in. ID pipes. This fact leaves some doubt as to the value of the flow parameter in large-diameter pipes.

For computing holdup and pressure drop in inclined systems, the Beggs and Brill[11] correlation is the most comprehensive empirical method available at present. On the surface, the correlation appears to account for the prevailing flow pattern in inclined flow. However, the flow pattern determined by this method is only applicable for a horizontal system. For an inclined system, the flow pattern discerned might not correspond to the actual pattern observed in the system but is used by Beggs and Brill as a correlating parameter only. Complications involved in the calculation procedure and the method's exclusive reliance on empiricism make it less than completely satisfactory. Nonetheless, performance of the Beggs and Brill correlation is usually very good.

For horizontal and near-horizontal systems, the Taitel et al.[1] model has become well established for determining flow patterns. In addition, the Taitel et al. model is useful in estimating holdup in stratified flow regimes. For estimating pressure gradient and holdup in horizontal/near-horizontal systems, we recommend the use of the Lockhart-Martinelli correlation for all flow regimes. For estimating frictional pressure gradient in horizontal wellbores, we recommend the Ouyang-Aziz[32] correlations. Note, however, that many horizontal wells are completed openhole and no simple solution exists.

4.4 Modeling Flow in Nonconventional Situations

Upward multiphase flow in vertical and deviated circular wellbores is the norm in petroleum production. However, exceptions occur in many applications. Some examples include:

- Performing a transient test in a sucker-rod pumping well requires holdup and pressure-drop estimations in the tubing/casing annulus.
- Designing steam injection and gas anchors demands understanding downward two-phase flow.
- Modeling phase redistribution during shut-in tests requires understanding bubble migration in countercurrent two-phase flow.

These situations add complexity to already complex flow phenomena. Models and correlations developed for vertical and deviated wells are not always directly applicable, although they form a basis for analyzing these systems.

In the rest of this chapter, we discuss two-phase gas/liquid flow in annulus, downward direction, and countercurrent flow. The last section discusses two-phase, oil/water flow in vertical and deviated wells.

4.4.1 Two-Phase Flow in Annulus. Two-phase flow patterns observed in an annular channel are similar to those observed in vertical and inclined upward flow; that is, bubbly and dispersed bubbly, slug, churn, and annular flow. As in the case of flow in inclined systems, slug and churn flow are combined and called intermittent flow. Another similarity between flow in deviated wells and flow in annular channels is the influence of geometry on the shape of bubbles and, therefore, their rise velocities.

Very little work is available on two-phase flow in an annulus. The early studies of Gipson and Swaim,[33] Godbey and Dimon,[34] Podio et al.,[35] and Hasan and Kabir[36] involved stagnant liquid columns. A mechanistic model for two-phase flow in annuli was first presented by Caetano et al.[37] Subsequently, we[38] presented a simplified approach to estimate liquid holdup and pressure gradient based on the models for vertical and deviated wellbores, discussed earlier. Because of its simplicity and accuracy, we present this work here.

The approach adapted for deviated circular channels appears to work well for vertical and deviated annuli. For bubbly flow in vertical or deviated annuli, we[38] found that holdup may be estimated using Eq. 3.20 (or Eq. 4.25) with $C_o = 1.2$ and v_∞ given by the Harmathy correlation (Eq. 3.6). Therefore, no modification in the estimation procedure of a vertical circular channel is needed. Indeed, as in circular channels, the transition from bubbly to slug flow occurs in an annulus when the gas-volume fraction exceeds 25%. Therefore, we used Eq. 4.7 [$v_{sg} > (0.43 v_{sL} + 0.357 v_\infty)\sin\alpha$] as the criterion for this transition in vertical and deviated annuli.

Similarly, for intermittent flow, we can use Eqs. 4.23 [$f_g = v_{sg}/(C_o v_m + \bar{v}_\infty)$] and 4.24 (for average rise velocity) to estimate holdup. We noted that a value of 1.2 for C_o worked well for both vertical and deviated annuli. However, we found the rise velocity of Taylor bubbles to be influenced by both pipe inclination and the inside-to-outside diameter ratio of the annulus. The expression for estimating the Taylor-bubble rise velocity in an annulus is written as

$$v_{\infty T\alpha} = \left[0.345 + 0.1 \left(d_i / d_o \right) \right] \left(1 + \cos\alpha \right)^{1.2}$$
$$\sqrt{\sin\alpha}\sqrt{g d_o \left(\rho_L - \rho_g \right)/\rho_L}, \quad \ldots\ldots\ldots\ldots (4.75)$$

where d_i is the diameter of the inner tubing (tubing OD) and d_o is that of the outer tubing (casing ID). Note that for a circular channel, when there is no inner tubing, d_i is zero, and Eq. 4.75 collapses into Eq. 4.32, which, in turn, reduces to Eq. 3.7 (Nicklin equation) for vertical systems in which $\cos\alpha$ is zero, and $\sin\alpha = 1.0$.

Using Caetano et al.[37] data, among others, we[38] showed that the volume-fraction data of three flow regimes can be modeled quite satisfactorily. **Figs. 4.16** through **4.18** provide the model's validation. Note that slug- and churn-flow patterns, presented as intermittent flow in this text, were treated separately.

Once holdup is estimated, pressure gradient in bubbly and intermittent flow regimes may be calculated with the usual approach,

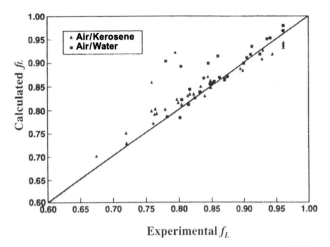

Fig. 4.16—Model mimics bubbly flow data of Caetano *et al.* (from Refs. 37 and 38).

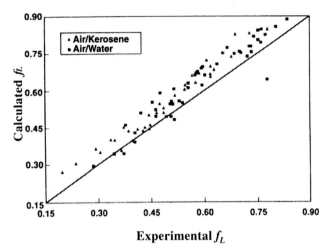

Fig. 4.17—Model mimics slug flow data of Caetano *et al.* (from Refs. 37 and 38).

$$-\frac{dp}{dz} = \frac{g \sin\alpha}{g_c}\left(\rho_L f_L + \rho_g f_g\right) + \frac{f_m v_m^2 \rho_m}{2g_c d} + \frac{\rho_m v_m}{g_c}\frac{dv_m}{dz}.$$

$$\dots \dots \dots \dots \dots \dots (4.27)$$

We recommend Eq. 3.11 for transition to annular flow in an annulus. That is because neither the pipe geometry nor its inclination affects this transition significantly. For the rare occurrence of annular flow in an annular geometry, pressure gradient may be computed with the Lockhart–Martinelli correlation, discussed in Chap. 2. However, for a rigorous and complete analysis of annular flow, as well as other flow regimes, refer to the study of Caetano *et al.*[37] A pressure-buildup test in a sucker-rod pumping well presents an essentially nonfrictional pressure-drop calculation situation. That is because low velocity of the annular fluids, whose movement is monitored by acoustic pulses, suggests hydrostatic head as the major contributor to the total pressure. **Fig. 4.19,** taken from Ref. 39, compares the performance of various f_g-models in computation of bottomhole pressures.

4.4.2 Downward Two-Phase Flow. Downward simultaneous flow of gas and liquid, although rare, is important in the chemical process industry and also in petroleum production. An example of two-phase downflow is the injection of wet steam in thermal recovery. Gas anchor design in pumped wells provides another example.

As mentioned earlier, the Beggs and Brill[11] correlation allows holdup and pressure-drop computation for all inclination angles, including when flow occurs in the downward direction. Mukherjee and Brill[12] also presented extensive data and a correlation for downward two-phase flow. Both correlations are quite robust. However, they are less reliable at low-liquid rates because of their parametric dependence on input liquid fraction.

Bornea[40] proposed a unified model for flow pattern transitions in both upward and downward flows. Crawford *et al.*[41] presented data and an empirical method for estimating pattern transitions in downflow by modifying the Weisman and Kang[2] approach for pattern transition in inclined upflow. Crawford *et*

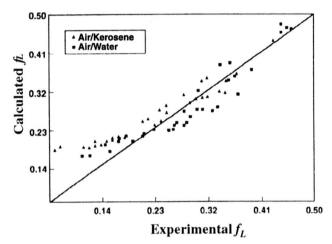

Fig. 4.18—Model mimics churn flow data of Caetano *et al.* (from Refs. 37 and 38).

al.[42] also proposed a simplified drift-flux approach to compute the gas volume fraction in downward bubbly and slug flow.

Based on the drift-flux approach, which has worked well for vertical and deviated upflow, Hasan[43] presented a model for estimating holdup in downward bubbly and intermittent two-phase flow. We present the essence of that study. Here, we assume that the behavior of vertical and inclined downward two-phase flow will be very similar to that of their counterpart in upflow, except that buoyancy will oppose the flow of the gas phase in downflow. Following Eq. 3.22 for upflow, we express the in-situ gas velocity, v_g, during downflow at all inclinations as $C_o v_m - v_\infty$. Therefore, the model expresses liquid holdup in these two flow regimes as

$$f_L \equiv 1 - f_g = 1 - \frac{v_{sg}}{C_o v_m - v_\infty}. \dots \dots \dots \dots (4.76)$$

The effect of buoyancy (i.e., the value of v_∞) and bubble distribution across the channel (i.e., the value of C_o) will depend on the existing flow pattern. Analysis of inclined downflow data, from diverse sources, show that Eq. 4.76 can be used for

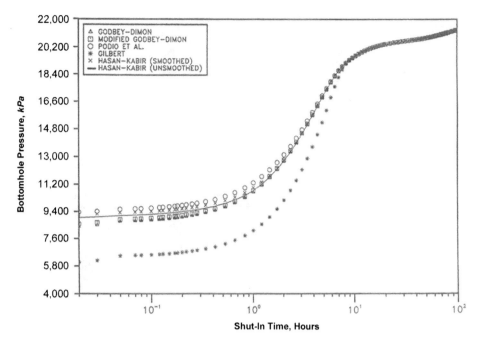

Fig. 4.19—Computing bottomhole pressures in a buildup test using f_g model (from Ref. 39).

bubbly flow with a value of 1.2 for C_o and that the Harmathy equation can estimate the rise velocity of bubbles for all inclination angles. Therefore, the only difference in computing liquid holdup during bubbly flow in downward direction, compared to that for upflow (Eq. 4.21), is the negative sign in front of the terminal rise velocity, v_∞, in Eq. 4.50.

For slug or intermittent flow, the approach used for deviated upflow can be extended to inclined downflow (Eq. 4.28), with a negative sign for the average rise velocity, $\bar{v}_{\infty\alpha}$ that is,

$$f_L \equiv 1 - f_g = 1 - \frac{v_{sg}}{C_o v_m - \bar{v}_{\infty\alpha}}, \quad \ldots\ldots\ldots\ldots (4.77)$$

where, as in upflow,

$$\bar{v}_{\infty\alpha} = v_{\infty T\alpha}(1 - e^{-v_t/v_{sg}}) + v_\infty e^{-v_t/v_{sg}} . \quad \ldots\ldots\ldots (4.29)$$

Analysis of slug flow holdup data suggests that Eq. 4.77 applies when a slightly lower value of 1.12 is used for C_o, instead of using 1.2 in upflow.

As in the case of upflow, a gas volume fraction of 25% (holdup of 75%) can be used as the transition criterion between bubbly and intermittent flow. This criterion also applies to deviated wells , if the actual superficial velocity of the gas phase at the upper section of the pipe is used, as shown earlier. Thus, we recommend using equation

$$v_{sg} = [0.43v_{sL} - 0.357v_\infty]\sin\alpha \quad \ldots\ldots\ldots\ldots (4.78)$$

to allow for the opposing effect of buoyancy. Transition data from various sources lend credence to Eq. 4.78. Note that Eq. 4.58 indicates a minimum required v_{sL} value below which v_{sg} becomes negative; that is, the system becomes unstable—a fact noted by Crawford *et al.*[41] **Fig. 4.20** provides testimony to the benefits of the recommended approach.

4.4.3 Countercurrent Two-Phase Flow. Countercurrent two-phase flow, in which liquid flows downward and the gas phase moves upward, may occur during oil production, transient testing, and well-control operations. Transient tests that are performed by shutting the well at the surface often lead to interpretation problems when high gas/liquid productions occur. The preferential upward movement of the gas may cause severe segregation, resulting in anomalous wellbore pressure increase. The increased pressure can cause the liquid to flow back into the formation, while the gas phase moves in the upward direction. Similarly, oil production often requires separating gas by reversing the direction of liquid flow to maintain high-pump efficiency. Countercurrent flow is also prevalent in the chemical industry in equipment such as absorption columns and bubble-column reactors.

Very few works exist in the petroleum literature that examine countercurrent two-phase flow. The work of Shah *et al.*,[44] among others, is essentially empirical in nature. Taitel and Bornea[45] were the first to report the existence of three flow regimes—bubbly, slug, and annular—and presented a map delineating the boundaries. The existence of annular regime during countercurrent flow, however, is likely to be limited because of the opposing flow direction of the phases.

The behavior of countercurrent flow may be viewed as a combination of simultaneous flow of two phases in the upward and downward directions. Indeed, Hasan *et al.*[46] proposed that the drift-flux approach can be used to estimate holdup and pressure drop during bubbly and slug flow, with appropriate signs for the flow velocities. Therefore, for bubbly flow, noting that v_m in the upward direction is given by $v_{sg} - v_{sL}$, we write

$$f_L \equiv 1 - f_g = 1 - \frac{v_{sg}}{C_o(v_{sg} - v_{sL}) + v_\infty} . \quad \ldots\ldots\ldots (4.79)$$

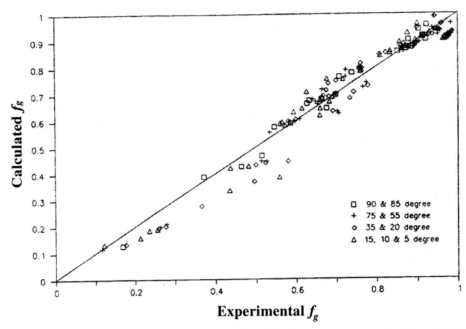

Fig. 4.20—Model mimics bubbly and intermittent flow data for various pipe angles (from Ref. 43).

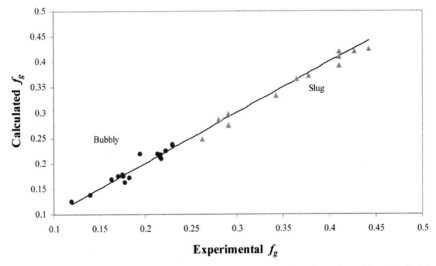

Fig. 4.21—Model explains countercurrent bubbly and slug flow data (from Ref. 46; reprinted with permission from Elsevier Science).

As in cocurrent flow, we recommend the use of the Harmathy correlation (Eq. 3.6) for estimating v_∞. Velocity data,[46] for single bubbles rising against downward liquid flow, agree well with those estimated with Eq. 3.6. Unlike the case of cocurrent flow, where $C_o = 1.2$, the holdup data suggest a higher value of 2.0 for the flow parameter, C_o, in countercurrent bubbly flow. Fluid recirculation causes the velocity profile to be sharper with a much higher maximum velocity at the channel center than in the case of cocurrent turbulent flow. Consequently, the value of C_o is higher than in cocurrent flow.

Similarly, for slug or intermittent flow, we suggest an average rise velocity approach to estimate holdup.

$$f_L \equiv 1 - f_g = 1 - \frac{v_{sg}}{C_o(v_{sg} - v_{sL}) + \bar{v}_{\infty\alpha}} , \qquad \ldots\ldots\ldots (4.80)$$

where, as in upflow, $\bar{v}_{\infty\alpha}$ is calculated from Eq. 4.28, with the Taylor-bubble rise velocity estimated from Eq. 3.7 for vertical systems. In this case, a value of $C_o = 1.2$ agrees very well with countercurrent slug flow data from several sources. **Fig. 4.21** shows the data of Hasan *et al.*[46] and those of the model presented by Eqs. 4.59 and 4.60.

As in case of cocurrent flow, we found that the transition from bubbly to slug flow occurs at a f_g of about 25% (f_L=75%). Using Eq. 4.79 with C_o=2.0, we can express the superficial gas velocity needed for bubbly/slug flow transition in countercurrent flow as

$$v_{sg} = 0.5v_\infty - v_{sL} \cdot \quad \text{..................... (4.81)}$$

No work has been reported for estimating holdup in deviated wells for countercurrent flow. We conjecture that the approach used for inclined cocurrent flow will apply to countercurrent flow. Therefore, Eq. 4.79 will be applicable to bubbly flow without modifications in deviated wells. Similarly, Eq. 4.80 may apply to countercurrent intermittent flow in deviated wells when the Taylor-bubble rise velocity, $v_{\infty T\alpha}$, is estimated with Eq. 4.28.

4.4.4 Oil/Water Two-Phase Flow.
As oil fields mature, coproduction of water with oil generally increases with time. Consequently, wellbore two-phase oil/water flow is encountered in most operations. A reliable holdup model is required so that production logs (PL) can be interpreted accurately. Controlling water production is one of the key elements in reservoir management. Therefore, any downhole remedial actions for water control are critically dependent on the accuracy of the model used in PL analysis. Liquid/liquid flow is also encountered when a power fluid, such as in a jet pump, is used to assist the lift. Despite diverse needs, only a handful of investigations attempt to explain the simultaneous flow of two immiscible liquids.

Flores *et al.*[47] presented a comprehensive study of oil/water flow patterns in vertical and deviated pipes. An important finding of their study is characterization of flow patterns into oil- and water-dominated regimes. Significant slippage occurs between oil and water phases in water-dominated flow; whereas, slippage is negligible in oil-dominated flow. Their study also shows that while the behavior of oil/water flow has many similarities with gas/liquid flow, important differences still remain. One significant difference is that the formation of a Taylor-like bubble is not evident in oil/water flow, although pseudoslug flow can be observed. Pseudoslugs are characterized by the oil droplets that tend to move as a packet interrupted by water breaks. Even in churn flow, the oil droplets tend to maintain their identity, although some irregular-shaped oil droplets can be observed visually.

Recently, Hasan and Kabir[48,49] and Flores *et al.*[50] proposed semimechanistic models, based on the drift-flux approach for estimating in-situ oil fraction, f_o, and pressure gradient for oil/water two-phase flow in vertical and deviated wells. The models are similar in nature and propose that the slip between the phases is negligible for oil-dominated flows, which occur when $f_o > 0.7$ (i.e., $f_w < 0.3$). In terms of superficial oil and water velocities, v_{so} and v_{sw}, respectively, we have

$$f_o \equiv 1 - f_w = \frac{v_{so}}{v_m} \cdot \quad \text{..................... (4.82)}$$

For all water-dominated flow regimes ($f_o < 0.7$) and well deviations ($<70°$), we[48] recommend the expression for in-situ oil volume fraction, f_o, which is written as

$$f_o \equiv 1 - f_w = \frac{v_{so}}{1.2v_m + v_{\infty\theta} f_w^2} \cdot \quad \text{.............. (4.83)}$$

Note the similarity between Eq. 4.83 for in-situ oil volume fraction and Eq. 4.28 for in-situ gas volume fraction in devi-

ated wells. A constant value of 1.2 for the flow parameter is used in both oil/water and liquid/gas systems for all deviations ($<70°$). The presence of the water-holdup term in the denominator of the right side of Eq. 4.83, recommended by both Hasan and Kabir[48] and Flores *et al.*,[50] reduces the effective rise velocity of oil bubbles. Therefore, the in-situ fraction calculated with Eq. 4.83 is higher than that of Eq. 4.28. Note that Eq. 4.83, implicit in holdup, requires a root solver, such as the secant-bisection method or an iterative procedure, for its evaluation.

For rise velocity of oil bubbles in vertical systems, we[48,49] recommended the use of the Harmathy correlation. Using Nicolas and Witterholt[51] data for a number of liquid/liquid systems with varying densities (1,000 to 773 kg/m³) and interfacial tensions (18 to 43 dynes/cm), we showed a good agreement between the bubble rise velocity data and the Harmathy correlation. For deviated wells, we[48] proposed an expression similar to Eq. 4.28.

$$\begin{aligned} v_{\infty\alpha} &= v_\infty \sqrt{\sin\alpha} \left(1 + \cos\alpha\right)^2 \\ &= 1.53 \sqrt[4]{g\sigma(\rho_w - \rho_o)/\rho_w^2} \sqrt{\sin\alpha} \left(1 + \cos\alpha\right)^2 \cdot \end{aligned}$$
$$\text{.................... (4.84)}$$

Note, however, that we[48] used the Harmathy correlation for bubble rise velocity for a vertical well for all flow regimes and that the factor accounting for well inclination has a slightly different exponent than does Eq. 4.28. In contrast, Flores *et al.*[50] used a Nicklin-type correlation with an empirically determined constant for bubble rise velocity in churn flow, $v_{\infty T}$.

$$v_{\infty T} = 0.25\sqrt{gd(\rho_w - \rho_o)/\rho_w} \cdot \quad \text{.............. (4.85)}$$

We presented data from a number of sources that lend strong support to Eqs. 4.82 through 4.84. For estimating frictional pressure head in oil/water flow, the no-slip approach is recommended because the frictional pressure gradient is expected to be small in all but near-horizontal systems. However, for greater accuracy, especially for near-horizontal systems, refer to Flores *et al.*,[50] who proposed the following expression for the mixture friction factor, f_{fm}, in terms of Reynolds number.

$$f_{fm} = C \operatorname{Re}_m^{-n} = C\left(\rho v_m d / \mu\right)^{-n} \cdot \quad \text{.............. (4.86)}$$

The values of the properties (density and viscosity) and the constants (C and n) depend on the phase that is continuous. For example, when water is the continuous phase, $C = 63.8$ and $n = 0.84$, and for continuous oil phase, $C = 207.3$ and $n = 1.27$.

To show robustness of the recommended modeling approach, we present data from our[48] work in **Figs. 4.22** and **4.23.**

Summary

In petroleum production, two-phase flow occurs in a variety of situations, other than the conventional upward flow of gas and liquid. In cases where flow occurs in deviated wells, occurs in vertical and inclined annuli, moves in downward directions, and is counter to each other, we show that the

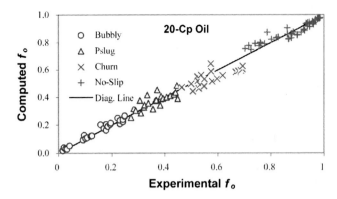

Fig. 4.22—Model mimics data in a 1.06-in. ID pipe (from Ref. 48).

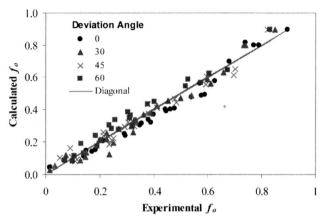

Fig. 4.23—Model mimics data in a 6.5-in. ID pipe (from Ref. 48).

drift-flux approach provides a good estimation of holdup. The same is also true when two immiscible liquid phases, such as oil and water, are involved in vertical or deviated wells. The method's simplicity and engineering accuracy are appealing.

Applications of some of these models are made elsewhere in the text. For instance, Chap. 9 discusses downward flow of wet steam, and Chap. 10 shows how oil/water flow modeling is used in production log interpretation.

Nomenclature

a = factor used in the Beggs-Brill holdup equation, Eq. 4.13

A = cross-sectional area for fluid flow, ft^2

A_g, A_L = cross-sectional area available for gas or liquid flow, ft^2

C = constant in Lockhart-Martinelli parameter, dimensionless

C_2 = constant for Taylor-bubble rise velocity in slug flow, dimensionless

C_{Da} = bubble drag coefficient for inclined channel, dimensionless

C_o = flow parameter in bubbly flow, dimensionless

d = flow-string diameter, ft

d_c, d_t = casing or tubing diameter, ft

E = fraction of the liquid phase entrained in the gas core, dimensionless

E_o = Eotvos number, $gd^2(\rho_L-\rho_g)/\sigma$, dimensionless

f = friction factor, dimensionless

f_c = film friction factor for the gas core in annular flow, dimensionless

f_g = gas in-situ volume fraction (void fraction), dimensionless

f_{gLS} = gas in-situ volume fraction in the liquid slug portion of the cell, dimensionless

f_{gTB} = gas in-situ volume fraction in the Taylor bubble portion of the cell, dimensionless

f_{fL} = single-phase liquid friction factor, used in Eq. 4.59, dimensionless

f_L = liquid holdup, (liquid in-situ volume fraction), dimensionless

f_{LLS} = liquid holdup in the liquid slug portion of the cell, dimensionless

f_{LTB} = liquid holdup in the Taylor bubble portion of the cell, dimensionless

f_m = friction factor for the two-phase mixture, dimensionless

f_n = friction factor calculated assuming no slip between the phases, dimensionless

f_w = water holdup, (water in-situ volume fraction), dimensionless

F = parameter in Taitel et al. horizontal flow-pattern map, dimensionless

F_B, F_T = force caused by buoyancy or turbulent fluctuation, lbf

F_p = friction geometry parameter, dimensionless

Fr = Froude number, v^2/gd, dimensionless

$F(\alpha)$ = parameter used by Beggas and Brill, defined by Eq. 4.21, dimensionless

g = acceleration caused by gravity, ft/sec^2

g_c = conversion factor, 32.17 (lbm-ft)/(lbf-sec^2)

G_m = mixture mass flux, $\rho_m v_m$, lbm/(hr-ft^2)

G_g, G_L = gas or liquid mass flux, $\rho_g v_{sg}=G_m x$, or $\rho_L v_{sL}=G_m(1-x)$, lbm/(hr-ft^2)

h = liquid height in horizontal/near-horizontal flow, ft

I = Gomez et al. inclination factor, dimensionless

I_H, I_V = Gomez et al. inclination factor horizontal or vertical systems, dimensionless

K = parameter in Taitel et al. horizontal flow-pattern map, dimensionless

Ku_{sg} = Kutadelaze number, $= v_{sg}\rho_g/[g(\rho_L-\rho_g)\sigma]^{0.25}$, dimensionless

L = total vertical well depth, ft

L = total length of a cell in slug flow, ft

L_R = relaxation distance, 1/ft

L_s, L_T = length of the liquid slug or Taylor bubble in slug flow, ft

N_f = inverse viscosity number, $[gd^3\rho_L(\rho_L-\rho_g)]^{1/2}/\mu_L$, dimensionless

p = pressure, psi

(dp/dz) = total pressure gradient, psi/ft

$(dp/dz)_A$ = accelerational (kinetic) pressure gradient, psi/ft

$(dp/dz)_F$ = frictional pressure gradient, psi/ft

$(dp/dz)_H$ = static pressure gradient, psi/ft

p_{wf} = flowing bottomhole pressure, psi

Pr = Prandtl number, $c_p \mu / k$, dimensionless

q = fluid flow rate at standard conditions, STB/D or MMscf/D

q_g, q_L = gas or liquid flow rate at standard conditions, MMscf/D or STB/D

q_{wh} = wellhead rate, STB/D or MMscf/D

Q = heat transfer rate per unit length of wellbore, Btu/(hr-ft)

r_w = wellbore radius, ft

r_D = dimensionless radial distance, r/r_w, dimensionless

Re = Reynolds number, $dv\rho/\mu$, dimensionless

Re_m = Reynolds number for the mixture, $\rho_m v_m d/\mu_m$, dimensionless

Re_g, Re_L = Reynolds number for the gas ($\rho_g v_g d/\mu_g$) or liquid phase ($\rho_L v_L d/\mu_L$), dimensionless

R_s = solution gas/oil ratio, scf/STB

s = parameter used by Beggs and Brill, defined by Eqs. 4.18 and 4.19, dimensionless

S_i = gas/liquid interface perimeter, ft

S_L = wetted liquid perimeter, ft

T = parameter in Taitel *et al.* horizontal flow-pattern map, dimensionless

V_B = bubble volume, ft^3

v = fluid velocity, ft/sec

v_c = core fluid velocity, ft/sec

v_d = drift velocity of the lighter phase, ft/sec

v_g, v_L = gas or liquid in-situ velocity, ft/sec

v_{gd}, v_{Ld} = dimensionless phase velocities, dimensionless

v_{gTB} = in-situ gas velocity in the Taylor bubble portion of the cell, ft/sec

v_{sg}, v_{sL} = superficial gas or liquid in-situ velocity, ft/sec

v_{tr} = superficial gas at the bubbly-slug transition zone, ft/sec

v_{TB} = in-situ velocity of the Taylor bubble, ft/sec

v_{gLS} = in-situ gas velocity in the liquid slug portion of the cell, ft/sec

$v_\infty, v_{\infty T}$ = terminal rise velocity of bubbles in bubbly flow or a Taylor bubble in slug flow, ft/sec

$v_{\infty T \alpha}$ = terminal rise velocity of a Taylor bubble in a horizontal well inclined by α degrees, ft/sec

w = mass flow rate of fluid, lbm/sec

x = gas mass fraction in tubing fluid mixture, dimensionless

X = Lockhart-Martinelli parameter, dimensionless

y = parameter used by Beggs and Brill, defined by Eq. 4.17, dimensionless

Y = ratio of gravitational to gas-phase frictional gradient, dimensionless

z = vertical well depth (measured from wellhead), ft

α' = Blassius friction factor, dimensionless

α = horizontal wellbore inclination, degrees

β = ratio of the length of the Taylor bubble to the total cell, L_T/L, dimensionless

δ = film thickness, ft

$\underline{\delta}$ = dimensionless film thickness

μ = oil viscosity, cp

ε = pipe roughness factor, ft

ϕ_g, ϕ_L = friction multiplier based on gas or liquid flowing alone in the channel in the Lockhart-Martinelli correlation, dimensionless

ϕ_1, ϕ_2 = parameters for the Weisman and Kang inclined flow-pattern map, dimensionless

ρ = density, lbm/ft^3

ρ_g, ρ_L = gas or liquid phase density, lbm/ft^3

ρ_c, ρ_e = core fluid or earth (formation) density, lbm/ft^3

λ = parameter for the Baker flow-pattern map, Eq. 4.35, dimensionless

σ = surface tension, lbm/sec^2

ψ = parameter for the Baker flow-pattern map, Eq. 4.36, dimensionless

γ = distortion coefficient used in Eq. 4.8, dimensionless

τ = shear stress, psi

ω = empirical constant in Eq. 4.71

Subscripts

a = annulus

A = air

c = casing

g = gas

L = liquid

LS = liquid slug

o = oil

P = projected (area of a bubble)

s = standard conditions for Weisman-Kang map

T = Taylor bubble

w = water

References

1. Taitel, Y., Lee, N., and Dukler, A.E.: "Transient Gas-Liquid Flow in Horizontal Pipes: Modeling the Flow Pattern Transitions," *AIChE J.* (September 1978) 920.

2. Weisman, J. and Kang, S. Y.: "Flow Pattern Transitions in Vertical and Upwardly Inclined Lines," *Int. J. Multiphase Flow* (1981) **7**, 271.

3. Bornea, D. *et al.*: "Gas-Liquid Flow in Inclined Tubes: Flow Pattern Transition for Upward Flow," *Chem. Eng. Sci.* (1985) **40**, 131.

4. Taitel, Y., Bornea, D. and Dukler, A.E.: "Modeling Flow Pattern Transition For Steady Upward Gas-Liquid Flow in Vertical Tubes," *AIChE J.* (May 1980) 345.

5. Hasan, A. R.: "Inclined Two-phase Flow: Pattern Transition, Void Fraction and Pressure Drop," *Particulate Phenomena & Multiphase Transport*, T.N. Veziroglu (ed.), Hemisphere Publications, New York (1988) **1**, 229.

6. Hasan, A. R. and Kabir, C. S.: "Predicting Multiphase Flow Behavior in a Deviated Well," *SPEPE* (November 1988) 474.

7. Harmathy, T.Z.: "Velocity of Large Drops and Bubbles in Media of Infinite or Restricted Extent," *AIChE J.* (1960) **6**, 281.

8. Patel, R.: "Multiphase Flow in Vertical and Inclined Annuli," MS thesis, U. of North Dakota, Grand Forks, North Dakota (1988).

9. Kaya, A.S., Sarica, C., and Brill, J.P.: "Mechanistic Modeling of Two-Phase Flow in Deviated Wells," *SPEPF* (August 2001) 156.

10. Beggs, H. D.: "An Experimental Study of Two-Phase Flow in Inclined Pipes," PhD dissertation, U. of Tulsa, Tulsa, Oklahoma (1972).

11. Beggs, H. D. and Brill, J. P.: "Study of Two-Phase Flow in Inclined Pipes," *JPT* (May 1973) 607.

12. Mukherjee, H. and Brill, J. P.: "Liquid Holdup Correlations for Inclined Two-Phase Flow," *JPT* (May 1983) 1003.

13. Singh, G. and Griffith, P.: "Determination of Pressure Drop Optimum Pipe Size for Two-Phase Slug Flow in an Inclined Pipe," *J. Eng. Ind.* (November 1970); *Trans., ASME,* **92**.

14. Bonnecaze, R. H., Erskine, W., and Greshkovich, E. J.: "Hold-up and Pressure Drop for Two Phase Slug Flow in Inclined Pipelines," *AIChE J.* (1971) **17**, 1109.

15. Mattar, L. and Gregory, G. A.: "Air-Oil Slug Flow in an Upward-Inclined Pipe-I: Slug Velocity, Holdup and Pressure Gradient," *Cdn. J. Pet. Tech.* (January–March 1974) 69.

16. Asheim, H.: "MONA, An Accurate Two-Phase Wellbore Flow Model Based on Phase Slippage," *SPEPE* (May 1986) 221.

17. Wallis, G.B.: *One Dimensional Two-Phase Flow*, McGraw-Hill Book Co. Inc., New York City (1969) 303–305.

18. Gomez, L.E. *et al.*: "Unified Mechanistic Model for Steady-State Two-Phase Flow: Horizontal to Vertical Upward Flow," *SPEJ* (September 2000) 339.

19. Ansari, A. M. *et al.*: "A Comprehensive Mechanistic Model for Upward Two-Phase Flow in Wellbores," *SPEPF* (May 1994) 143; *Trans.*, AIME, **297**.

20. Hughmark, G. A.: "Holdup and Heat Transfer in Horizontal Slug Gas-Liquid Flow," *Chem. Eng. Sci.*(1962) **20**, 1007.

21. Gregory, G. A. and Scott, D. S.: "Correlation of Liquid Slug Velocity and Frequency in Horizontal Cocurrent Gas-Liquid Slug Flow," *AIChE J* (1969) **15**, No. 6, 933.

22. Lau, C.W.: "Bubbly and Slug Flow Pressure Drop in An Inclined Pipe," SB thesis, Mass. Inst. Tech., Cambridge, Massachusetts (1972).

23. Bendiksen, K. H.: "An Experimental Investigation of the Motion of Long Bubbles in Inclined Tubes," *Int. J. Multiphase Flow* (1984) **10**, 467.

24. Hewitt, G.F. and Hall-Taylor, N.S.: *Annular Two-Phase Flow,* Pergamon Press, Oxford (1970).

25. Baker, O.: "Design of Pipe Lines For Simultaneous Flow of Oil and Gas" *Oil & Gas J.* (26 July 1954) **26**, 185.

26. Xiao, J.J., Shoham, O., and Brill, J.P.: "A Comprehensive Mechanistic Model for Two-phase Flow in Pipelines," paper SPE 20631 presented at the 1990 SPE Annual Technical Conference and Exhibition, New Orleans, Louisiana, 23–26 September.

27. Mandhane, J.M., Gregory, G.A. and Aziz, K.: "A Flow Pattern Map for Gas-Liquid Flow in Horizontal Pipes," *Int. J. Multiphase Flow* (1974) **1**, 537.

28. Govier, G. W. and Aziz, K.: *The Flow of Complex Mixtures in Pipes*, van Nostrand Reinhold Co., New York City (1972).

29. Henstock, W.H. and Hanratty, T.J.: "The Interfacial Drag and the Height of the Wall Layer in Annular Flow," *AIChE J.* (November 1976) **22**, No. 6, 990.

30. Ihara, M., Kikuyama, K., Hasegawa, Y., and Mizuguchi, K.: "Flow in Horizontal Wellbores with Influx Through Porous Walls," paper SPE 28485 presented at the 1994 SPE Annual Technical Conference and Exhibition, New Orleans, Louisiana, 25–28 September.

31. Dikken, B. J.: "Pressure Drop in Horizontal Wells and its Effect on Production Performance," *JPT* (November 1990) 1426.

32. Ouyang, L. and Aziz, K.: "A New Homogeneous Model for Gas-Liquid Flow in Horizontal Wells," *J. Pet. Sci. & Eng.* (2000) **27**, No. 2, 119.

33. Gipson, F.W. and Swaim, H.W.: "Designed Beam Pumping," *Proc.*, 19th Annual Southwestern Petroleum Short Course, Lubbock, Texas (April 1972) 95.

34. Godbey, J.K. and Dimon, C.A.: "Automatic Liquid Level Monitor for Pumping Wells," *JPT* (August 1977) 1019.

35. Podio, A.L., Tarrillion, M. J., and Roberts, E. T.: "Laboratory Works Improves Calculations," *Oil and Gas J.* (25 August 1980) 137.

36. Hasan, A.R. and Kabir, C.S.: "Determining Bottomhole Pressures in Pumping Wells," *SPEJ* (December 1985) 823; *Trans.*, AIME, **279**.

37. Caetano, E. F., Shoham, O. & Brill, J. P.: "Upward Vertical Two-Phase Flow Through an Annulus, Part I: Single Phase Friction Factor, Taylor Bubble Rise Velocity and Flow Pattern Prediction; Part II: Modeling Bubble, Slug, and Annular Flow," *J. Energy Resources Tech.*(March 1992) **114**, 1.

38. Hasan, A.R. and Kabir, C.S.: "Gas Void Fraction in Two-Phase Up-Flow in Vertical and Inclined Annuli," *Int. J. Multiphase Flow* (1992) **18**, No. 2, 279.

39. Kabir, C.S. and Hasan, A.R.: "Two-Phase Flow Correlations as Applied to Pumping Well Testing," *J. Energy Resources Tech.* (June 1994) **116**, 121.

40. Bornea, D.: "A Unified Model for Predicting Flow Pattern Transition for the Whole Range of Pipe Inclination," *Int. J. Multiphase Flow* (1986) **13**, 1.

41. Crawford, T.J., Weinberger, C.B. and Weisman, J.: "Two-Phase Flow Patterns and Void Fractions in Downward Flow. Part I: Steady-State Flow Patterns," *Int. J. Multiphase Flow* (1986) **11**, 761.

42. Crawford, T.J., Weinberger, C.B. and Weisman, J.: "Two-Phase Flow Patterns and Void Fractions in Downward Flow. Part II: Void Fractions and Transient Flow Patterns," *Int. J. Multiphase Flow* (1986) **13**, 219.

43. Hasan, A.R.: "Void Fraction in Bubbly and Slug Flow in Downward Two-Phase Flow in Vertical and Inclined Wellbores," *SPEPE* (August 1995) 172.

44. Shah, Y.T., Stiegel, G.J., and Sharma, M.M.: "Backmixing in Gas-Liquid Reactors," *AIChE J.* (1978) **24**, 369.

45. Taitel, Y. and Bornea, D.: "Counter Current Gas-Liquid Vertical Flow, Model for Flow Pattern and Pressure Drop," *Int. J. Multiphase Flow* (1983) **9**, 637.

46. Hasan, A.R., Kabir, C.S., and Srinivasan, S.: "Void Fraction Estimation in Countercurrent Vertical Two-Phase Flow," *Chem. Eng. Sci.* (1994) **49**, No. 16, 2567.

47. Flores, J.G. *et al.*: "Characterization of Oil-Water Flow Patterns in Vertical and Deviated Wells," *SPEPF* (May 1999) 102.

48. Hasan, A.R. and Kabir, C.S.: "A Simplified Model for Oil-Water Flow in Vertical and Deviated Wellbores," *SPEPF* (February 1999) 56.

49. Hasan, A.R. and Kabir, C.S.: "A New Model for Two-Phase Oil/Water Flow: Production Log Interpretation and Tubular Calculations," *SPEPE* (May 1990) 193; *Trans.,* AIME, **287**.

50. Flores, J.G. *et al.:* "Investigation of Holdup and Pressure Drop Behavior for Oil-Water Flow in Vertical and Deviated Wells," *Trans.*, ASME (March 1998) **120**, 8.

51. Nicolas, Y. and Witterholt, E.J.: "Measurement of Multiphase Fluid Flow," paper SPE 4023 presented at the 1972 SPE Annual Fall Meeting, San Antonio, Texas, 8–11 October.

SI Metric Conversion Factors

°API	$141.5/(131.5 + °API)$		$= \text{g/cm}^3$
Btu	$\times\ 1.055\ 056$	$\text{E} + 00$	$= \text{kJ}$
cp	$\times\ 1.0^*$	$\text{E} - 03$	$= \text{Pa s}$
dyne	$\times\ 1.0^*$	$\text{E} - 02$	$= \text{mN}$
ft	$\times\ 3.048^*$	$\text{E} - 01$	$= \text{m}$
ft^2	$\times\ 9.290\ 304^*$	$\text{E} - 02$	$= \text{m}^2$
ft^3	$\times\ 2.831\ 685$	$\text{E} - 02$	$= \text{m}^3$
ft/sec^2	$\times\ 9.290\ 304^*$	$\text{E} - 02$	$= \text{m/s}^2$
°F	$(°F - 32)/1.8$		$= °\text{C}$
in.	$\times\ 2.54^*$	$\text{E} + 00$	$= \text{cm}$
lbf	$\times\ 4.448\ 222$	$\text{E} + 00$	$= \text{N}$
lbm	$\times\ 4.535\ 924$	$\text{E} - 01$	$= \text{kg}$
lbm/sec	$\times\ 4.535\ 924$	$\text{E} - 01$	$= \text{kg/s}$
lbm/ft^3	$\times\ 1.601\ 846$	$\text{E} + 01$	$= \text{kg/m}^3$
psi	$\times\ 6.894\ 757$	$\text{E} + 00$	$= \text{kPa}$

* Conversion factor is exact.

Chapter 5
Wellbore Heat Transport

5.1 Introduction

Hydrocarbon production or fluid injection inevitably involves significant heat exchange between the wellbore fluid and its surroundings. Presence of seawater and air in the riser adds complexity to the heat transfer process in an offshore environment. During production, the hot fluid continues to lose heat to the increasingly cold surroundings, as it ascends the borehole. In contrast, the injected fluid may either gain (cold water) or lose (steam or hot water) heat upon descent.

The heat-transfer process just described impacts fluid properties and, in turn, the dynamics of fluid flow. Consequently, the coupled nature of momentum and energy transport may require simultaneous solutions for both processes. While steady-state flow modeling is adequate for designing tubular hardware en route to optimal wellhead production, transient-pressure testing may demand rigorous treatment of the coupled and transient nature of momentum, fluid, and heat flows. Similar treatment may be required when shut-in passes are made during production logging runs.

When oil is produced, its sandface temperature is about the same as that of the formation. Only very large drawdown will precipitate a temperature increase, owing to the Joule-Thompson (J-T) effect. By contrast, the gas may exhibit cooling for the same reason. In either case, fluid temperature at the sandface may be estimated from the knowledge of formation temperature and the J-T effect. However, as the fluid rises up the well, its temperature becomes higher than the surrounding earth because of the decline in earth temperature with decreasing depth. A wellbore fluid temperature profile and a static (undisturbed) earth temperature profile for an oil well are shown in **Fig. 5.1.**

The temperature difference between the wellbore fluid and the formation causes transfer of heat from the fluid to its surroundings. As Fig. 5.1 shows, the temperature difference increases with decreasing depth, causing greater heat transfer and lower fluid temperature as the fluid rises up the wellbore. At any given depth, the formation temperature will vary with radial distance from the well. The near-wellbore formation temperature also varies somewhat with production or injection time. Therefore, heat loss from the producing fluid decreases with time. Fig. 5.1 also depicts the increase in the injected fluid temperature with well depth.

The importance of various aspects of heat transfer between a wellbore fluid and the formation has generated rich literature on the subject. For instance, the usefulness of measuring wellbore fluid temperature was pointed out as early as 1937 by Schlumberger *et al.*[1] Perhaps the earliest application of the heat-transfer principle was the use of temperature logs for estimating water and gas injection profiles in the 1950's.[2,3] However, a lack of complete understanding of physics of heat flow led to a few problems in the field in the early days. Thermal stress failure of casings in steam-injection wells is a case in point.

A theoretical model for estimating fluid temperature as a function of well depth and production or injection time was first presented by Ramey.[4] Ramey's pioneering work spawned a number of applications. Some of these applications include heat loss estimation in steam injection and geothermal wells, production log interpretation, and estimation of fluid circulation temperature and static formation temperature.

Although Ramey's method gave us a much-needed impetus for further development, the method does have a few limitations. For example, the effects of kinetic energy and friction are neglected, and flow of only a single-phase fluid can be handled. Equally important, Ramey suggested the well radius to be vanishingly small in most cases; that is, the line-source well. This assumption can prove untenable in many instances. However, the work of Carslaw and Jaeger[5] may be adapted to remove the restrictive line-source approximation. Methods have also been proposed to handle two-phase flow,[6-9] thereby removing the other assumption. The work of Hasan and Kabir[10] shows how both assumptions can be removed for the general case of steady-state, wellbore two-phase flow.

In the following sections, we first model the formation temperature distribution. We then present the energy balance for the wellbore fluid as it exchanges heat with the surrounding earth. In Sec. 5.4, we develop expressions for wellbore fluid temperature for both production and injection wells. Our development closely follows the work of Hasan and Kabir.[10]

5.2 Formation Temperature Distribution

5.2.1 Diffusivity Equation. During production, the hot wellbore fluid provides a source of heat to the formation while, during fluid injection, the wellbore acts as a heat sink. To model heat flow and the resulting temperature distribution in such systems, we treat the formation as a homoge-

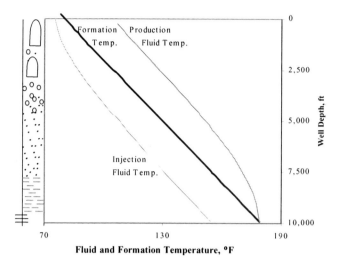

Fig. 5.1—Fluid and formation temperature profiles during production and injection.

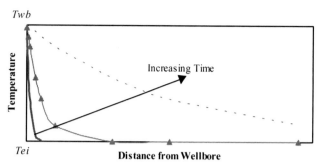

Fig. 5.2—Schematic of formation temperature profile at a given depth around the wellbore.

neous solid. Assuming symmetry around the well simplifies the three-dimensional (3D) problem into a two-dimensional (2D) problem. In addition, heat diffusion in the vertical direction may be ignored, owing to small vertical temperature gradients. Neglecting vertical heat flow reduces the system to a one-dimensional (1D) heat-diffusion problem. This approach, adapted by Hasan and Kabir[10] and others, introduces very little error and allows an analytical solution for the problem. The analytic approach is often preferred to the alternative numerical solutions, which may prove tedious and time consuming.

An energy balance on the formation then leads to the partial-differential equation, derived in cylindrical coordinates, for the variation of formation temperature with radial distance from the well and production time,

$$\frac{\partial^2 T_e}{\partial r^2} + \frac{1}{r}\frac{\partial T_e}{\partial r} = \frac{c_e \rho_e}{k_e}\frac{\partial T_e}{\partial t} \cdot \quad\quad (5.1)$$

In Eq. 5.1, T_e is the formation temperature at an arbitrary depth at time, t, and distance, r, measured from the center of the wellbore. Heat capacity, density and thermal conductivity of formation are given by c_e, ρ_e, and k_e, respectively. The thermal diffusivity equation is analogous to that used in pressure diffusion while solving pressure-transient problems.

The three boundary conditions needed for the solution of Eq. 5.1 can be obtained from the examination of the physical system. Fig. 5.2 is a schematic of the temperature distribution in the formation around a producing well at a given depth. At very early times, the formation temperature retains its initial value (T_{ei}) except near the wellbore, as shown by the inner curve. Thus, initially ($t=0$), we assume T_e equals T_{ei} everywhere in the formation. As time increases, heat, transferred from the warm wellbore fluid, will raise the formation temperature in its vicinity. The formation temperature profile at such a time will look somewhat like the middle curve shown in Fig. 5.2. However, at the outer boundary, formation temperature does not change with radial distance; that is, the slope is zero, or $\partial T/\partial r = 0$. Finally, the heatflow rate at the wellbore/formation interface is governed by Fou-

rier's law of heat conduction. Therefore, one can write the three boundary conditions,

$$\lim_{t \to 0} T_e = T_{ei}, \quad\quad (5.2)$$

$$Q = 2\pi k_e \frac{r\partial T_e}{\partial r}\bigg|_{r=r_{wb}}, \quad\quad (5.3)$$

and $$\lim_{r \to \infty} \frac{\partial T_e}{\partial r} = 0 \cdot \quad\quad (5.4)$$

In Eq. 5.4, Q is the heat flow rate from the formation to the well per unit length of the well, and r_{wb} is the outer radius of the wellbore.

As production continues, heat transfer from the wellbore causes a gradual rise in the temperature of the surrounding formation, which, in turn, causes a slow decrease in the rate of heat flow. Ameen[11] used the superposition principle to account for changing heat flux using a numerical approach. His solution showed that the assumption of constant heat flux introduced very little inaccuracy.

5.2.2 Solution of Diffusivity Equation. Eq. 5.1 is generally solved in terms of dimensionless variables r_D (dimensionless radial distance$=r/r_{wb}$), and t_D (dimensionless time$=k_e t/\rho_e c_e r_{wb}^2$). Hasan and Kabir[10] solved the resulting equation with the Laplace transform, following the approach suggested by van Everdingen and Hurst[12] for a similar set of equations used for pressure transients. They presented the expression for formation temperature as a function of radial distance and time. For estimating flowing fluid temperature, the formation temperature and its spatial derivative at the wellbore/formation interface ($r_D=1$) are needed. We can write the expression for the temperature at the wellbore/formation interface as

$$T_{wb} = T_{ei} + \frac{Q}{\pi^2 k_e} I, \qu\quad (5.5)$$

where $$I = \int_0^\infty \frac{1-e^{-u^2 t_D}}{u^2}\frac{Y_1(u)J_0(u) - J_1(u)Y_0(u)}{J_1^2(u)+Y_1^2(u)}du \cdot$$

$$\qu\quad\quad (5.6)$$

Analogous to the dimensionless pressure, p_D, used in pressure-transient analysis, we define dimensionless temperature, T_D, as

$$T_D \equiv -\frac{2\pi k_e}{Q}\left(T_{wb} - T_{ei}\right). \quad \ldots\ldots\ldots\ldots\ldots (5.7)$$

Thus, $T_D = -2I/\pi$. Note that T_D is always positive and that it represents heat flow from the formation towards a well. For the more usual case of fluid production, T_{wb} is greater than T_{ei}, causing the computed value of Q to be negative, meaning that the wellbore fluid loses heat to its surroundings.

Computations using Eqs. 5.5 through 5.7 require tedious evaluation of an integral involving modified Bessel functions of zero and first orders over the limits of zero and infinity. Hasan and Kabir[10] found the following algebraic expressions for dimensionless temperature, T_D, in terms of dimensionless time, t_D, to represent the solutions quite accurately.

$$T_D = \left[0.4063 + \frac{1}{2}\ln t_D\right]\left[1 + \frac{0.6}{t_D}\right], \text{ if } t_D > 1.5, \quad \ldots (5.8)$$

and $T_D = 1.1281\sqrt{t_D}\left(1 - 0.3\sqrt{t_D}\right)$, if $t_D \leq 1.5$. $\ldots\ldots$ (5.9)

The above expressions for T_D are discontinuous at $t_D = 1.5$. The continuous expression for T_D may be more suitable in some applications and is written as

$$T_D = \ln\left[e^{-0.2t_D} + \left(1.5 - 0.3719e^{-t_D}\right)\sqrt{t_D}\right]. \quad \ldots\ldots (5.10)$$

At large times, both Eqs. 5.8 and 5.10 reduce to the expression,

$$T_D = 0.4063 + \frac{1}{2}\ln t_D. \quad \ldots\ldots\ldots\ldots\ldots\ldots (5.11)$$

The log-linear representation of T_D, given by Eq. 5.11, was first used by Ramey[4] and Edwardson et al.[13] and is valid for wells of small diameters. Therefore, the expressions proposed by Hasan and Kabir[10] and Ramey[4] are equivalent at late times, although significant differences may occur at early times.

Eq. 5.7 is a convenient expression that relates heat flow to the temperature-difference driving force, $(T_{wb} - T_{ei})$, and allows heat-transfer computation with Eqs. 5.8 through 5.11. However, the temperature at the wellbore/formation interface, T_{wb}, is unknown and must be replaced by the wellbore fluid temperature. This substitution of T_{wb} by T_f is accomplished by using an energy balance for the wellbore fluid.

5.3 Energy Balance for Wellbore Fluid

Temperature difference between the wellbore fluid and the surrounding formation results in energy exchange. An energy balance for the fluid may be performed following any standard text on thermodynamics. Ramey[4] made an energy balance for the fluid by assuming single-phase flow. A general energy balance[10] for either a single- or two-phase system is presented here.

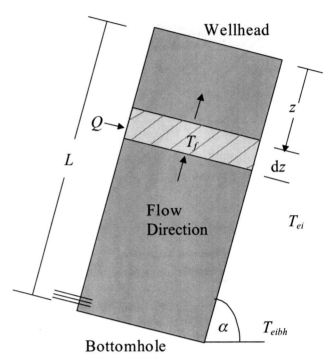

Fig. 5.3—Energy balance for wellbore fluid.

Fig. 5.3 shows a production system using single tubing, inclined at an angle, α, to the horizontal. Consider a control volume of length dz at a distance z from the wellhead in this system, where the distance coordinate, z, is positive in the downward direction. The amount of heat $(wH|_{z+dz})$ enters the element at $(z+dz)$ by convection, while conduction from the formation adds Q to the element.

Similarly, $(wH|_z)$ heat leaves the element at z by convection. Adding potential and kinetic energies to the heat energy of the fluid, we obtain

$$wH|_{z+dz} + \frac{(z+dz)wg\sin\alpha}{Jg_c} + \frac{wv^2|_{z+dz}}{2Jg_c} + Qdz$$

$$= wH|_z + \frac{zwg\sin\alpha}{Jg_c} + \frac{wv^2|_z}{2Jg_c}. \quad \ldots\ldots\ldots\ldots (5.12)$$

During injection, every term except Q in Eq. 5.12 changes sign. We can generalize the energy balance equation for both production and injection systems as

$$\frac{dH}{dz} + \frac{g\sin\alpha}{Jg_c} + \frac{v}{Jg_c}\frac{dv}{dz} = \mp\frac{Q}{w}, \quad \ldots\ldots\ldots\ldots (5.13)$$

where the negative sign on the right side applies to production and the positive sign to injection. In Eq. 5.13, g_c and J represent appropriate conversion factors. For a fluid undergoing no phase change, that is, when heat effects owing to evaporation/condensation, solution and mixing are negligible; enthalpy is a function of pressure and temperature and is given by

FLUID FLOW AND HEAT TRANSFER IN WELLBORES

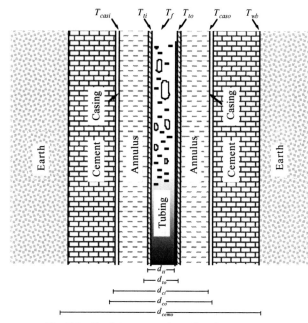

Fig. 5.4—Resistances to heat flow in a wellbore.

$$dH = \left(\frac{\partial H}{\partial T}\right)_p dT + \left(\frac{\partial H}{\partial p}\right)_T dp = c_p dT - C_J c_p dp \,,$$

$$\dots \dots \dots \dots \dots \dots \dots (5.14)$$

where C_J represents the Joule-Thompson coefficient and c_p is the mean heat capacity of the fluid at constant pressure. Note that because of significant evaporation/condensation during steam injection, Eq. 5.14, is inapplicable. We discuss issues related to steam injection or geothermal production in Chap. 9, Sec.9.3. Using Eq. 5.14, we can write the expression for the wellbore fluid temperature as a function of depth as

$$\frac{dT_f}{dz} = C_J \frac{dp}{dz} + \frac{1}{c_p}\left[\mp\frac{Q}{w} - \frac{g\sin\alpha}{Jg_c} - \frac{v}{Jg_c}\frac{dv}{dz}\right]. \quad \dots (5.15)$$

Combining Eq. 5.15 with Eqs. 5.7 and 5.10, one can arrive at an expression for T_f. However, to eliminate T_{wb} from the resultant expression, one must use the overall-heat-transfer coefficient for the wellbore.

5.3.1 Overall-Heat-Transfer Coefficient for Wellbores. Radial heat transfer occurs between the wellbore fluid and the earth, overcoming resistances offered by the tubing wall, tubing insulation, tubing-casing annulus, casing wall, and cement, as shown in **Fig. 5.4.** These resistances are in series, and except for the annulus, the only energy transport mechanism is conductive heat transfer. At steady state, the rate of heat flow, through a wellbore per unit length of the well, Q, can be expressed as

$$Q = -2\pi r_{to} U_{to}\left(T_f - T_{wb}\right) \cdot \dots \dots \dots \dots \dots (5.16)$$

In Eq. 5.16, U_{to} is defined as the overall-heat-transfer coefficient, based on the tubing outside surface area, $2\pi r_{to}$, and the temperature difference between the wellbore fluid and well-

bore/formation interface, $(T_f - T_{wb})$. Thus, the overall-heat-transfer coefficient for a given well is a very important parameter. Discussion on this topic has been presented by a number of authors[10,14] and is summarized in Appendix A.

When heat transfer occurs at steady state, heat, flowing through each of the elements (see Fig. 5.4), must be the same. Steady-state heat transfer allows us to derive the expression for the overall-heat-transfer coefficient,[10,14]

$$\frac{1}{U_{to}} = \frac{r_{to}}{r_{ti}h_{to}} + \frac{r_{to}\ln\left(r_{to}/r_{ti}\right)}{k_t} + \frac{r_{to}\ln\left(r_{ins}/r_{to}\right)}{k_{ins}}$$

$$+ \frac{r_{to}}{r_{ins}\left(h_c + h_r\right)} + \frac{r_{to}\ln\left(r_{co}/r_{ci}\right)}{k_c} + \frac{r_{to}\ln\left(r_{wb}/r_{co}\right)}{k_{cem}}.$$

$$\dots \dots \dots \dots \dots \dots \dots (5.17)$$

Most of the terms in Eq. 5.17 are easily computed. However, the resistance to heat transfer, offered by the annulus, represented by the fourth term in Eq. 5.17, is somewhat difficult to estimate. In case of steam injection or geothermal production, the large temperature difference between the tubing and annular fluids may cause both radiation and natural convection. Details of radiative and natural-convective heat-transfer mechanisms are also discussed in Appendix A.

5.3.2 Heat Loss to the Formation. We may rewrite the expression for T_D (Eq. 5.7) in heat transfer from the formation to the wellbore/formation interface as

$$Q \equiv -\frac{2\pi k_e}{T_D}\left(T_{wb} - T_{ei}\right) \cdot \dots \dots \dots \dots \dots (5.18)$$

Combining Eqs. 5.16 and 5.18 and eliminating T_{wb}, we obtain

$$Q \equiv -L_R wc_p\left(T_f - T_{ei}\right) = -\frac{wc_p}{A}\left(T_f - T_{ei}\right), \dots (5.19)$$

where L_R is the relaxation length parameter defined as

$$L_R \equiv \frac{2\pi}{c_p w}\left[\frac{r_{to}U_{to}k_e}{k_e + \left(r_{to}U_{to}T_D\right)}\right]. \dots \dots \dots \dots (5.20)$$

Note that the relaxation parameter, L_R, is inverse of the parameter, A, which is defined by Ramey[4] as

$$A \equiv \frac{c_p w}{2\pi}\left[\frac{k_e + \left(r_{to}U_{to}T_D\right)}{r_{to}U_{to}k_e}\right]. \dots \dots \dots \dots (5.21)$$

5.3.3 Relaxation Parameter, L_R (1/A). Eq. 5.19 shows that the heat loss (or gain) by the fluid in the wellbore to the formation is directly proportional to $(T_f - T_{ei})$ and the parameter, L_R. Thus, L_R may be viewed as a type of overall-heat-transfer coefficient for the formation/wellbore system having the units of 1/length, ft^{-1} or m^{-1}. Note that the expression for L_R contains thermal properties of both the formation and wellbore. It also includes the dimensionless temperature function, T_D, which varies with time. However, T_D is a weak function of

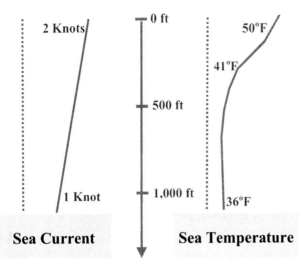

Fig. 5.5—Measured seawater temperature and velocity profiles (from Ref. 15).

time, especially that at late times. Therefore, constant L_R assumption works well in most practical applications.

The overall-heat-transfer coefficient for the wellbore system may vary with well depth because of the changing well configuration. In addition, as Eq. 5.17 suggests, natural convection in the annulus can contribute significantly to the value of U. Temperature difference, driving natural convection, varies with well depth, causing L_R to be a function of depth. However, variation of L_R with depth is usually small and generally neglected because U_{to} appears both in the numerator and the denominator of Eq. 5.20. The assumption of constant L_R has important consequences for the solution of the differential equation representing wellbore fluid temperature, which is discussed in Sec. 5.4.

5.3.4 Heat Transport in Offshore Riser. Computing wellbore fluid temperature in an offshore environment is a demanding task. That is because energy transport through seawater and air must be accounted for in an offshore riser. Depending on the riser length and water temperature, the wellbore fluid temperature might be affected significantly.

For production through seawater, a tubing/casing configuration without the cement sheath is assumed. The heat transfer rate, Q, through successive layers of cylindrical resistances, is given by

$$Q = -2\pi r_{to} U_{to} \left(T_f - T_{ei} \right), \quad \dots\dots\dots\dots (5.22)$$

where T_{ei} represents the static seawater temperature far away from the well at a given depth. The variation in seawater temperature with depth is needed to apply Eq. 5.22. In most cases, the water temperature decreases with depth, but in a nonlinear fashion. **Fig. 5.5** illustrates measured sea current and temperature profiles. The overall-heat-transfer coefficient, U_{toc}, based on the tubing outside surface area, is given by

$$\frac{1}{U_{to}} = \frac{r_{to}}{r_{ti}h_t} + \frac{1}{h_a} + \frac{r_{to}\ln\left(r_{to}/r_{ti}\right)}{k_t} + \frac{r_{to}\ln\left(r_{co}/r_{ci}\right)}{k_c} + \frac{r_{to}}{r_{co}h_c}. $$
$$\dots\dots\dots\dots\dots (5.23)$$

Eq. 5.22 may be recast in the same form as Eq. 5.21. Comparing these two equations for the case of production/injection through submerged tubulars, we derived the expression for relaxation parameter, L_{Rc}, as

$$L_{Rc} = \frac{2\pi r_{to} U_{toc}}{c_p w}. \quad \dots\dots\dots\dots\dots (5.24)$$

During production through seawater, natural current will make forced convection the most likely mode of heat transfer, especially near the air/water interface. Fishenden and Saunders[16] have studied forced convection and recommend the correlation for flow across long vertical pipes, which is written as

$$\mathrm{Nu} = 0.26 \left(\mathrm{Re}\right)^{0.6} \left(\mathrm{Pr}\right)^{0.3}, \quad \dots\dots\dots\dots (5.25)$$

where Nusselt and Prandtl numbers are given by $\mathrm{Nu} = h_c d/k_e$, and $\mathrm{Pr} = c_{pc}\mu_c/k_c$. Gebhart[17] presents a slightly different correlation.

$$\mathrm{Nu} = \left[0.35 + 0.56\left(\mathrm{Re}\right)^{0.52}\right]\left(\mathrm{Pr}\right)^{0.3} \quad \dots\dots\dots (5.26)$$

In the range of parameter values of interest, Eqs. 5.25 and 5.26 yield very similar results. Note that these expressions are also applicable to the wellbore exposed to air currents.

5.4 Wellbore Fluid Temperature

We relate fluid temperature to well depth by substituting the expression for heat loss to the formation, Q, (Eq. 5.19) into the energy balance equation (Eq. 5.15).

$$\frac{dT_f}{dz} = \pm\left(T_f - T_{ei}\right)L_R - \frac{g\sin\alpha}{c_p J g_c} - \frac{v}{c_p J g_c}\frac{dv}{dz} + C_J\frac{dp}{dz},$$
$$\dots\dots\dots\dots (5.27)$$

where the + sign applies to production, and the − sign applies to injection. We assume that the undisturbed formation temperature, T_{ei}, varies linearly with depth. Therefore, one can write an expression for T_{ei} for a deviated well of length, L, as

$$T_{ei} = T_{eibh} - (L - z)g_G \sin\alpha, \quad \dots\dots\dots\dots (5.28)$$

where g_G represents the geothermal gradient in terms of vertical depth, and T_{eibh} is the static earth temperature at the bottomhole. Note that z is positive in the downward direction. Even when the earth temperature is not linear with depth, it may be reasonably well represented by a few linear equations. Eq. 5.27 may be written as

$$\frac{dT_f}{dz} = \pm L_R(T_f - T_{ei}) - \frac{g\sin\alpha}{c_p J g_c} + \phi, \quad \dots\dots\dots (5.29)$$

where $\phi = -\dfrac{v}{c_p J g_c}\dfrac{dv}{dz} + C_J\dfrac{dp}{dz}$. $\cdots\cdots\cdots\cdots$ (5.30)

As expected, Eq. 5.29 shows that the change in fluid temperature with depth depends on the difference in temperature between the wellbore fluid and the surrounding formation. During production when $T_f > T_{ei}$, the fluid temperature decreases as the fluid moves up (Δz negative) the wellbore.

5.4.1 Producing Fluid Temperature. *Single-Phase Liquid Flow.* Liquids, being essentially incompressible, allow a number of simplifications to Eq. 5.29 for single-phase oil or water flow. For example, fluid velocity change with depth, (dv/dz), becomes negligible. In addition, because liquid density variation with pressure is usually very small, one can write

$$dH = dE + d(pV) = cdT + Vdp , \quad \cdots\cdots\cdots\cdots (5.31)$$

and $C_J \equiv \dfrac{1}{c_p}\left[\dfrac{\partial H}{\partial p}\right]_T = \dfrac{V}{c_p} = \dfrac{1}{\rho c_p}$. $\cdots\cdots\cdots\cdots$ (5.32)

Therefore, for liquids

$$\phi \equiv -\dfrac{v}{c_p J g_c}\dfrac{dv}{dz} + C_J\dfrac{dp}{dz} = \dfrac{1}{c_p \rho}\dfrac{dp}{dz} . \quad \cdots\cdots\cdots (5.33)$$

However, for single-phase liquid flow, the static head loss nearly equals the total pressure gradient. In other words, $dp/dz \sim \rho(g/g_c)\sin\alpha$. Therefore, Eq. 5.29 reduces to

$$\dfrac{dT_f}{dz} = L_R(T_f - T_{ei}) = L_R T_f - T_{eibh} + (L-z)g_G \sin\alpha .$$
$$\cdots\cdots\cdots\cdots (5.34)$$

We can also arrive at Eq. 5.34 by noting that, for liquids, the energy balance (Eq. 5.13) may be simplified to $c_p dT/dz = -Q/w = (T_f - T_{ei})L_R$.

If the relaxation length, L_R, is assumed invariant with well depth, Eq. 5.34 becomes a simple first-order linear differential equation, which can be solved with the integrating factor method. The solution is

$$T_f = T_{ei} + (g_G \sin\alpha/L_R) + IC e^{(z-l)L_R} , \quad \cdots\cdots\cdots (5.35)$$

where IC, representing the integration constant, is evaluated by noting that, at the bottomhole ($z=L$), the fluid temperature is equal to the formation temperature ($T_f = T_{eibh}$). Therefore,

$$T_f = T_{ei} + g_G \sin\alpha\left(1 - e^{(z-L)L_R}\right)/L_R$$
$$= T_{eibh} - g_G \sin\alpha\left[(L-z) - \left(1 - e^{(z-L)L_R}\right)/L_R\right] .$$
$$\cdots\cdots\cdots\cdots (5.36)$$

Eq. 5.36 shows that the fluid temperature decreases exponentially from the bottomhole ($z=L$) to the wellhead. It also shows that while the temperature of the fluid and the formation are the same at the bottomhole, the fluid temperature is higher than the formation temperature at any other location in the well. The difference in temperature between the well-

bore fluid and the formation gradually increases as the fluid ascends the well. For deep wells, $(z-L)L_R$ might become a large negative number leading to the expression for the temperature difference between the wellbore fluid and the formation, written as

$$T_f - T_{ei} = g_G \sin\alpha/L_R . \quad \cdots\cdots\cdots\cdots (5.37)$$

Eqs. 5.36 and 5.37 show that for very deep wells, the temperature difference ($T_f - T_{ei}$) might asymptotically approach a constant value. The magnitude of this temperature difference depends on the value of L_R. Thus, if the asymptotic approach holds, temperature logs may be used to estimate the value of L_R. When the thermal properties needed to calculate L_R (Eq. 5.21) are available, one may use temperature logs to calculate flow rates from various producing zones, as was proposed by Curtis and Witterholt.[18] This estimation is possible because L_R is inversely proportional to the mass flow rate. However, various assumptions, inherent in this approach, often render such estimates very approximate.

Single-Phase Gas Flow. Gas wells present a little more complication than oil wells because the static head is not canceled by the ϕ term. However, for gases at low pressures, ϕ is usually small and may be neglected. In that case, with the procedure used for solving Eq. 5.34, the following expression for fluid temperature may be derived from Eq. 5.29.

$$T_f = T_{ei} + \dfrac{1 - e^{(z-L)L_R}}{L_R}\left[g_G \sin\alpha - \dfrac{g\sin\alpha}{c_p J g_c}\right] . \quad \cdots\cdots (5.38)$$

At high pressures, when the density of gases are comparable to those of liquids, Eq. 5.37 will be more appropriate than Eq. 5.38.

Gas/Liquid Flow. For wells producing multiphase fluids, and for some gas wells, Eq. 5.29 must be solved in its entirety. If we assume that ϕ and L_R are independent of well depth, Eq. 5.29 becomes a first-order linear differential equation. The solution to Eq. 5.29, with $T_f = T_{eibh}$ at the bottomhole, is

$$T_f = T_{ei} + \dfrac{1 - e^{(z-L)L_R}}{L_R}\left[g_G \sin\alpha + \phi - \dfrac{g\sin\alpha}{c_p J g_c}\right] . \quad \cdots (5.39)$$

Note that, Eq. 5.39 is general and applies to the flow of single-phase liquid or gas and to two-phase fluids. For single-phase liquid flow, when ϕ equals the hydrostatic head ($= g\sin\alpha/Jg_c$), Eq. 5.39 reduces to Eq. 5.36, while single-phase gas flow with ϕ neglected, reduces to Eq. 5.38.

The value of the parameter, ϕ, needed in Eq. 5.39, depends on many variables, such as flow rate, gas/liquid ratio, and wellbore pressure. Hasan and Kabir[10] used the empirical expression for ϕ, developed by Sagar *et al*,[8] which is valid for flow rates less than 5 lbm/sec,

$$\phi = -0.002978 + 1.006 \times 10^{-6} p_{wh} + 1.906 \times 10^{-4} w$$
$$-1.047 \times 10^{-6} GLR + 3.229 \times 10^{-5} API$$
$$+0.004009\gamma_g - 0.3551 g_G . \quad \cdots\cdots\cdots\cdots (5.40)$$

For flow rates higher than 5 lbm/sec, Sagar *et al.* set $\phi=0$. An alternative to this empirical approach is the use of Joule-Thompson coefficient for two-phase flow, which is derived from first principles[9] and is given by

$$C_J \equiv \frac{1}{c_p}\left[\frac{x}{\rho_g}\left(-\frac{T}{Z}\left(\frac{\partial z}{\partial T}\right)_p\right)+\frac{1-x}{\rho_L}\right], \quad \dots\dots (5.41)$$

where x is the mass fraction of the vapor phase. We recommend use of Eq. 5.41, which has more general applicability. The parameter, ϕ, calculated from C_J will vary somewhat with well depth for both gas and multiphase fluids. Use of an average value, evaluated at the midpoint of the well, offers sufficient accuracy in most cases.

5.4.2 Fluid Temperature in Injection Wells. Injection wells are common occurrence in oil-field operations. Sometimes part of the produced water or gas is injected back into the formation for pressure maintenance. Secondary and tertiary recovery schemes also demand fluid injection. Injecting live steam into the formation often helps reduce reservoir fluid viscosity by raising its temperature. In these and other applications, one must be able to calculate the injection fluid temperature as it flows down the wellbore.

The differential equation describing flowing fluid temperature in wellbores, Eq. 5.29 with the negative sign, is valid for injection wells without evaporation/condensation. Eq. 5.29 is integrated for an injection well with the wellhead fluid, T_{fwh}, and surface earth temperatures, T_{es}, are used as boundary conditions to yield

$$T_f = T_{ei} - \frac{1-e^{(z-L)L_R}}{L_R}\left[g_G\sin\alpha+\phi-\frac{g\sin\alpha}{c_p Jg_c}\right]$$

$$+e^{-zL_R}\left(T_{fwh}-T_{es}\right). \quad \dots\dots\dots (5.42)$$

Condensable systems are treated in Chap. 9, Sec 9.3.

5.4.3 Variable Geothermal Gradient. Sometimes, one may encounter geologic formations with different heat-transfer characteristics, leading to a variable geothermal gradient. In such a case, Eq. 5.29 may be integrated by dividing the well into a number of intervals, with constant geothermal gradients being applied to each interval. The fluid temperature, calculated at the end of the interval, is used as the entrance fluid temperature for the interval above or beneath it. Therefore, production from a formation with two values of geothermal gradient, g_{G1} and g_{G2}, the expression for fluid temperature at the bottom interval is still given by Eq. 5.39, while that for the upper interval is given by

$$T_f = T_{ei} + \frac{1-e^{(z-L)L_R}}{L_R}\left[g_{G2}\sin\alpha+\phi-\frac{g\sin\alpha}{c_p Jg_c}\right]$$

$$+e^{(z-L)L_R}\left(T_{f1}-T_{ei1}\right), \quad \dots\dots\dots (5.43)$$

where T_{f1} and T_{ei1} represent fluid and earth temperatures at the interface of the two intervals. The procedure, of course, can be extended to an infinite number of intervals.

Field Example 5.1. Data reported by Sagar *et al.*[8] from a vertical flowing well is used to show the procedure for calculating fluid temperature in a producing well. The flow rates and well dimensions are given next.

q_o = 59 STB/D.
q_w = 542 STB/D.
q_g = 41 MScf/D.
γ_o = 34.3 API.
γ_w = 1.01.
γ_g = 1.04.
d_{ti} = 2.875 in.
d_{to} = 3.00 in.
d_{wb} = 9.00 in.
d_{ci} = 6.46 in.
d_{co} = 7.00 in.
p_{wh} = 113 psig.
T_{ewh} = 76°F.
T_{eibh} = 108°F=T_{fbh}.
Depth = 5,355 ft.
t_p = 158 hr.

The following typical values for the thermal properties of the various elements were used.

k_e = 1.40.
k_{cem} = 4.021.
k_a = 0.383.
k_f = 0.1 Btu/(hr-ft-°F).
c_p = 0.947 Btu/(lbm-°F).
μ_a = 1.5 cp.
μ_t = 1.1 cp.
α = 0.04 ft/sec².

To calculate the overall-heat-transfer coefficient with Eq. 5.17, we must estimate h_c with Eq. A-9 in Appendix A. This step requires an evaluation of the annular-fluid Grashof number according to Eq. A-10, which requires the temperature difference across the annular fluid $(T_{ins}-T_{ci})$. Because calculation of $T_{ins}-T_{ci}$ requires an estimate of U_{to}, an iterative approach is called for at each depth location of the well. As pointed out in Appendix A, use of the full value of h_c calculated from Eq. A-9 generally results in a slightly lower wellbore fluid temperature. Therefore, in calculating U_{to}, we used only 25% of the value of h_c estimated with the Dropkin-Sommerscales[19] correlation (i.e., h^*_c) because we think that this correlation significantly overestimates natural convective heat-transfer coefficients in wellbore annuli. Thus, for the wellhead conditions, we calculate

Gr = 92,040,
h_c = 38.51 Btu/(hr-ft²-°F),
h^*_c = $h_c/4$ = 9.63 Btu/(hr-ft²-°F),
U_{to} = 8.91 Btu/(hr-ft²-°F),
and L_R = 2.9×10^{-4} ft⁻¹ (A=3,449 ft).

Note that these values of U and A (=1/L_R) differ considerably from those computed by Sagar *et al.* [4.57 Btu/(hr-ft²-

TABLE 5.1—FLUID TEMPERATURE AND OTHER DATA FOR THE FIELD EXAMPLE						
Depth, ft	h_c[Btu/(hr-ft²-°F)]	U[Btu/(hr-ft²-°F)]	A [=(1/L_R) ft]	Formation Temperature, °F	Calculated Fluid Temperature, °F	Measured Fluid Temperature, °F
0	38.51	29.2	3,449	76	90.5	88
500	37.89	29.0	3,468	79	93	93
1,000	37.57	28.6	3,478	82	95.3	96
1,500	36.92	28.2	3,499	85	97.5	98
2,000	36.12	27.7	3,525	88	99.6	100
2,500	35.17	27.2	3,559	91	101.5	102
3,000	34.04	26.4	3,601	94	103.2	103
3,500	32.39	25.5	3,667	97	104.8	105
4,000	30.24	24.1	3,765	100	106.1	106
4,500	27.12	22.2	3,934	103	107.1	107
5,000	21.69	18.6	4,343	106	107.8	108
5,355	3.57	3.5	14,591	108	108	108

°F) and 5,000 ft, respectively] because they neglected convection in the annulus. In this example, we used the Sagar *et al.* correlation (Eq. 5.40) to evaluate ϕ. For this system, in which w is 2.41 lbm/sec, we calculate a value of 0.00074 for ϕ. Eq. 5.39 then yields the fluid temperature at the wellhead to be 90.5°F, compared to a measured value of 88°F. **Fig. 5.6** and **Table 5.1** report the flowing fluid temperature calculation carried out at various depths and compare these estimates against the measured data.

The agreement of the computed fluid temperatures (bottom heavy curve) with the measured values (open circles) appears quite good. Our experiences with this and other field data show that one-quarter of the h_c value calculated with Eq. 5.50 works well in practice. Computations suggest that a higher value for k_e near the wellhead, when compared to the rest of the formation, provides a better agreement. The top curve in Fig. 5.5 shows flowing fluid temperature that would be calculated if convection in the annulus is ignored.

Table 5.1 shows that the overall-heat-transfer coefficient, U_{to}, is much smaller at the bottomhole than at the wellhead. The marked variation in the U_{to} values with well depth is a direct result of the contribution of the natural convective heat-transfer coefficient of the annular fluid to the overall-heat-transfer coefficient. Because of small temperature differences between the tubing fluid and the earth near the bottomhole, temperature difference across the annulus (i.e., $T_{ins}-T_{ci}$) is small, and so is h_c. This low-h_c value leads to a smaller value for U_{to}. At the wellhead, the reverse is true, resulting in a much larger overall-heat-transfer coefficient. Of course, the annulus is not usually filled with liquid up to the wellhead; quite often, gas occupies most of the annulus. In such cases, computations must be done in segments, allowing for variable h_c with well depth, thereby honoring fluid composition in the annulus.

Summary

Estimating fluid temperature in a production or an injection well is a challenging task, owing to complex interaction of wellbore fluids with its surroundings. A part of the complexity arises from the transient nature of heat dissipation in the formation, even when wellbore fluid flow occurs at steady state. In this chapter, we present simplified relations for the dimensionless temperature representing heat flow from formation toward wellbore. Doing energy balance for the wellbore fluid and coupling it with that in the formation develops relations for wellbore fluid temperature. Using simplifying assumptions, we arrived at desired fluid-temperature expressions for flow of single-phase liquid, gas, and two-phase gas/liquid mixture.

Usually, appropriate sign reversal accounts for flow in the opposite direction for injection wells. The treatment also includes offshore wells where both seawater and air are encountered in the riser. Experiences show that convective heat transport through the annular fluid is important and

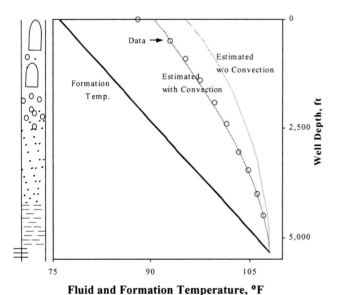

Fig. 5.6—Wellbore fluid temperature profile—a field example.

should be included in all cases. The material in this chapter is designed for flow of noncondensable fluids. Issues related to steam injection and geothermal production are discussed in Chap. 9, Sec 9.3.

Nomenclature

A = inverse relaxation distance parameter, ft

c_a = heat capacity of annular fluid, Btu/(lbm-°F)

c_e = formation heat capacity, Btu/(lbm-°F)

c_p = heat capacity, Btu/(lbm-°F)

c_{pa}, c_{pt} = heat capacity of annular or tubing fluid, Btu/(lbm-°F)

c_{pm} = heat capacity of wellbore fluid mixture, Btu/(lbm-°F)

c_t = total system compressibility, 1/psi

C_J = Joule-Thomson coefficient, °F/psi

d = pipe or well diameter, in.

d_c, d_t = casing or tubing diameter, in.

E = internal energy, Btu/lbm

f = friction factor, dimensionless

f_c = film friction factor for the gas core in annular flow, dimensionless

f_g = gas in-situ volume fraction (void fraction), dimensionless

F = force, lbf

g = acceleration owing to gravity, ft/sec^2

g_c = conversion factor, 32.17(lbm-ft)/(lbf-sec^2)

g_G = geothermal gradient, °F/ft

Gr = Grashof number (defined by Eq. A-10), dimensionless

h = formation thickness, ft

h_a, h_t = convective heat-transfer coefficient for annular or tubing fluid, Btu/(°F-hr-ft)

h_c = convective heat-transfer coefficient, Btu/(°F-hr-ft)

H = fluid enthalpy, Btu/lbm

I = integral defined by Eq. 5.6, dimensionless

J_0, J_1 = Bessel functions of the first kind of order zero and one, dimensionless

k_a = conductivity of annular fluid, Btu/(hr-ft-°F)

k_c = conductivity of casing material, Btu/(hr-ft-°F)

k_{cem} = conductivity of cement, Btu/(hr-ft-°F)

k_e = conductivity of earth or formation, Btu/(hr-ft-°F)

Ku_{sg} = Kutadelaze number $[=v_{sg}\rho_g/\{g(\rho_L-\rho_g)\sigma\}^3]$, dimensionless

L = total measured well depth, ft

L_R = relaxation distance parameter, 1/ft

m = mass of fluid in a control volume, lbm

M = mass of mud per unit well depth, lbm/ft

N_f = inverse viscosity number $[=gd^3\rho_L(\rho_l-\rho_g)]^{1/2}/\mu_L]$, dimensionless

Nu = Nusselt number $[=hd/k]$, dimensionless

p = pressure, psi

p_D = dimensionless pressure $(=\Delta p/141.2qB\mu)$

p_{wf} = flowing bottomhole pressure, psi

Pr = Prandtl number $[=c_p\mu/k]$, dimensionless

q = fluid flow rate at standard conditions, STB/D or MMscf/D

q_{wh} = wellhead rate, STB/D or MMscf/D

Q = heat transfer rate per unit length of wellbore, Btu/(hr-ft)

r_w = wellbore radius, ft

r_D = dimensionless radial distance $[=r/r_w]$, dimensionless

R = universal gas constant

Re = Reynolds number $[=dv\rho/\mu]$, dimensionless

Re_m = Reynolds number for the mixture $[=\rho_m v_m d/\mu_m]$, dimensionless

Re_g, Re_L = Reynolds number for the gas $(=\rho_g v_g d/\mu_g)$ or liquid phase $(=\rho_L v_L d/\mu_L)$, dimensionless

R_s = solution gas/oil ratio, scf/STB

t = production or injection time, hr

t_e = effective superposition time, hr

t_D = dimensionless time, $ket/\rho_e c_e r_{wb}^2$

Δt = shut-in time, hr

T = temperature, °F

T_a, T_t = temperature of annulus or tubing fluid, °F

T_{ai}, T_{ti} = inlet-temperature of annular or tubing fluid, °F

T_{ei}, T_e = formation temperature at initial condition or at any radial distance, °F

T_{eibh}, T_{ew} = static formation temperature at the bottomhole or wellhead, °F

T_f = fluid temperature, °F

T_{wb} = temperature at wellbore/formation interface, °F

T_{ws}, T_{wso} = mud temperature, initial mud temperature, °F

T_D = dimensionless temperature $= (2\pi k_e)(T_{wb}-T_{ei})/Q$

U = overall-heat-transfer coefficient, Btu/(hr-ft^2-°F)

v = fluid velocity, ft/sec

w = mass flow rate of fluid, lbm/hr

x = gas mass fraction in tubing fluid mixture, dimensionless

Y_0, Y_1 = Bessel function of the second kind of order zero and one

z = variable well depth from surface, ft

α = wellbore inclination with horizontal, degrees

$\hat{\alpha}$ = heat diffusivity of formation $(=k_e/c_e\rho_e)$, ft^2/hr

β = fluid thermal expansion coefficient, 1/°F

μ = oil viscosity, cp

ρ = density, lbm/ft^3

ρ_c, ρ_e = core fluid or earth (formation) density, lbm/ft^3

ρ_g, ρ_L = gas or liquid phase density, lbm/ft^3

σ = surface tension, lbm/sec^2

γ_g = gas gravity (air=1)

γ_o = oil gravity, °API

Subscripts

a = annulus

c = casing

cem = cement

ins = insulation

g = gas

$L =$ liquid
$o =$ oil
$t =$ tubing
$ta =$ tubing to annulus for heat-transfer coefficient
$ti =$ tubing inside
$to =$ tubing outside
$w =$ water
$wb =$ wellbore

References

1. Schlumberger, M., Doll, H.G, and Perebinossoff, A.A.: "Temperature Measurements in Oil Wells," *J. Inst. Pet. Technologists* (January 1937) **23**, 159.
2. Bird, J.M.: "Interpretation of Temperature Logs in Water-and Gas-Injection Wells and Gas-Producing Wells," *Drill. & Prod. Prac.* (1954) 187.
3. Lesem, I.B. *et al.*: "A Method of Calculating the Distribution of Temperature in Flowing Gas Wells," *Trans.*, AIME (1957) **210**, 169.
4. Ramey, H.J., Jr.: "Wellbore Heat Transmission," *JPT* (April 1962) 427; *Trans.*, AIME, **225**.
5. Carslaw, H.S. and Jaeger, J.C.: *Conduction of Heat in Solids*, Oxford U. Press, London (1959).
6. Satter, A.: "Heat Losses of Steam Down a Wellbore," *JPT* (July 1965) 845.
7. Shiu, K.C. and Beggs, H.D.: "Predicting Temperatures in Flowing Oil Wells," *J. Energy Resources Tech.* (March 1980) 1.
8. Sagar, R.K., Dotty, D.R., and Schmidt, Z.: "Predicting Temperature Profiles in a Flowing Well," *SPEPE* (November 1991) 441.
9. Alves, I.N., Alhanati, F.J.S., and Shoham, O.: "A Unified Model for Predicting Flowing Temperature Distribution in Wellbores and Pipelines," *SPEPE* (November 1992) 363.
10. Hasan, A.R. and Kabir, C.S.: "Aspects of Heat Transfer During Two-phase Flow in Wellbores," *SPEPF* (August 1994) 211.
11. Ameen, M.M.: *Unified Model for Two-Phase Flow and Heat Transfer in Wellbores*, MS thesis, U. of North Dakota, Grand Forks, North Dakota (1992).
12. van Everdingen, A.F. and Hurst, W.: "The Application of the Laplace Transformation to Flow Problems in Reservoirs," *Trans.*, AIME (1949) **186**, 305.
13. Edwardson, M.J. *et al.*: "Calculation of Formation Temperature Disturbances Caused by Mud Circulation," *JPT* (April 1962) 416; *Trans.*, AIME, **225**.
14. Willhite, G.P.: "Overall Heat Transfer Coefficients in Steam and Hot Water Injection Wells," *JPT* (May 1967) 607.
15. Romero, J. and Touboul, E.: "Temperature Prediction for Deepwater Wells: A Field Validated Methodology," paper SPE 49056 presented at the 1998 SPE Annual Technical Conference and Exhibition, New Orleans, 27–30 September.
16. Fishenden, M. and Saunders, O.A.: *An Introduction to Heat Transfer*, first edition, Oxford U. Press, London (1950) 103.
17. Gebhart, B.: *Heat Transfer*, second edition, McGraw-Hill Book Co. Inc., New York City (1971) 272.
18. Curtis, M.R. and Witterholt, E.J.: "Use of the Temperature Log for Determining Flow Rates in Producing Wells," paper SPE 4637 presented at the 1973 SPE Annual Fall Meeting, Las Vegas, Nevada, 1–3 October.
19. Dropkin, D. and Sommerscales, E.: "Heat Transfer by Natural Convection in Liquids Confined by Two Parallel Plates Inclined at Various Angles with respect to the Horizontal," *J. Heat Transfer, Trans.* ASME, Series C (February 1965) **87**, 77.

SI Metric Conversion Factors

°API	$141.5/(131.5 + °API)$	$= g/cm^3$
Btu	$\times 1.055\ 056$	$E + 00 = kJ$
Btu/(hr-ft²-°F)	$\times 5.674\ 466$	$E + 00 = [W/(m^2 \cdot k)]$
Btu/lbm	$\times 2.326^*$	$E + 03 = (J/kg)$
cp	$\times 1.0^*$	$E - 03 = Pa\ s$
ft	$\times 3.048^*$	$E - 01 = m$
ft²	$\times 9.290\ 304^*$	$E - 02 = m^2$
ft/sec²	$\times 9.290\ 304^*$	$E - 02 = m/s^2$
°F	$(°F - 32)/1.8$	$= °C$
in.	$\times 2.54^*$	$E + 00 = cm$
lbf	$\times 4.448\ 222$	$E + 00 = N$
lbm	$\times 4.535\ 924$	$E - 01 = kg$
lbm/ft³	$\times 1.601\ 846$	$E + 01 = kg/m^3$
lbm/hr	$\times 1.259\ 979$	$E - 04 = (kg/s)$
psi	$\times 6.894\ 757$	$E + 00 = kPa$

*Conversion factor is exact.

Chapter 6
Wellbore Temperature Profiles in Multiple Strings

6.1 Introduction

Ordinarily, solutions of most fluid- and heat-flow problems in a wellbore deal with unidirectional fluid flow in a single production string. Chap. 5 presents working equations for estimating fluid temperature in such systems. However, oil production often involves more than the traditional single-string scenario. Economic necessity dictates coproduction of fluids through the annulus and tubing, through two independent strings, and injection down one string and production up the other in the same wellbore. The heat-transfer issue gets complicated when production through seawater and air occurs in an offshore environment. These and other complex configurations demand knowledge of temperature and pressure profiles for optimization of production and/or injection in each string.

In subsequent chapters we discuss a number of complex heat-transfer issues. For example, modeling unsteady-state heat transfer during transient testing of gas and oil wells, presented in Chap. 7, aids understanding of wellbore phenomena, leading to improved test interpretation and design. Similarly, temperature estimation during steady fluid circulation through tubing/annulus in drilling and during gas injection through an annulus into tubing in gas lift, are discussed in Chap. 8, Sec. 8.2 and Chap. 9, Sec. 9.2. Chap. 9, Sec. 9.1 presents other heat-transfer issues as they pertain to petroleum production. All these treatments involve a single production string, however.

Estimating fluid temperature in bundled tubes can be demanding in deepwater producing environments, where considerable heat transfer may occur. To address some of the plausible scenarios, in this chapter we present analytic solutions for temperature profiles when flow occurs simultaneously in multiple strings. Our motivation stems from the difficulty of using the systems analysis,[1,2] as discussed in Chap. 9, Sec. 9.1, which was originally intended for single-string completions to complex systems. That is because unknown fluid temperature profiles may have significant bearing on the fluid properties and, in turn, on pressure-drop computation. Besides pursuing issues related to systems analysis, this chapter presents building blocks for interpreting temperature logs, which can pose significant challenges because of complex heat-transfer issues in systems with multiple strings.

6.2 Production Through Tubing and Annulus

6.2.1 Mathematical Model. To segregate fluids, production from geologically contrasting horizons often occurs through two separate completions. **Fig. 6.1** schematically shows that the primary production occurs through the tubing, while a secondary production is up the annulus. The energy balance for a differential fluid element in the annulus involves heat transfer to the annular fluid from the formation, Q [$=c_{pa}(T_{ei}-T_a)L_R$; Eq. 5.20], from the annular fluid to the tubing fluid, Q_{ta}, enthalpy change in the annular fluid, and energy related to fluid static and kinetic heads. Thus, the energy balance on a unit-flow-rate basis for the annulus fluid contained in a differential element, dz, is given by[3,4]

$$
H_a(z) + \frac{zg\sin\alpha}{g_cJ} + \frac{v^2(z)}{g_cJ} + \frac{Q_{ta}}{w_a}dz
$$

$$
= H_a(z+dz) + \frac{(z+dz)g\sin\alpha}{g_cJ} + \frac{v^2(z+dz)}{g_cJ} + \frac{Q}{w_a}dz \ .
$$

Rearranging, $\dfrac{Q_{ta}-Q}{w_a} = \dfrac{dH_a}{dz} + \dfrac{g\sin\alpha}{g_cJ} + \dfrac{v_a}{g_cJ}\dfrac{dv_a}{dz}$.

$$\dots\dots\dots\dots\dots\dots\dots (6.1)$$

Heat transferred from the annulus fluid to the tubing fluid per unit length is given by

$$
Q_{ta} = 2\pi r_t U_t (T_a - T_t) = \frac{c_{pa}}{B_a}(T_a - T_t) , \quad \dots\dots\dots (6.2)
$$

where $B_a = \dfrac{w_a c_{pa}}{2\pi r_t U_t}$. $\dots\dots\dots\dots\dots\dots\dots (6.3)$

By combining Eqs. 6.1, 6.2, and 5.20, and expressing enthalpy change in terms of changes in temperature and pressure, $dH = c_p dT - C_J c_p dp$ (Eq. 5.19), we obtain

$$
c_{pa}\frac{dT_a}{dz} - \frac{C_J c_{pa}}{J}\frac{dp_a}{dz} + \frac{g\sin\alpha}{g_cJ} + \frac{v_a}{g_cJ}\frac{dv_a}{dz}
$$

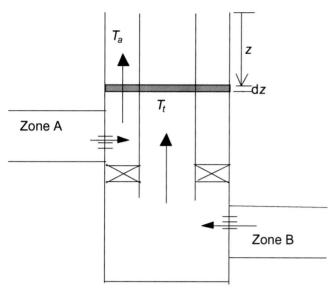

Fig. 6.1—Production through tubing and annulus.

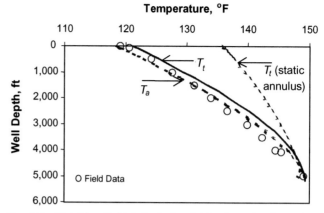

Fig. 6.2—Matching field data during tubing/annulus flow, Well A28.

$$= -L_R c_{pa}(T_{ei} - T_a) + \frac{c_{pa}}{B_a}(T_t - T_a),$$

or $c_{pa}\dfrac{dT}{dz} + D_a = -L_R c_{pa}(T_{ei} - T_a) + \dfrac{c_{pa}}{B_a}(T_t - T_a).$

$$\dots\dots\dots\dots\dots\dots (6.4)$$

We use D_a to combine those terms whose total contribution in Eq. 6.4 is small and whose value remain relatively constant throughout the length of the wellbore. D_a is given by

$$D_a = -\frac{C_J c_{pa}}{J}\frac{dp_a}{dz} + \frac{g\sin\alpha}{g_c J} + \frac{v_a}{g_c J}\frac{dv_a}{dz}. \quad \dots\dots (6.5)$$

The energy balance for the tubing fluid may be similarly written as

$$c_{pt}\frac{dT}{dz} + D_t = \frac{w_a c_{pa}}{w_t B_a}(T_t - T_a), \quad \dots\dots\dots (6.6)$$

where D_t is the term analogous to D_a for the tubing fluid.

Eq. 6.6 can be used to write T_a in terms of T_t for substitution in Eq. 6.4 as

$$T_a = T_t - B'\frac{dT_t}{dz} - B'\frac{D_t}{c_{pt}}, \quad \dots\dots\dots\dots (6.7)$$

where $B' = \dfrac{w_t c_{pt}}{2\pi r_t U_t}. \quad \dots\dots\dots\dots\dots (6.8)$

Combining Eqs. 6.4 and 6.7, we derive the governing differential equation for fluid temperature, which is written as

$$-\frac{B'}{L_R}\frac{d^2 T_t}{dz^2} + B''\frac{dT_t}{dz} - T_t + T_{es} + g_G z\sin\alpha + D' = 0,$$

$$\dots\dots\dots\dots\dots (6.9)$$

where $B'' = B' + \dfrac{B'}{BL_R} + \dfrac{1}{L_R}, \quad \dots\dots\dots\dots (6.10)$

and $D' = B'\dfrac{D_t}{c_{pt}} + B'\dfrac{D_t}{c_{pt}}\dfrac{1}{B_a L_R} - \dfrac{D_a}{L_R c_{pa}}. \quad \dots\dots (6.11)$

The solution of Eq. 6.9 is similar to that of the gas-lift problem[5] (Chap. 9, Sec. 9.2). The solution leads to the expressions for the temperature of the annular and tubing fluids above Zone A, which are written as

$$T_t = \alpha' e^{\lambda_1 z} + \beta e^{\lambda_2 z} + g_G z\sin\alpha + B'' g_G\sin\alpha + T_{es} + D',$$

$$\dots\dots\dots\dots\dots (6.12)$$

and $T_a = (1 - \lambda_1 B')\alpha' e^{\lambda_1 z} + (1 - \lambda_2 B')\beta e^{\lambda_2 z}$

$$+ g_G\sin\alpha(B'' - B') + g_G z\sin\alpha + T_{es} + D'.$$

$$\dots\dots\dots\dots\dots (6.13)$$

Appendix B presents the expressions for various parameters. Note that tubing fluid temperature below Zone A can be estimated with Eq. 5.39.

Field Example 6.1. Well A28. This well produces up the tubing and tubing/casing annulus. Field measurements were made in the tubing string during flowing condition at various depths, called stations. At each station, 15 minutes were allowed for thermal equilibration to occur between the external temperature probe with its surrounding fluids. Sec. B.4, in Appendix B, presents relevant field data needed for computation.

Fig. 6.2 shows that Eq. 6.12, represented by the solid line, reproduces the measured tubing fluid temperature within engineering accuracy. The temperature difference between the tubing and annulus is small because flow in both strings promotes heat transfer. Note that production of annular fluid causes higher dissipation of heat because of forced convection than would be the case if the annular fluid were stationary, as shown by the dashed line in Fig. 6.2 (static annulus). The temperature difference between the two cases is rather large, strongly indicating the need for rigorous modeling.

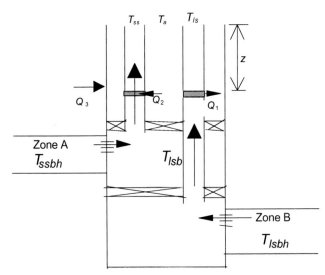

Fig. 6.3—Production through two tubing strings.

6.3 Production Through Two Tubing Strings

6.3.1 Mathematical Model. **Fig. 6.3** shows the schematic for the case where two tubing strings are used to produce from two separate zones with stationary fluid in the annulus. We let subscript ls denote the long string, producing from the deeper horizon (Zone B), and subscript ss stands for the short string, producing from the shallower horizon (Zone A). In writing the energy balance for this case, we have denoted Q_2 as the energy entering the short string from the annulus, while Q_1 is the energy entering the annulus from the long string. Heat gained from the annulus to the formation is designated Q_3. The energy balance for the annulus is then written as

$$Q_2 = Q_1 + Q_3 \cdot \quad \dots\dots\dots\dots\dots\dots (6.14)$$

These energy transfer terms—Q_1, Q_2, and Q_3—can be expressed in terms of temperature-difference driving forces and heat-transfer coefficients as

$$Q_1 = 2\pi r_1 U_1 \left(T_{ls} - T_a\right), \quad \dots\dots\dots\dots\dots (6.15)$$

$$Q_2 = 2\pi r_2 U_2 \left(T_a - T_{ss}\right), \quad \dots\dots\dots\dots\dots (6.16)$$

$$\text{and } Q_3 = w_{ls} c_{pls} \left(T_{ei} - T_a\right) L_R \cdot \quad \dots\dots\dots\dots (6.17)$$

Energy balance for the annular fluid, given by Eq. 6.14, may then be rewritten as

$$\left(T_{ls} - T_a\right)\left(2\pi r_{ls} U_{ls}\right) = \left(T_a - T_{ss}\right)\left(2\pi r_{ss} U_{ss}\right)$$

$$+ \left(T_a - T_{ei}\right)\left(w_{ls} c_{pls} L_R\right) \cdot \quad \dots\dots\dots\dots (6.18)$$

Energy balance for the long string is given by

$$\frac{dT_{ls}}{dz} = \left(T_{ls} - T_a\right)\frac{2\pi r_{ls} U_{ls}}{c_{pls} w_{ls}} - \frac{g \sin \alpha}{c_{pls}} + \phi_{ls} \cdot \quad \dots\dots (6.19)$$

Similarly, for the short string, the energy balance is

$$\frac{dT_{ss}}{dz} = \left(T_a - T_{ss}\right)\frac{2\pi r_{ss} U_{ss}}{c_{pss} w_{ss}} - \frac{g \sin \alpha}{c_{pss}} + \phi_{ss} , \quad \dots\dots (6.20)$$

where parameters ϕ_{ls} and ϕ_{ss} are defined as

$$\phi_{ls} = \left\{ C_{Jls}\left(\frac{dp}{dz}\right)_{ls} - \frac{v_{ls}}{c_{pls}}\frac{dv_{ls}}{dz} \right\}, \quad \dots\dots\dots (6.21)$$

$$\text{and } \phi_{ss} = \left\{ C_{Jss}\left(\frac{dp}{dz}\right)_{ss} - \frac{v_{ss}}{c_{pss}}\frac{dv_{ss}}{dz} \right\} \cdot \quad \dots\dots\dots (6.22)$$

Eqs. 6.18 through 6.20 have three unknowns—T_{ls}, T_{ss}, and T_a; therefore, they can be solved easily. These equations are rewritten in the following forms using parameters $a_1, a_2, \dots a_7$, which are defined in Appendix B.

$$a_1 T_{ls} + a_2 T_a + a_3 T_{ss} + a_4(L - z) + a_5 = 0 , \quad \dots\dots (6.23)$$

$$\frac{dT_{ls}}{dz} = -a_6 \left(T_{ls} - T_a\right) + \phi_{ls} - \frac{g \sin \alpha}{c_{pls}} , \quad \dots\dots\dots (6.24)$$

$$\text{and } \frac{dT_{ss}}{dz} = a_7 \left(T_{ss} - T_a\right) + \phi_{ss} - \frac{g \sin \alpha}{c_{pss}} \cdot \quad \dots\dots\dots (6.25)$$

The general solutions for temperature in the long and short strings are given by

$$T_{ls} = c_1 e^{\lambda_{ls} z} + c_2 e^{\lambda_{ss} z} + \frac{b_4}{b_3} z + \frac{b_3 b_5 - b_2 b_4}{b_3^2} , \quad \dots\dots (6.26)$$

$$\text{and } T_{ss} = d_1 c_1 e^{\lambda_{ls} z} + d_2 c_2 e^{\lambda_{ss} z} + d_3 z + d_4 \cdot \quad \dots\dots\dots (6.27)$$

The expression for the annular fluid temperature is given by

$$T_a = d_1 c_1 e^{\lambda_{ls} z}\left(1 - \frac{w_{ss} c_{pss} \lambda_{ls}}{2\pi r_{ss} U_{ss}}\right) + d_3 z + d_4$$

$$+ d_2 c_2 e^{\lambda_{ss} z}\left(1 - \frac{w_{ss} c_{pss} \lambda_{ss}}{2\pi r_{ss} U_{ss}}\right) + \frac{w_{ss} c_{pss}}{2\pi r_{ss} U_{ss}}\left(\phi_{ss} - d_3\right) \cdot$$

$$\dots\dots\dots\dots\dots (6.28)$$

Appendix B presents the parameters of the previous equations.

Field Example 6.2. Well C39. Fluids are produced up two separate tubing strings in this well. Relevant data are presented in Appendix B, Sec. B.4. We attempted to reproduce the temperature profile recorded in the long string. **Fig. 6.4** exhibits Eq. 6.13 in solid line, mimicking the long-string fluid temperature data very well. As in the previous case, the temperature difference between the tubing and annular fluid is small. However, unlike the previous case, a temperature difference of about 8°F occurs at the wellhead when the short string remains idle, suggesting lesser dominance of annular fluid in controlling the convective-heat transfer. Producing through the short string and keeping the long string idle produces a temperature trace very similar to that in the short string.

FLUID FLOW AND HEAT TRANSFER IN WELLBORES

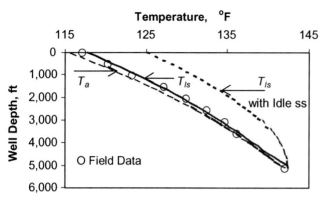

Fig. 6.4—Matching field data during flow up two independent strings, Well C39.

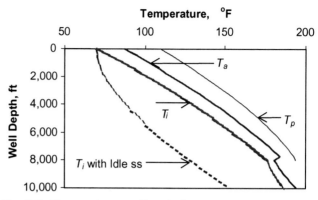

Fig. 6.5—Temperature profiles during a production/injection scenario.

6.4 Production and Injection Through Common Wellbore

6.4.1 Mathematical Model.
When simultaneous production and injection occurs through the same wellbore, questions rise whether cold-water injection will promote formation of hydrates during gas production or of paraffin during oil production. **Fig. 6.5** shows a schematic for the dual injection-production scheme. In this case, a fluid is injected into a deeper horizon (long string or *ls*), while production occurs through a shallower interval (short string or *ss*) through two independent strings.

The governing differential equations in this case, obtained from energy balances, are exactly the same as those for the last case. Thus, Eqs. 6.18, 6.19, and 6.20 apply to the case of production and injection through two strings as well. Solutions for these equations are also the same; that is, Eqs. 6.26 through 6.28 represent fluid temperatures of the conduits in this case. However, differences in the flow direction in this case, compared to the previous one, causes a slight difference in boundary conditions for the two cases, which leads to somewhat different expressions for the various parameters in the temperature equations. These differences are clearly noted in Appendix B.

Illustrative Example. We present a synthetic case (**Fig. 6.6**) to show the variation in temperature profiles when simultaneous injection and production occur through two strings in the same wellbore. Here, cold water is injected at 10,000 ft, while oil production occurs from an interval of 8,000 ft. The kinks in both the injected and annular fluid temperatures at 8,000 ft are a direct reflection of the abrupt fluid entry. Input parameters are detailed in Appendix B. Note that the injected fluid assumes a much lower temperature profile in absence of oil production, thereby suggesting poor heat convection in the annulus. In other words, while the phase behavior of the producing fluid may be favorable during simultaneous operation, problems may arise during start-up, if contingencies go unplanned. These types of computations during completion design are needed to avoid potential production/operation problems.

Summary

In this chapter, we discuss how temperature profiles could be computed in three scenarios involving multiple strings. Solutions for each case, including those presented here, are needed to aid completion design, perform systems analysis, and evaluate temperature logs.

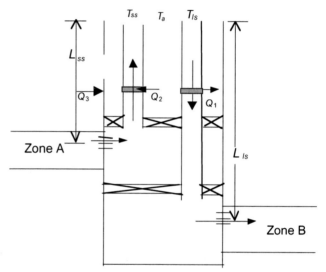

Fig. 6.6—Production and injection through two independent strings.

Complications arise when production or production-injection occurs through two strings in the same wellbore. For example, we learned that heat loss is promoted in the tubing string when simultaneous production occurs in both the tubing and tubing-casing annulus. Consequently, the tubular fluid experiences lower temperature than the static-annular-fluid situation. In contrast, the static-annular fluid controls heat exchange with its surrounding formation when production in two independent production strings are involved. Therefore, production or shut-in of the short string has a marginal impact on the temperature profile in the long string and vice versa. When cold water is injected in one of the two strings, the temperature profile in the production string may be altered significantly, which may promote solid precipitation problems, such as hydrates, paraffins, and asphaltenes. We discuss how asphaltenes and paraffin may be combated in Chap. 9, Sec. 9.4, as well as issues related to systems analysis in Chap. 9, Sec. 9.1.

Nomenclature

B_a = parameter defined by Eq. 6.2, ft/lbm
B' = parameter defined by Eq. 6.8, ft
B'' = parameter defined by Eq. 6.10, ft
c_p = heat capacity of fluids, Btu/(lbm-°F)
C_J = Joule-Thompson coefficient, °F/psi
g = gravitational acceleration, ft/sec²
g_G = geothermal temperature gradient, °F/ft
D_a = parameter defined by Eq. 6.5, Btu/(lbm-ft)
D_t = parameter defined by Eq. 6.6, Btu/(lbm-ft)
D' = parameter defined by Eq. 6.11, °F
H = fluid enthalpy, Btu/lbm
J = ft-lbf to Btu conversion factor, dimensionless
k_e = earth or formation conductivity, Btu/(hr-ft-°F)
L = well length, ft
L_R = relaxation distance parameter, 1/ft
p = pressure, psi
q = volumetric oil flow rate, STB/D
Q = heat flow rate per unit length from or to the formation, Btu/(hr-ft)
r = radius of flow string, L
T = fluid or formation temperature, °F
T_D = dimensionless temperature {=$2\pi k_e \Delta T/Q$}
U = overall-heat-transfer coefficient for a string, Btu/(hr-ft²-°F)
v = fluid velocity, ft/sec
w = mass flow rate, lbm/sec
z = variable well depth from surface, ft
α = inclination angle from horizontal, degree
α' = parameter used in Eq. 6.12, °F
β = parameter used in Eq. 6.12, °F
ϕ = parameter used in Eq. 6.20, °F/ft

Subscripts

a = annulus
bh = bottomhole
es = earth static
ls = long string
ss = short string
t = tubing

References

1. Brown, K.E. and Lea, J.F.: "Nodal Systems Analysis of Oil and Gas Wells," *JPT* (October 1985) 1751.
2. Brown, K.E. *et al.:* "Production Optimization of Oil and Gas Wells by Nodal Systems Analysis," *Technology of Artificial Lift Methods*, PennWell Publishing Co., Tulsa, Oklahoma (1984) **4.**
3. Hasan, A.R. and Kabir, C.S.: "Aspects of Wellbore Heat Transfer During Two-Phase Flow," *SPEPF* (August 1994) 211.
4. Alves, I.N., Alhanati, F.J.S., and Shoham, O.: "A Unified Model for Predicting Flowing Temperature Distribution in Wellbores and Pipelines," *SPEPE* (November 1992) 363.
5. Hasan, A.R. and Kabir, C.S.: "A Mechanistic Model for Computing Fluid Temperature Profiles in Gas-Lift Wells," *SPEPF* (August 1996) 179.

SI Metric Conversion Factors

Btu × 1.055 056	E + 00 = kJ
Btu/(hr-ft²-°F) × 5.674 466	E + 00 = [W/(m²·k)]
Btu/lbm × 2.326*	E + 03 = (J/kg)
ft × 3.048*	E – 01 = m
ft/sec² × 9.290 304*	E – 02 = m/s²
°F (°F – 32)/1.8	= °C
lbm × 4.535 924	E – 01 = kg
psi × 6.894 757	E + 00 = kPa

*Conversion factor is exact.

Chapter 7
Transient Fluid and Heat Flows in Wellbores

7.1 Introduction

When production of fluids occurs from moderate to high-temperature (>300°F) reservoirs, considerable heat exchange takes place between the fluid and its surroundings. This flow condition is further exacerbated in an offshore, deepwater-producing environment as fluids get transported through segments of cold seawater and air in the riser. Chap. 5 deals with the steady-state fluid flow, which is accompanied by unsteady-state heat flow. Here, we consider modeling of unsteady-state fluid and heat flow processes.

Transient flows of mass, momentum, and energy occur whenever the coupled wellbore/reservoir system is perturbed either by design or inadvertently. By perturbation, we mean changes in volumetric flow rates. Multipoint drawdown and buildup tests are cases in point. Although transient tests are obvious candidates for a rigorous treatment, we will show that a fully transient wellbore/reservoir simulator is useful for a variety of production operation applications. Some of these examples include computing dynamic productivity and injectivity indices, doing fully transient systems or Nodal analysis, and designing or interpreting temperature logs. Estimation of flowing bottomhole pressure and, in turn, flow rates and the volume lost during a well blowout is another example where the transient simulation becomes essential. Transient simulations are also required for designing and maintaining flowlines, equipment, and facilities, particularly in an offshore environment. However, transient pressure analysis is beyond the scope of this book.

A few simulators have been reported in the literature to study transient flow problems in a coupled wellbore/reservoir system. They can be categorized into two groups. One approach considers an isothermal wellbore and the other deals with the general case of nonisothermal flow problems. Models of Winterfeld[1] and Alhmehaideb et al.[2] fall into the first category. Unless we address onshore production from shallow reservoirs, near-isothermal boreholes are hard to find. Fully implicit numeric coupling of the wellbore and the reservoir were reported by Miller,[3] Stone et al.,[4] and Su and Lee,[5] among others, to treat nonisothermal flow problems. In this modeling approach, the energy equation is solved in addition to the mass and momentum equations for two-phase, gas/liquid flow.

We present a hybrid approach to couple the wellbore with the reservoir in this chapter. The wellbore that solves the

mass, momentum, and energy equation is numeric, while the reservoir, where single-phase fluid flow occurs, is analytic. This approach reduces computational time significantly. Some of the other advantages of this approach include easy simulation inputs and desktop or laptop computation. Ramey[6] was the first to show the usefulness of this coupling procedure, while modeling the steady-state steam injection process.

Here, we briefly describe wellbore/reservoir simulators for modeling single-phase gas, oil, and the two-phase gas/oil flow problems. Much of the material presented here is drawn from Refs. 7 through 9.

7.2 Modeling Single-Phase Gas Flow

7.2.1 Model Formulation. Mass, momentum, and energy balances, along with gas PVT relation, are used to generate the constitutive equations. **Fig. 7.1** sketches the basis of these balances for a control volume of unit length, within the wellbore.

Material Balance. The mass balance equation for a differential depth, dz, of the well, in terms of wellbore fluid density, ρ, fluid velocity, v, and cross-sectional flow area, A, is written as

$$\frac{\partial(A\rho)}{\partial t} + \frac{\partial}{\partial z}(A\rho v) = 0 \cdot \quad \dots \dots \dots \dots \dots (7.1)$$

Momentum Balance. The momentum balance equation is given by

$$\frac{\partial v}{\partial t} + v\frac{\partial v}{\partial z} = -\frac{1}{\rho}\frac{\partial p}{\partial z} - g - \frac{2fv^2}{d} \cdot \quad \dots \dots \dots \dots (7.2)$$

Energy Balance. The energy balance is written by noting the conductive heat loss to the formation, plus the convective energy transport into and out of the control volume of unit length. In terms of fluid internal energy, E, fluid enthalpy, H, fluid mass flow rate, w, fluid mass in the control volume, m, and the internal energy and mass of the wellbore system (the tubular and cement sheaths combined), $(m'E)_w$, the energy balance equation, as shown in Fig. 7.1, gives

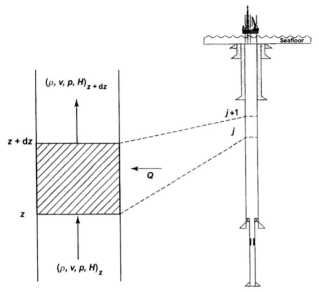

Fig. 7.1—Schematic of mass, momentum, and energy balances.

$$Q = \frac{d(mE)_{cv}}{dt} + \frac{d(m'E)_w}{dt} \frac{d}{dz}\left[w\left(H + \frac{1}{2}v^2 + gz\sin\theta\right)\right]$$

$$\quad\quad\quad\quad\quad\quad\quad\quad\quad\quad\quad\quad (7.3)$$

The second term on the right side of Eq. 7.3 represents the energy absorbed or released by the tubulars and cement sheaths in the wellbore. Omitting this term can lead to serious error because it accounts for a significant fraction of the total energy exchange between the wellbore and the formation. In our simulations, we noted an anomalously sharp increase at early times in computed wellbore fluid temperatures during drawdowns and a decrease during buildups when this term was neglected.

The heat lost to (or received from) the formation, Q, is given by[10] (Eq. 5.20)

$$Q \equiv \rho v c_p \left(T_{ei} - T_f\right) L_R , \quad\quad\quad\quad\quad (7.4)$$

where L_R is the relaxation distance parameter defined in Chap. 5 (Eq. 5.20) and given by

$$L_R = \frac{2\pi}{c_P w}\left[\frac{r_{to}U_{to}k_e}{k_e + (r_{to}U_{to}T_D)}\right] . \quad\quad (7.5)$$

The dimensionless temperature-distribution function, T_D, was defined in Chap. 5. It is reproduced here for convenience.

$$T_D = \ln\left\{e^{(-0.2t_D)} + \left(1.5 - 0.3719e^{-t_D}\right)\sqrt{t_D}\right\} \quad (7.6)$$

Dimensionless time is given by $t_D = k_e t / \rho_e c_e r_w^2$. Eq. 7.5 is valid only when heat loss from the wellbore is constant. In general, energy exchange between the fluid and formation gradually changes with time because of the steady change in the formation temperature surrounding the wellbore. The

superposition principle can be used to account for changes in both heat and mass flow rate with time.

Change in fluid enthalpy is related to changes in its temperature and pressure, which is written as

$$\frac{dH}{dz} = -C_J c_p \frac{dp}{dz} + c_p \frac{dT_f}{dz} , \quad\quad\quad\quad (7.7)$$

where c_p is the gas heat capacity at constant pressure and C_J is the Joule-Thompson coefficient given by

$$C_J = \frac{1}{c_p}\left[\frac{1}{\rho_g}\left(-\frac{T}{Z}\left(\frac{\partial Z}{\partial T}\right)_p\right)\right] . \quad\quad\quad (7.8)$$

Eq. 7.3 is rewritten by replacing the internal energy of the gas in control volume with its enthalpy, H, and its pressure and volume, noting that $m = A\rho$.

$$Q = A\rho \frac{\partial H}{\partial t} + \frac{\partial(m'cT_f)}{\partial t} - A\rho R \frac{\partial(ZT_f)}{\partial t}$$

$$+ A\left(H - \frac{ZRT_f}{M}\right)\frac{\partial\rho}{\partial t} + \frac{d}{dz}\left[(A\rho v)\left(H + \frac{v2}{2} + gz\sin\theta\right)\right],$$

$$\quad\quad\quad\quad\quad\quad\quad\quad\quad\quad\quad\quad (7.9)$$

where c represents the weighted-average specific heat of the wellbore cement/tubular material. Note that Eq. 7.9 allows for changes in the flow cross-sectional area in the well. Modeling the heat absorbed or released by the annular fluid, tubulars, and cement sheath is important. However, to account for the individual heat capacity and transient temperature of each element of the wellbore becomes prohibitively time-consuming. We suggest the use of a weighted-average temperature of the fluid/cement/tubular material and assume that at any given time, the temperature rise of this composite system is a fraction of the rise in the fluid temperature. This approximation simplifies mathematical formulation and saves computation time without significantly affecting accuracy, as our field experiences show.

Note that in arriving at Eq. 7.9, we used the gas law to replace pressure, p, by temperature, T_f, as

$$p = \frac{Z\rho RT_f}{M} , \quad\quad\quad\quad\quad\quad\quad\quad\quad (7.10)$$

where M represents the molecular weight of the gas.

Wellbore-Fluid Temperature. The development of the finite-difference form of Eq. 7.9, using j to denote the spatial coordinate and l to denote the time coordinate, is shown in Appendix C. The final form of wellbore fluid temperature as a function of time and depth is

$$\left(T_f\right)_j^{l+1} = \frac{(\sigma_j^l / A) - \psi_j^l + \left(\rho v T_{ei}c_p(L_R)\right)_j^{l+1} + \xi_j^l (T_f)_j^l \omega_j^l}{\left(\rho v c_p L_R\right)_j^{l+1} + \xi_j^l - \lambda_j^l} .$$

$$\quad\quad\quad\quad\quad\quad\quad\quad\quad\quad\quad (7.11)$$

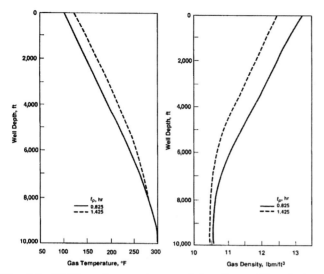

Fig. 7.2—Wellbore temperature and density profiles during gas flow.

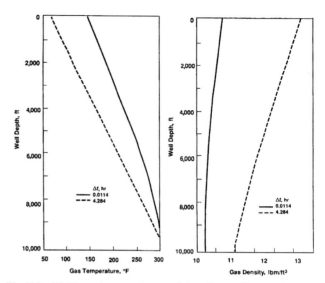

Fig. 7.3—Wellbore temperature and density profiles during well shut-in.

Expressions for the various terms, σ, ψ, ξ, λ, and ω are given in Appendix C. Temperature computation generally begins with a well in thermal equilibrium with its surroundings so that the initial fluid temperature at any depth is known. Temperature at the next timestep, $l+1$, is then computed with Eq. 7.11, using values of parameters at the earlier timestep. L_R does not vary significantly with time; thus, L_R^{l+1} may be approximated by L_R^l.

The relaxation parameter, L_R, in Eq. 7.11 is normally defined by Eq. 7.5, which accounts for conductive heat transport in the formation. However, in offshore, a portion of the wellbore is exposed to convective heat transport of seawater and ambient air in the riser. Exposure of this nature may significantly affect the wellhead fluid temperature. As discussed in Chap. 5, Eq. 7.11 may be used as long as L_R is defined properly to account for these convective effects as (see Eq. 5.24)

$$L_{Rc} = \frac{2\pi r_{to} U_{toc}}{c_p w}, \quad \dots \dots \dots \dots \dots \dots \dots (7.12)$$

where the overall-heat-transfer coefficient, U_{toc}, accounts for the convective heat transfer outside the flow string and those for the wellbore system. In Appendix A, we show how the overall-heat-transfer coefficients, U and U_{toc}, are calculated for various situations.

Sandface Flow Rate. The diffusivity equation for single-phase flow in a homogeneous reservoir is given by

$$\frac{\partial p_{pn}}{\partial t} = \frac{k}{\phi \mu c} \frac{1}{r} \frac{\partial}{\partial r}\left(r \frac{\partial p_{pn}}{\partial r}\right). \quad \dots \dots \dots \dots (7.13)$$

The numerical solution of the formation flow equation (Eq. 7.13) is often time-consuming. We used an analytical solution for the case of constant-production rate, which is written as

$$p_i - p_w = m^* q \left(p_D + s\right). \quad \dots \dots \dots \dots \dots (7.14)$$

The reservoir influence function or model, p_D, for a cylindrical source well may be expressed in terms of the dimensionless time analogous to Eq. 7.6. Alternatively, one may use Laplace space solutions to retain generality. Note that for pressure transients, dimensionless time is given by $t_D = \beta_m t / r_w^2$, where the momentum diffusivity, β_m, equals $2.64 \times 10^{-4} k / \phi \mu c_t$.

Fluid influx into the wellbore changes rapidly at early times during either drawdown or buildup. Superposition in time is used to account for the variation in influx rate q with time. The resulting expression for bottomhole flow rate at a time step, $l+1$, in terms of flow rates at earlier times, is

$$q_n = q_{n-1} + \frac{p_i - p_{wn}}{m^*\left[p_D(t_{Dn} - t_{Dn-1}) + s + Dq_n\right]}$$

$$- \frac{\sum_{i=1}^{n-1}(q_i - q_{i-1})\left[p_D(t_{Dn} - t_{i-1}) + s + Dq_i\right]}{p_D(t_D - t_{n-1}) + s + Dq_n}, \quad \dots (7.15)$$

where $t_{D0} = 0$, and $q_0 = 0$. For a nonequilibrium initial condition, $p_i = p_{wf1}$, q_1 is the prevailing flow rate, and $Dq_i = |D(q_1 - q_{i-1})|$. Note that the D_q term represents the skin associated with non-Darcy flow. Eq. 7.15 is general and any reservoir model, p_D, can be inserted for a given system, such as double-porosity, composite, or fractured.

7.2.2 Sensitivity Study: Single-Phase Gas Example. In this section we discuss the results of a simulated case generated by the model. This vertical well has a depth of 10,000 ft with a bottomhole temperature of 300°F.

Fig. 7.2 shows the wellbore fluid density and temperature profiles corresponding to a production rate of 5 MMscf/D. **Fig. 7.3** shows similar results during the subsequent well shut-

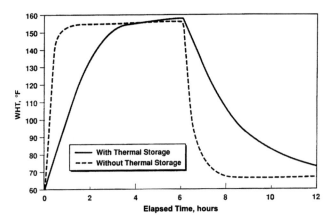

Fig. 7.4—Occurrence of thermal storage during flow and shut-in tests.

in. The nonlinear and time-dependent nature of these profiles is noteworthy. These profiles underscore the importance of accounting for thermal effects whenever conversion of wellhead pressure (WHP) to bottomhole pressure (BHP) is desired.

Fig. 7.4 presents the wellhead temperature transients from the last two simulations. Note the gradual rise in the wellhead-fluid temperature during drawdown and the subsequent gentle decline during well shut-in. Also shown in the figure are profiles generated by neglecting the heat absorption or rejection by the wellbore system, comprising tubulars, annular fluid, and the cement sheath. Note the sharp increase in wellbore fluid temperature (WHT) at early times during drawdown and a similar sharp decrease during shut-in compared to the base case. Differences between the two WHT signatures are analogous to that observed for either the BHP or WHP when the wellbore fluid storage is included or excluded during a transient test. Because of this analogy, we term this phenomenon associated with the WHT as *thermal storage.*

By thermal storage we mean the ability of the wellbore system to store or release heat, thereby causing delay for the WHT to attain an equilibrium value when the production rate is held constant. In any real system, the tubulars will provide significant storage of heat, thereby causing any analysis to be erroneous that neglects thermal storage. Note that the phenomenon of thermal storage is not limited to the wellbore system; any physical body in thermal contact with another body at a different temperature may experience it. Temperature logging tools provide another example of this phenomenon. We discuss that particular thermal storage situation in Chap. 8, Sec. 8.2.

To study the effect of the production rate on the transient behavior of pressure and temperature, we simulated both drawdown and buildup tests for three flow rates. **Fig. 7.5** shows the WHP's and WHT's corresponding to rates of 2.5, 5.0, and 7.5 MMscf/D. Increase in WHT with rate is a direct consequence of increased associated total fluid energy (*wH*). Simulations of this nature are prerequisite to the design of both subsurface and surface equipment and facilities to handle high WHT's. This point is made clear by evaluating a real case as examined next.

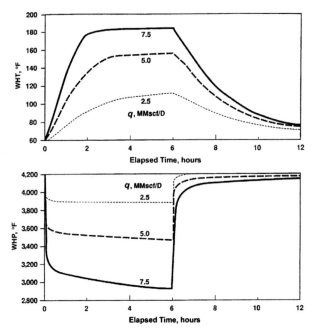

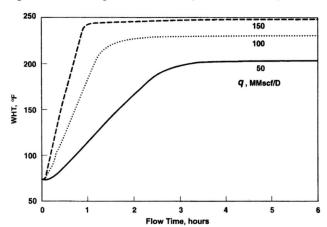

Fig. 7.5—Flow rate governs wellhead pressure and temperature.

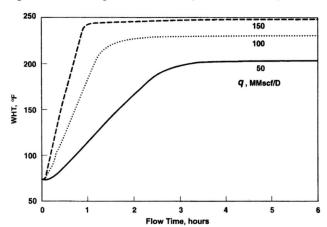

Fig. 7.6—Subsea wellhead temperature depends on the production rate.

In this actual scenario, the operator was interested in learning about the WHT's because at certain temperatures, CO_2-induced corrosion becomes very pronounced. While a steady-state simulator yields only the final equilibrium WHT value, severity and duration of the critical temperature range experienced can be discerned only by using a transient simulator. Knowledge of WHT's and subsequent cooling during the pipeline transport of this sour-gas/condensate mixture dictates the metallurgy requirements of the entire system. Besides, the transient output (fluid composition and temperature) of this simulation is necessary for the input of the transient pipeline simulation. We now discuss the results of these simulations.

Fig. 7.6 shows the subsea wellhead temperature (WHT) transients for various flow rates for the deviated (about 45°) well case. Note that the temperature plateau occurs at different times because of the thermal storage effect. At the lowest rate, such as 50 MMscf/D, thermal storage lasts longer because of correspondingly lower associated fluid energy. In other words, a low-mass rate will take longer to heat up tubu-

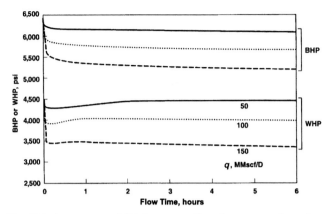

Fig. 7.7—Low rates exhibit longer wellhead pressure distortion owing to thermal storage.

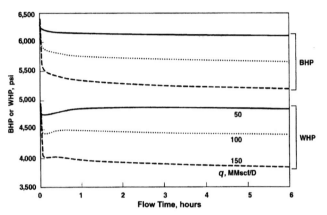

Fig. 7.9—Higher pressures are experienced in a vertical well.

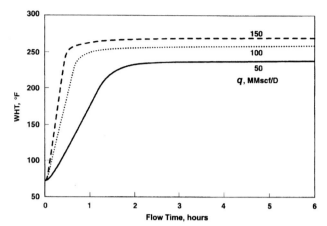

Fig. 7.8—Gas in a vertical well retains more heat because of shorter residence time.

lars and attain temperature equilibrium. The corresponding pressures at the bottomhole (BHP) and wellhead (WHP) are shown in **Fig. 7.7.**

Figs. 7.8 and **7.9** show the WHT and WHP/BHP plots, respectively, for a vertical-well case. The WHT values in this case are considerably higher than its deviated well counterpart. For example, we observe a 29°F higher equilibrium WHT when the rate is 100 MMscf/D. The rationale for this observation is that the gas must traverse an additional well length of about 8,000 ft in the deviated-well case, thereby losing more heat than the vertical-well situation.Simulations were also made for the platform well scenario by adding about 1,000 ft of seawater and air segments to the subsea completion model. These simulation runs show that the gas experiences marginal cooling because of low-residence time in the riser (seabed-to-rigfloor) section. For instance, at the lowest rate of 50 MMscf/D, an element of gas is exposed for less than three minutes in the riser. Consequently, a decrease of about 2°F is observed for the equilibrium WHT. For the same reason, a WHT decrease of less than 1°F is observed when the rate is 150 MMscf/D. Note, however, that these simulations presupposed a constant ambient air temperature of 75°F during each flow period.

Based on these calculations, the operator considered drilling longer well lengths to produce gas at relatively low temperatures at the subsea completion. In this way, corrosion hazards were thought to be minimized.

The annular fluid offers significant resistance to heat flow, making its conductivity an important determinant of the well-bore-fluid temperature. Then, from a metallurgical design standpoint, fluid WHT's dictate the makeup of surface equipment and flowlines. In the next section, we discuss how the conductivity of annular fluid influences the wellhead temperature.

7.3 Modeling Single-Phase Oil Flow

7.3.1 Model Formulation. Formulation of this model is analogous to the gas model described earlier in this chapter. The resulting expression for flowing fluid temperature is reported in Appendix C. Details of the formulation can be found in Ref. 8.

7.3.2 Sensitivity Study: Single-Phase Oil Example. We explore the sensitivity of certain essential parameters on the transient behavior of pressure and temperature both at the wellhead and bottomhole in an oil well. **Table 7.1** presents the wellbore/reservoir data used to generate the synthetic cases.

Fig. 7.10 shows the effect of the producing rate on WHP, WHT, and BHP. Increasing WHT with a higher rate is a result of increased associated fluid enthalpy. While the BHP shows the expected smooth trend, the early-time WHP suggests otherwise. This behavior is a direct consequence of thermal storage, precipitated by storage (during drawdown) or release (during buildup) of thermal energy by tubulars, cement sheaths, and annular fluid. **Fig. 7.11** compares the derivative curves generated for buildup using WHP data. One observes that the WHP's associated with decreasing flow rate exhibit larger thermal-storage distortion, as indicated by the increasing departure of the derivative signature from the flat response, which signifies lack of storage. Low rates simply take a longer time to promote heat exchange between the fluids and its surroundings, thereby contributing to distortion. Thus, Fig. 7.11 underscores an important point. That is, one cannot simply add the hydrostatic head to the WHP for computing the BHP without proper accounting of fluid temperature variation with time and depth, as **Figs. 7.12** and **7.13** testify. Figs. 7.12 and 7.13 show these profiles for both drawdown and buildup cases.

Note the increasing WHT with an increasing production rate because of the associated fluid energy.

Similarly, for the same volumetric rate, energy increases with increasing fluid density (decreasing API gravity), as shown in **Fig. 7.14.** Therefore, the total mass rate dictates the WHT behavior.

TABLE 7.1—WELL, RESERVOIR, AND FLUID DATA	
Reservoir pressure, psia	7,000
Well depth, ft	10,000
Tubing ID, in.	2.75
Tubing OD, in.	3.5
Casing ID, in.	8.9
Casing OD, in.	9.375
Pipe roughness, ft	$1.8\times10^-$
Production rate, STB/D	2,000
Formation permeability, md	500
Formation thickness, ft	100
Formation porosity, fraction	0.2
Oil gravity, °API	28
Gas gravity (air=1)	0.75
Total system compressibility, 1/psi	8×10^{-5}
Damaged skin	0
Reservoir temperature, °F	220
Geothermal gradient, °F/ft	0.015
Formation thermal conductivity, Btu/(ft-°F-hr)	2.5
Formation density, lbm/ft³	165
Formation heat capacity, Btu/(lbm-°F)	0.625
Tubing/Casing material thermal conductivity, Btu/(ft-°F-hr)	30
Annular fluid thermal conductivity, Btu/(ft-°F-hr)	0.2
Cement thermal conductivity, Btu/(ft-°F-hr)	0.38
Cement sheath diameter to 270 ft, in.	30
Cement sheath diameter from 270 ft to TD, in.	20

Questions may arise about the effect of initial-formation temperature distribution on WHP because fluid circulation during drilling and completion can potentially distort the virgin geothermal gradient in the wellbore vicinity. Experiences with transient fluid circulation modeling, as discussed in Chap. 8, Sec. 8.1, show that fluid temperatures in the annulus (formation/drillpipe) and tubing (drillpipe) are not very sensitive to various heat-transfer parameters, including those at surface and subsurface. Moreover, the entire formation acts essentially as an infinite heat source or sink. Therefore, the initial-formation temperature profile is not distorted to any appreciable degree owing to fluid circulation.

We performed some simulations nonetheless to address the distorted geothermal gradient issue. **Fig. 7.15** shows the

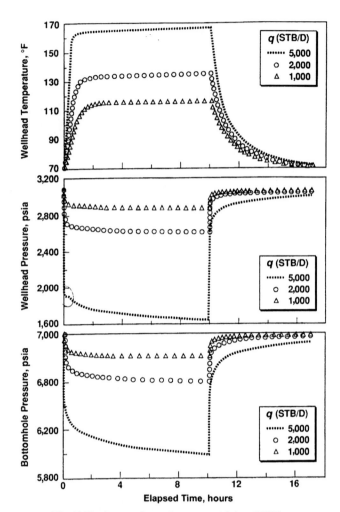

Fig. 7.10—Increasing rate causes higher WHT's.

transient WHT corresponding to various geothermal gradient values. The underlying thought is to simulate cases assuming fluid circulation before testing caused enough cooling to distort the geothermal gradient itself. As expected, very little

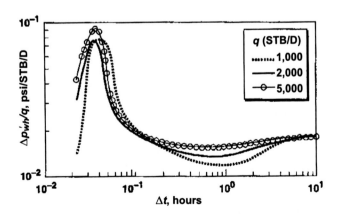

Fig. 7.11—Buildup WHP behavior shows flow-rate-dependent thermal storage distortion.

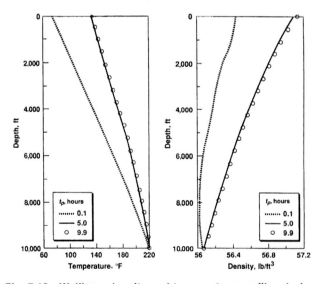

Fig. 7.12—Wellbore density and temperature profiles during single-phase oil flow.

FLUID FLOW AND HEAT TRANSFER IN WELLBORES

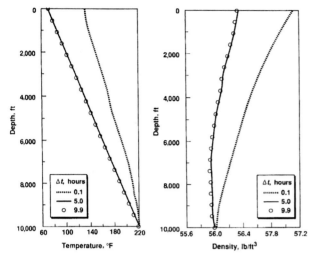

Fig. 7.13—Wellbore density and temperature profiles during well shut-in.

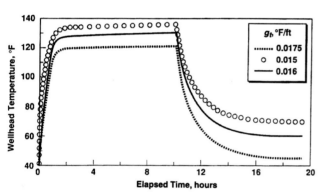

Fig. 7.15—Geothermal gradient influences WHT.

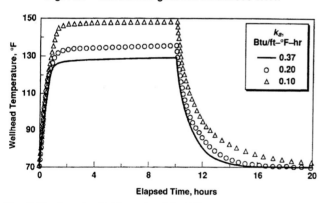

Fig. 7.17—Annular fluid conductivity influences WHT response.

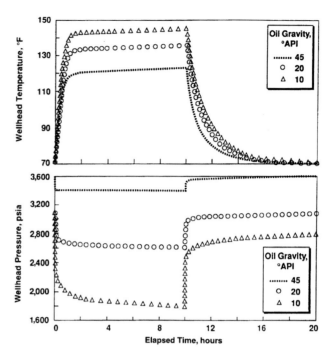

Fig. 7.14—WHT increases with increasing oil density.

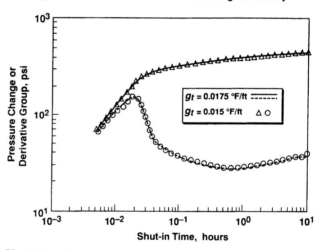

Fig. 7.16—Minor difference occurs in WHP response with changes in geothermal gradient.

difference in WHP's occurs as **Fig. 7.16** shows, with no differences in BHP's. Although this simulation approach does not mimic reality, the approach represents the worst possible scenario. Therefore, the aspect of near-wellbore cooling appears unimportant.

High WHT can potentially increase the project development cost by raising the metallurgy requirements of tubular, flowlines, and surface facilities. This problem is compounded further when corrosion considerations arise because of sour crudes. Predictably, this approach provides a vehicle for addressing the issue at the project's inception. For example,

one can explore consequences of using water-based mud instead of its oil-based counterpart to establish the anticipated WHT. **Fig. 7.17** shows that oil-based mud, having a low-thermal conductivity, is inefficient in losing heat to the surroundings. Consequently, high WHT's are reported. Although not germane to this discussion, retaining wellbore heat is highly desirable when either steam is injected or geothermal fluids are produced.

If high WHT is a concern and oil-based mud must be used because of corrosion considerations, a viable option of losing heat to the surroundings lies in drilling a deviated well. **Fig. 7.18** shows how well deviation increases fluid residence time, thus, leading to a cooler WHT for wells of the same true vertical depth.

In an offshore producing environment, besides using water-based or higher conductive mud, fluid cooling may be

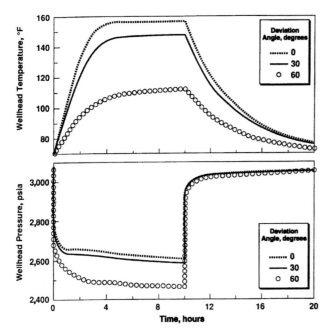

Fig. 7.18—Well deviation can potentially reduce WHT.

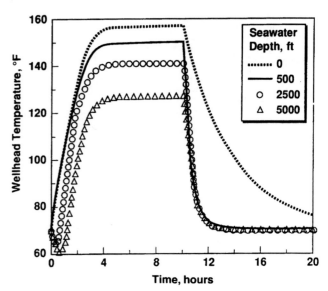

Fig. 7.19—Significant fluid cooling occurs with increasing seawater depth.

augmented by the presence of seawater. **Fig. 7.19** shows that unlike in the case of a gas well, significant cooling occurs in an offshore oil well. The reason for greater heat loss in oil wells than gas wells is the higher residence time owing to lower velocity experienced in oil wells. Note the temperature reversal occurring soon after the flow initiation when the water depth exceeds 2,000 ft. Production of cold fluid is responsible for this seemingly anomalous temperature response. Accordingly, **Fig. 7.20** indicates a shorter thermal-storage distortion period during buildups for the same reason. Note that this beneficial cooling effect starts to diminish with an increasing production rate, leading to an optimal withdrawal rate when temperature considerations are important.

7.4 Modeling Two-Phase Gas/Oil Flow

7.4.1 Model Formulation. Formulation of this model is analogous to the gas and oil modeldescribed earlier in this-

chapter. The resulting expression for flowing two-phase fluid temperature is reported in Appendix C. Ref. 9 presents the details of the formulation.

7.4.2 Sensitivity Study. Fig. 7.21 shows that an increase in the gas/oil ratio (GOR) decreases the WHT. Higher turbulence with increased gas causes greater heat transfer for the high-GOR cases. The corresponding increase in WHP is caused by an increase in wellbore gas volume with the attendant decrease in static-head loss. Consequently, we observe a progressively diminishing change in WHP (shut-in minus flowing wellhead pressure for a given GOR) because of increasing compressibility of the wellbore fluid. This observation also suggests that reliable reverse simulation to trans-

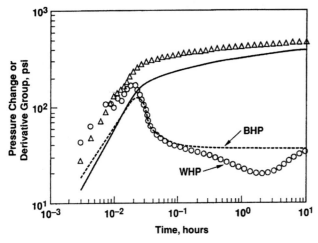

Fig. 7.20—Thermal storage distorts WHP response in 5,000-ft water.

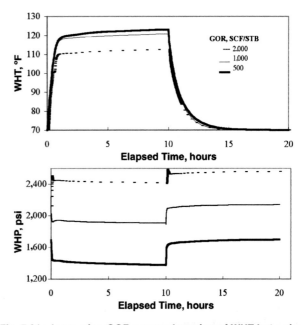

Fig. 7.21—Increasing GOR causes lowering of WHT but a rise in WHP.

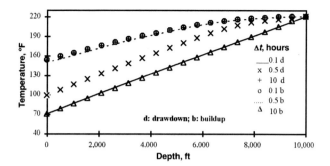

Fig. 7.22—Wellbore temperature profiles during two-phase transient tests.

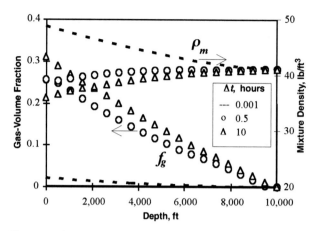

Fig. 7.23—Changing gas volume and mixture density during a buildup test.

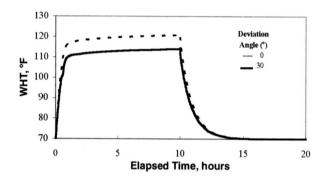

Fig. 7.24—Well deviation causes reduced WHT.

late wellhead p and T measurements to downhole pressures will be harder to perform because the WHP response is dampened by the fluid compressibility.

Perhaps the preceding discussion is better understood by examining the wellbore fluid characteristics during the flow and shut-in conditions for the base case. **Fig. 7.22** shows the fluid temperature profiles at various drawdown and buildup times. As shown, the early-time (0.1 hr) drawdown and the late-time (10 hr) buildup has very similar linear character. The implication is that the wellbore has not exchanged significant heat with the formation. Conversely, the late-time (10 hr) drawdown and the early-time (0.1 hr) buildup exhibits a very similar nonlinear response, suggesting considerable heat transfer. We can gain insight by examining the wellbore in-situ gas-volume fraction and density profiles. **Fig. 7.23** shows the gradual progression of these two entities during a drawdown test. As expected, the gas occupies an increasingly larger space in the flow string with an increasing production time, until a steady flow rate is attained at the surface, beyond the storage period. Storage is induced by both compressible fluid and heat flows.

One implication of this observation is that any in-situ measurements, temperature for instance, made during the transient wellbore flow period can potentially lead to misdiagnosis of downhole flow problems. Duration of this transient period may last from a few minutes to several days depending on the formation and wellbore characteristics. For example, shallow wellbores in high-transmissivity reservoirs will exhibit a very short wellbore-induced transient period. In contrast, deep wells in tight reservoirs may take several days before stabilizing, from the standpoint of both heat and fluid flows.

As one may surmise intuitively, the heat and fluid storage problem are more acute for two-phase flow because of the added phase and its distribution in the wellbore. Complications stem from both depth- and time-depended mixture density profiles. In a two-phase flow situation, both in-situ gas volume and thermal effects contribute to the nonlinearity of the wellbore-mixture density profile. In contrast, for single-phase flow, only thermal effects influence the depth-depended fluid density, hence, the wellbore pressure at any point in the fluid column.

Transient p-T behavior in environments, where enhanced heat exchange takes place, provides some interesting observations. A deviated offshore well is a case in point, as illustrated by **Fig. 7.24**. Here, the well deviation causes

increased heat exchange because of increased residence time for the same vertical depth in the deviated segment, leading to cooler WHT. As **Fig. 7.25** shows, an increasing submerged well length causes significant cooling, especially when the well is opened for flow after attaining thermal equilibrium with the surroundings.

We can surmise that one cannot translate the WHP into BHP very easily. The solution of this problem is difficult even when single-phase oil flow occurs. Complications arising from changing gas-volume and temperature effects can limit our ability to translate WHP values into BHP values, when we treat a two-phase mixture. Any notion of the use of WHP for deliverability calculations must be done very cautiously because of the transient nature of the flow problem. This statement is true even when a stable surface rate has

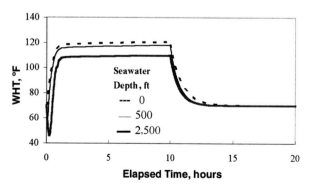

Fig. 7.25—Increased water depth causes reduced WHT.

been attained. We explore this point further when we discuss systems analysis in Chap. 9, Sec. 9.1.

Summary

In this chapter, we showed the development of rigorous wellbore/reservoir simulators to compute transient pressure and temperature at any point in the wellbore. Large wellbore-temperature differences cause severe distortion of transient wellhead-pressure response even when single-phase liquid production occurs. Duration of this distortion period is system specific, however. Results of various computations also show that the nonlinear nature of the wellbore density profile makes simple WHP conversion to BHP a difficult proposition, regardless of the nature of the wellbore fluid.

As expected, general heat-transfer characteristics of all fluids are very similar. While single-phase oil retains most of the heat relative to gas while ascending the well, a gas/oil mixture's performance lies between the two single-phase fluids. Heat transfer, in terms of importance, is governed by the conductivity of the annular fluid, well length and its deviation, and the geothermal gradient itself.

These simulators serve a multitude of needs. For instance, we can design a mud system from a heat-loss standpoint; compute WHT's associated with flow rates so that surface equipment and facilities can be designed properly; and assist flowline design when corrosion considerations are important. The cooling of production fluids in the seawater segment is rather marginal unless deepwater wells of more than 2,000 ft are considered.

Nomenclature

A = flow cross-sectional area, ft^2

B = formation volume factor, RB/STB

c' = weighted-average heat-capacity of tubulars, Btu/(lbm-°F)

c_p = heat capacity of fluids, Btu/(lbm-°F)

c_t = total system compressibility, 1/psi

C_J = Joule-Thompson coefficient, °F/psi

C_o = velocity profile correction factor, dimensionless

d = pipe diameter, ft

D = non-Darcy flow coefficient, D/scf or D/STB

E = internal energy, Btu/lbm

f = friction factor, dimensionless

f_g = in-situ gas volume fraction, dimensionless

f_L = liquid holdup, dimensionless

g = gravitational acceleration, ft/sec^2

g_T = geothermal temperature gradient, °F/ft

H = enthalpy, Btu/lbm

h = formation thickness, ft

j = depth index for discretization, dimensionless

k = formation permeability, md

k_e = earth or formation conductivity, Btu/(hr-ft-°F)

l = time coordinate for discretization, dimensionless

L = cell length, L

m = mass in a control volume per unit well length, lbm/ft

m' = mass of tubulars per unit length, lbm/ft

M = molecular weight, lbm/lbmole

L_R = inverse relaxation distance, 1/ft

p = pressure, psia

p_i = initial reservoir pressure, psia

p_{pn} = normalized pseudopressure, psia

p_w = wellbore pressure, psia

Δp = pressure drop, psi

q = volumetric gas or oil flow rate, MMscf/D or STB/D

Q = heat flow rate per unit length from or to the formation, Btu/(hr-ft)

r = radial distance, ft

r_w = radial distance, ft

R = universal gas-law constant, psia-ft^3/lbmole-°R

s = skin factor, dimensionless

t = time, hr

t_D = dimensionless time [$=2.64 \times 10^{-4} kt/\phi\mu c_t r_w^2$]

t_p = production time, hr

Δt = shut-in time, hr

T = temperature, °F

T_D = dimensionless temperature

T_f = fluid temperature in the wellbore, °F

U = overall-heat-transfer coefficient, Btu/(hr-ft^2-°F)

v = velocity, ft/sec

V = cell volume, ft^3

w = mass rate of fluid, lbm/hr

x = mass fraction of gas, dimensionless

z = variable well depth from surface, ft

Z = gas-law deviation factor, dimensionless

α = well angle from horizontal, degree

β = expansivity of fluid [$=-1/\rho(d\rho/dT)_p$], 1/°F

β_m = momentum diffusivity ($=2.64 \times 10^{-4} k/\phi\mu c_t$)

ϕ = formation porosity, dimensionless

ρ = density, lbm/ft^3

μ = oil viscosity, cp

Subscripts

c = convective

cv = control volume

D = dimensionless

e = earth

ei = earth initial

f = fluid

g = gas

i = initial

j = cell index

L = liquid

m = mixture

n = indicator for last timestep in discretization

o = outside

to = tubing outside

toc = tubing outside, convective

w = well

∞ = terminal

Superscripts

$l =$ timestep index

$' =$ average property

References

1. Winterfeld, P.H.: "Simulation of Pressure Buildup in a Multiphase Wellbore/Reservoir System," *SPEFE* (June 1989) 247.

2. Almehaideb, R.A., Aziz, K., and Pedrosa, O.A.: "A Reservoir/Wellbore Model for Multiphase Injection and Pressure Transient Analysis," paper SPE 17941 presented at the 1989 SPE Middle East Oil Show, Manama, Bahrain, 11–14 March.

3. Miller, C.W.: "Wellbore Storage Effect in Geothermal Wells," *SPEJ* (December 1980) 555.

4. Stone, T.W., Edmunds, N.R., and Kristoff, B.J.: "A Comprehensive Wellbore/Reservoir Simulator," paper SPE 18419 presented at the 1989 SPE Reservoir Simulation Symposium, Houston, 6–8 February.

5. Su, H-J. and Lee, S.H.: "Modeling Transient Wellbore Behavior in Horizontal Wells," paper SPE 29961 presented at the 1995 SPE International Meeting on Petroleum Engineering, Beijing, 14–17 November.

6. Ramey, H.J., Jr.: "Wellbore Heat Transmission", *JPT* (April 1962) 427; *Trans.*, AIME, **225**.

7. Kabir, C.S. *et al.*: "A Wellbore/Reservoir Simulator for Testing Gas Wells in High-Temperature Reservoirs," *SPEFE* (June 1996) 128.

8. Hasan, A.R., Kabir, C.S., and Wang, X.: "Development and Application of a Wellbore/Reservoir Simulator for Testing Oil Wells," *SPEFE* (September 1997) 182.

9. Hasan, A.R., Kabir, C.S., and Wang, X.: "Wellbore Two-Phase Flow and Heat Transfer During Transient Testing," *SPEJ* (June 1998) 174.

10. Hasan, A.R. and Kabir, C.S.: "Wellbore Heat Transfer During Two-Phase Flow," *SPEPF* (August 1994) 211.

SI Metric Conversion Factors

°API	$141.5/(131.5 + °API)$	$= g/cm^3$
Btu	$\times 1.055\ 056$	$E + 00 = kJ$
Btu/(hr-ft²-°F)	$\times 5.678\ 263$	$E + 00 = W/(m^2 \cdot K)$
Btu/lbm	$\times 2.326^*$	$E + 03 = J/kg$
cp	$\times 1.0^*$	$E - 03 = Pa\ s$
ft	$\times 3.048^*$	$E - 01 = m$
ft²	$\times 9.290\ 304^*$	$E - 02 = m^2$
ft³	$\times 2.831\ 685$	$E - 02 = m^3$
ft/sec	$\times 3.048^*$	$E - 01 = m/s$
ft/sec²	$\times 3.048^*$	$E - 01 = m/s^2$
°F	$(°F - 32)/1.8$	$= °C$
°F	$(°F + 459.67)/1.8$	$= K$
in.	$\times 2.54^*$	$E + 00 = cm$
lbm/ft³	$\times 1.601\ 846$	$E + 01 = kg/m^3$
lbm/hr	$\times 1.259\ 979$	$E - 04 = kg/s$
psi	$\times 6.894\ 757$	$E + 00 = kPa$
°R	$(°R/1.8)$	$= K$

* Conversion factor is exact.

Chapter 8
Drilling Operations

8.1 Fluid Circulation Temperature

8.1.1 Introduction. In drilling operations, the knowledge of accurate temperature with circulating time has a direct bearing on drilling fluid rheology and, hence, its design; determination of thermal stresses on tubular (particularly in permafrost or high-temperature regions); design of cementing programs; logging-tool design; and log interpretation. The estimation of fluid temperature becomes critical for high-temperature and geothermal reservoirs, where significant heat exchange occurs. In these reservoirs, problems compound when dealing with temperature-sensitive fluid properties, such as non-Newtonian fluid.

Similar to drilling, production and well control or dynamic kill operations also demand accurate computations of fluid circulation rates. Fluid temperature, both as a function of depth and elapsed time, dictates the intrinsic fluid properties of density and viscosity and, in turn, the pressure drop or the maximum allowable pumping rate. Offshore wells present another dimension to the heat-transfer problem in that heat exchange through the seawater and air must be incorporated.

There are a few reliable predictive tools for temperature estimation. For instance, the popular API thickening-time schedule for cementing operations is unreliable because it often over- or under-estimates the true temperature. Although direct temperature measurements can be made at a given depth during certain operations, we cannot overemphasize the need for computing temperature profiles for the entire wellbore by simulating the transient processes. Note that the earlier analytic models, proposed by Edwardson et al.[1] and Tragesser et al.[2] are unsuitable as a generalized computational tool because they require a detailed knowledge of the drilling history.

Two approaches, numerical and analytical, have emerged for estimating the circulating fluid temperature. In the numerical approach, solution of the governing finite-difference equations dealing with the unsteady-state, heat-transfer problem is sought. Raymond[3] proposed the first numerical model for computing circulating fluid temperatures during both unsteady- and pseudosteady-state conditions. Subsequently, many improvements were offered by others.[4-6]

In the second approach, analytical solutions were obtained for system geometry of lesser complexity, that is, in absence of multiple casing strings. For example, Holmes and Swift[7] obtained solution for steady-state heat transfer in both conduits and the formation. Recently, complete unsteady-state formulations were presented[8,9] for both forward and reverse circulation cases. In this chapter, we discuss simple but realistic analytic models that allow calculation of the inlet and outlet mud temperatures with time, as fluid is circulated in and out of a tank. These models are also capable of tracing the time-dependent temperature profile for the entire borehole.

8.1.2 Constant Tank-Fluid Temperature. In flowing down the tubing and back up the annulus (forward circulation), or down the annulus and up the tubing (reverse circulation), the circulating fluid generally gains heat from the hotter formation. The heat transfer rate for the fluid in the annulus depends on the formation temperature from which it gains heat, and on the tubing fluid temperature to which it loses heat. A schematic for the reverse circulation case is shown in **Fig. 8.1.** Kabir et al.[8] derived the following equations for the tubing (T_t) and annulus (T_a) fluid temperatures by doing an energy balance for a fluid element.

$$\frac{B}{L_R}\frac{d^2 T_t}{dz^2} \pm B\frac{dT_t}{dz} - T_t + T_{es} + g_G z \sin\alpha = 0 , \quad \cdots\cdots (8.1)$$

$$\text{and } T_a = T_t \mp B\frac{dT_t}{dz} , \quad \cdots\cdots\cdots\cdots\cdots\cdots (8.2)$$

$$\text{where } L_R = \frac{2\pi}{c_{fl}w}\left[\frac{r_c U_a k_e}{k_e + r_c U_a T_D}\right] , \quad \cdots\cdots\cdots\cdots (8.3)$$

$$\text{and } B = \frac{w c_{fl}}{2\pi r_t U_t} . \quad \cdots\cdots\cdots\cdots\cdots\cdots (8.4)$$

Note that the upper signs (+ in Eq. 8.1 and − in Eq. 8.2) apply to the reverse-circulation case, and the lower signs apply to the forward-circulation case. Solutions for the two flow directions differ because of the boundary conditions. We reproduce the solution from Ref. 9, which is written as

$$T_t = \alpha e^{\lambda_1 z} + \beta e^{\lambda_2 z} + g_G z \sin\alpha \pm B g_G + T_{es} , \quad \cdots\cdots (8.5)$$

$$\text{and } T_a = \left(1 \mp B\lambda_1\right)\alpha e^{\lambda_1 z} + \left(1 \mp B\lambda_2\right)\beta e^{\lambda_2 z}$$

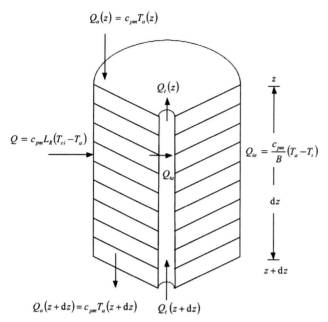

$$Q_a(z) = c_{pm}T_a(z)$$

$$Q_t(z)$$

$$Q = c_{pm}L_R(T_{ei} - T_a)$$

$$Q_{ta} = \frac{c_{pm}}{B}(T_a - T_t)$$

$$Q_{ta}$$

$$Q_a(z+dz) = c_{pm}T_a(z+dz) \qquad Q_t(z+dz)$$

Fig. 8.1—Schematic representation of the heat-transfer model.

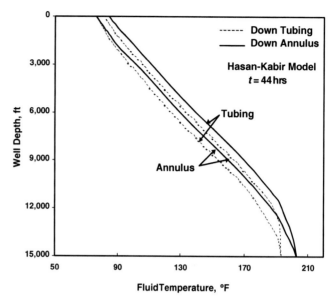

Fig. 8.2—Influence of flow direction on a fluid-temperature profile.

$$+g_G z \sin\alpha + T_{es} \cdot \quad \dots\dots\dots\dots\dots (8.6)$$

Again, the upper signs (+ in Eq. 8.5 and – in Eq. 8.6) apply to reverse flow, and the lower ones apply to the forward flow situation. The constants, α, β, λ_1, and λ_2, are dependent on boundary conditions and thermal properties, which are presented in Appendix D, Sec. D.1. **Fig. 8.2** shows how the flow direction influences the temperature profiles.

8.1.3 Variable Tank-Fluid Temperature. The solutions previously presented were deduced based on the condition that the circulating fluid inlet temperature is constant (either T_{ai} or T_{ti}). Fluid, circulating through tubing (or a drillpipe) and a tubing/casing (or casing/formation) annulus gains heat from the formation, which is usually at a higher temperature than the flowing fluid. Therefore, the fluid exiting the wellbore and entering the tank is at a temperature higher than the average value. Adding this hotter fluid gradually raises the tank fluid temperature with time. In other words, the wellbore acts as a heat exchanger supplying heat to the tank from the formation. However, as the tank temperature increases, heat loss from the tank to the surrounding air also increases. The tank temperature finally approaches a steady value when the heat, gained from the circulating fluid (from formation), equals the heat lost to the ambient air.

The transient energy balance for the tank may be made by noting the energy gain from the hot wellbore fluid and energy loss to the surrounding air. First, consider the case of forward circulation through a rectangular tank, as depicted in **Fig. 8.3.** Here, the fluid is at an initial temperature, T_o, which is often equal to the ambient air temperature, T_{air}. The energy balance comprises three elements. First, the energy is added to the tank by the entering circulating fluid at a temperature of T_{ae} (exit temperature of the annular fluid); second, the energy is lost by the fluid exiting the tank (and entering the

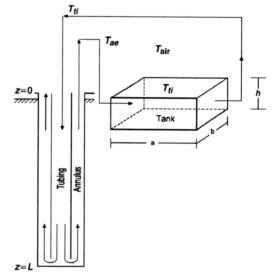

Fig. 8.3—Schematic representation of the mud-circulation model.

wellbore) at a temperature of T_{ti}; third, the heat that is lost to the ambient air. In other words,

$$wc_{fl}(T_{ae} - T_{ti}) - Uab(T_{ae} - T_{air}) = (abh)\rho_{fl}c_{fl}\frac{dT_{ti}}{dt},$$

$$\text{or} \quad \frac{dT_{ti}}{dt} + \Omega T_{ti} = Y, \quad \dots\dots\dots\dots\dots\dots (8.7)$$

$$\text{where } \Omega = \frac{w + (Uab/c_{fl})}{abh\rho_{fl}}, \quad \dots\dots\dots\dots (8.8)$$

$$\text{and } Y = \frac{wT_{ae} + (UabT_{air}/c_{fl})}{abh\rho_{fl}} \cdot \quad \dots\dots\dots (8.9)$$

Eq. 8.7 is a linear-differential equation, which yields a solution with the boundary condition ($T_{ti} = T_{air}$ at $t = 0$), and is written as

$$T_{ti} = \frac{Y}{\Omega} + \left(T_{air} - \frac{Y}{\Omega} \right) e^{-\Omega t} \cdot \quad \dots \dots \dots \dots \quad (8.10)$$

Note that in arriving at the expression (Eq. 8.10) for tank temperature variation with time, we assumed that Y is a constant, although it contains a term T_{ae}. As the tank temperature increases, the exit-fluid temperature from the annulus, T_{ae}, will also increase gradually with time. However, assuming T_{ae} to be constant is still reasonable because the variation in the value of T_{ae} with time is small and because the term wT_{ae} is generally much smaller than the term $UabT_{air}/c_{fl}$. A simplified expression for Eq. 8.10 may be written as[9]

$$T_{ti} = T_{ae} + \left(T_o - T_{ae} \right) e^{-\Omega t} \cdot \quad \dots \dots \dots \dots \quad (8.11)$$

Eq. 8.11 shows that the tank-fluid temperature asymptotically approaches the terminal exit-fluid temperature. This expression also holds when reverse circulation occurs, with wT_{ae} being replaced by wT_{te} in all appropriate equations.

8.1.4 Variable Heat Flux at Formation/Wellbore Interface.
In contrast to fluid flow, heat flow occurs throughout the length of the wellbore and not just at the perforated intervals. Therefore, the variable heat flux is considered along the entire wellbore/formation interface.

Expressions for fluid temperature in the tubing and annulus, given by Eqs. 8.5 and 8.6, include the exponents, λ_1 and λ_2, which are dependent on the relaxation distance, L_R. The development of the expression for L_R, given by Eq. 8.3, involves the solution of the thermal-diffusivity equation. One boundary condition in the solution includes constant heat flux at the wellbore/formation interface.[10,11] However, with increased circulation time, the wellbore fluid temperature tends to approach that of its immediate surroundings, thereby decreasing the heat-transfer rate with time and invalidating this boundary condition. To account for this changing heat flux, the superposition principle can be used, as shown in Ref. 9. The governing differential then becomes

$$\frac{B}{L_{Rn}} \frac{d^2 T_t}{dz^2} \pm B \frac{dT_t}{dz} - T_t$$
$$+ T_{es} + g_G z \sin \alpha + \omega_{1'} - \omega_{2'} = 0 \cdot \quad \dots \dots \quad (8.12)$$

Unlike Eq. 8.1, Eq. 8.12 includes terms involving heat flux, which must be linear in well depth, z, for the differential equation to be linear and yield an analytic solution. If each heat flux is represented by a linear equation, solutions to Eq. 8.12 are given by

$$T_t = \alpha e^{\lambda_1 z} + \beta e^{\lambda_2 z} + \Lambda z \pm B\Lambda + T_{es} + \omega_1 - \omega_2 , \quad \dots (8.13)$$

and
$$T_a = \left(1 \mp B\lambda_1 \right) \alpha e^{\lambda_1 z} + \left(1 \mp B\lambda_2 \right) \beta e^{\lambda_2 z}$$
$$+ \Lambda z + T_{es} + \omega_1 - \omega_2 . \quad \dots \dots \dots \dots \quad (8.14)$$

The constants $\Lambda, \alpha, \beta, \lambda_1, \lambda_2, \omega_1,$ and ω_2 are reported in Appendix D.

8.1.5 Fluid Temperature Inversion.
One interesting aspect of studying the forward circulation behavior is that the maximum temperature occurs in the annulus away from the bottom of the borehole. Here, we present a simple analytic expression for the depth at which the maximum fluid temperature occurs and offer a physical explanation of this phenomenon.

By differentiating Eq. 8.6 with respect to the well depth, z, and setting it equal to zero, we obtain

$$\frac{dT_a}{dz} = 0 = \left(1 + \lambda_1 B \right) \alpha \lambda_1 e^{\lambda_1 z} + \left(1 + \lambda_2 B \right) \beta \lambda_2 e^{\lambda_2 z} + g_G ,$$
$$\dots \dots \dots \dots \dots \quad (8.15)$$

or $e^{\lambda_1 z_{Tmax}} = -\dfrac{g_G}{\left(1 + \lambda_1 B \right) \alpha \lambda_1} - \dfrac{\left(1 + \lambda_2 B \right) \beta \lambda_2 e^{\lambda_2 z_{Tmax}}}{\left(1 + \lambda_2 B \right) \beta \lambda_1} .$
$$\dots \dots \dots \dots \dots \quad (8.16)$$

Because z_{Tmax} is implicit in Eq. 8.16, a trial-and-error solution is required. Alternatively, one can also differentiate the temperature profile numerically to find z_{Tmax} as shown later.

The temperature inversion is precipitated by heat flow equilibrium attained by the fluid as it ascends the annulus. In forward circulation, the drillpipe fluid temperature continues to rise upon receiving heat from the annular fluid, reaching a maximum at the bottomhole. This high-temperature fluid then flows up the annulus. The annular fluid, being lower than the formation temperature, receives heat from the formation. Initially, this gain in heat is larger than the heat it loses to the fluid in the drillpipe, with a consequent net increase in enthalpy and temperature as the fluid rises up the annulus. However, the rate of heat gain diminishes as the annular fluid encounters cooler formation with decreasing depth, while the annular fluid loses heat to the relatively colder tubing fluid. At some depth away from the bottomhole, the net heat gained by the fluid equals the net heat loss, and the maximum fluid temperature is reached.

The preceding discussion is best understood by inspecting **Fig. 8.4**. As the rate of heat transfer between the wellbore and the formation diminishes with increasing circulation time, the temperature profiles in both conduits approach the geothermal temperature showing a cooling effect. Only the annular temperature profiles are captured in Fig. 8.4. Although temperature inversion is apparent for each curve on Fig. 8.4, the depth at which the maximum temperature occurs is best amplified on a derivative graph. **Fig. 8.5** displays the same depth (13,776 ft or 4,199 m) for all the curves when the derivative goes to zero. Note that the derivative was taken with respect to the logarithm of depth to retain the same units for the x-axis (°F or °C) and facilitate plotting on the same

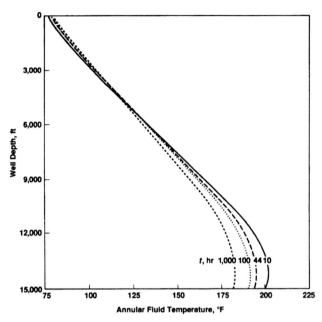

Fig. 8.4—Effect of circulation time on an annular temperature profile.

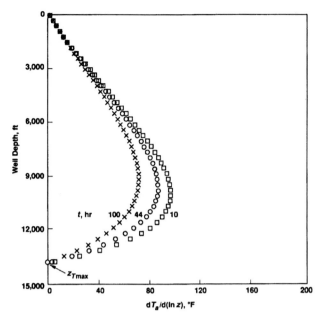

Fig. 8.5—Temperature derivative aids locating the temperature maxima.

graph. **Fig. 8.6** shows such a combined plot, where the derivative was taken by using the central-difference scheme. We also observe maxima on the derivative.

8.1.6 Influence of Parameters on Circulation Temperature.

We explore the effects of tank-fluid temperature variation and heat flux variation at the wellbore/formation interface on the circulating-fluid temperature using the Holmes-Swift[7] data set, given in **Table 8.1.** The tank, as shown in Fig. 8.2, has the dimension of $100 \times 10 \times 5$ ft³.

Tank Temperature Variation. **Fig. 8.7** shows the fluid temperature profile obtained after about 44 hours (44.14 hr)

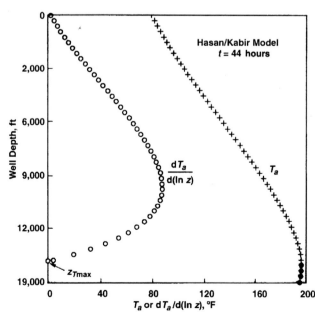

Fig. 8.6—Combined fluid temperature and its derivative show the temperature maxima.

of circulation. Here, the annular inlet temperature of the fluid is assumed to be constant at 75°F, compared to that when the inlet temperature is allowed to increase with time as indicated by Eq. 8.10. The difference in the two profiles, e.g., more than 25% increase in the wellhead fluid temperature, emphasizes the importance of accounting for such variations in temperature-sensitive applications.

The variations of tank-fluid temperature and temperature of the exiting annular fluid with time are shown in **Fig. 8.8** for two different initial temperatures, 35°F and 75°F. As indicated by Eq. 8.10, the tank temperature initially increases rapidly with time and then gradually levels off in both cases. The increase in tank-fluid temperature causes a gradual increase in the annular-fluid exit temperature, which is also shown in Fig. 8.8. An interesting feature of Fig. 8.8 is the gradual

TABLE 8.1—WELL AND MUD DATA FROM HOLMES AND SWIFT	
Well depth, ft	15,000
Drillstem OD, in.	6 5/8
Drillbit size, in.	8 3/8
Circulation rate, bbl/hr	300
Inlet mud temperature, °F	75
Mud viscosity, lbm/(ft-hr)	110
Mud thermal conductivity, Btu/(ft-°F-hr)	1.0
Mud specific heat, Btu/(lbm-°F)	0.4
Mud density, lbm/gal	10
Formation thermal conductivity, Btu/(ft-°F-hr)	1.3
Formation specific heat, Btu/(lbm-°F)	0.2
Formation density, lbm/ft³	165
Surface earth temperature, °F	59.5
Geothermal gradient, °F/ft	0.0127

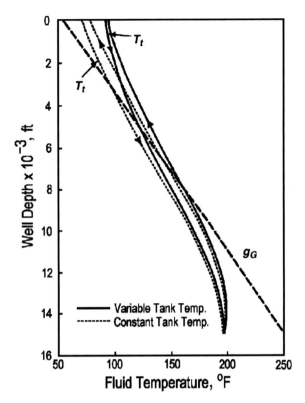

Fig. 8.7—Fluid temperature profiles for the variable inlet-temperature model.

decline in the difference between the annular-fluid exit temperature and the tubing-fluid inlet temperature with increasing time. We can explain this decrease in the temperature difference in the following manner: as the wellbore-fluid temperature increases, the temperature difference driving heat flow from the formation to the wellbore decreases. Thus, the net energy gain for the fluid gradually decreases with time,

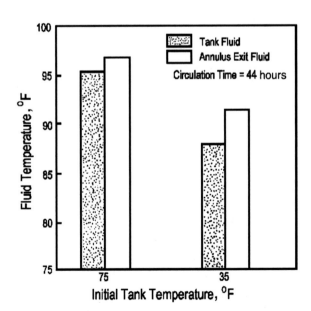

Fig. 8.9—Influence of initial tank fluid temperature on the final fluid temperatures.

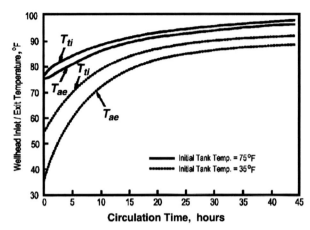

Fig. 8.8—Effect of circulation time on the wellhead fluid inlet/exit temperature.

leading to an ever-decreasing temperature difference of the two streams at the wellhead.

As Eq. 8.10 implies, many variables influence the rise in the tank fluid temperature. Parameters that are likely to have the largest effect are the initial-tank temperature, the area of the tank exposed to the air (heat transfer area=ab), the heat-transfer coefficient between the tank and the air (which can change dramatically with wind velocity), and the tank volume. The sensitivity of the calculated tank and annular exit temperatures to these variables is displayed in **Figs. 8.9** through **8.12.** Note that in these figures, we report tank and annular-fluid exit temperatures at the end of 44 hours of circulation.

Fig. 8.9 shows that the initial tank temperature does not appear to affect the tank-fluid temperature after 44 hours of circulation: the large initial difference of 40°F between the two cases reduces to only 5.5°F. This observation implies that the heat transported from the formation and lost to the ambient air has a more pronounced effect than the initial tank temperature for establishing the equilibrium inlet and exit temperatures. This trend is also indicated in Fig. 8.10, which

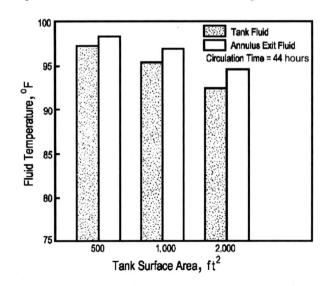

Fig. 8.10—Final fluid temperatures are insensitive to the heat-transfer area.

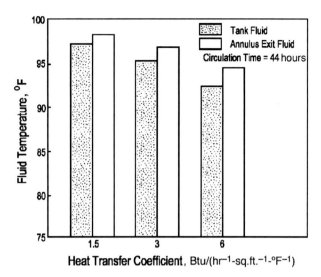

Fig. 8.11—Final fluid temperatures are insensitive to heat-transfer coefficients.

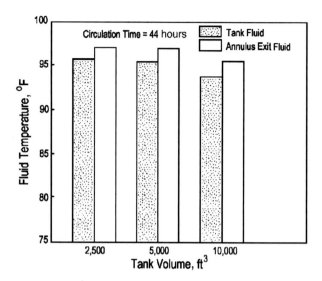

Fig. 8.12—Final fluid temperatures are insensitive to the tank volume.

shows that the tank temperature at the end of 44 hours is 5°F lower when the tank area is four times larger. The increased heat loss from a larger surface area causes the lower temperature. Fig. 8.11 similarly shows a lower tank temperature for the case when the heat transfer coefficient is larger. The effect of tank volume, which is displayed in Fig. 8.12, is small. Reduction of tank volume by 400% shows an increase of only 2.1°F in tank temperature, after 44 hours of circulation.

Heat Flux Variation. The base case illustrated in the last section is used here to show the effect of variable heat flux on circulating fluid temperature. In these applications, we used a constant wellbore-inlet temperature of 75°F; that is, a constant-tank temperature. **Fig. 8.13** shows the temperature profile for the case of forward flow, after 44 hours of circulation. The bottomhole temperature, for the case when variable heat flux is accounted for, is about 7°F (about 3.5%) higher than when heat flux is assumed constant. The difference would be more pronounced in deeper wells with higher temperature differentials between the wellhead and the bottomhole. Note that the two profiles are quite similar near the wellhead and the difference becomes significant only near the bottom. **Fig. 8.14** shows a similar case for the reverse-circulation case. Here, the variable heat flux appears to have negligible effect on the estimated temperature in both conduits.

Field Example 8.1. To illustrate application of the model (Eqs. 8.10 or 8.11) discussed, we used the data of Davies et al.[12] for both Cases One and Two. They reported wellhead or inlet fluid temperature with inlet flow-rate variations in Case One. For simplicity, we attempted to reproduce most of the measured data beyond the initial 100 minutes into the circulation. Because detailed reporting of individual parameters were lacking, we estimated the constants Ω and Y with Eqs. 8.8 and 8.9, respectively. To do this calculation, we observed that the tank-fluid temperature at the start of first (3 bbl/min) and second (7 bbl/min) circulation rates were 30°C and 32.5°C, respectively. For the second circulation period, the fluid attained an asymp-

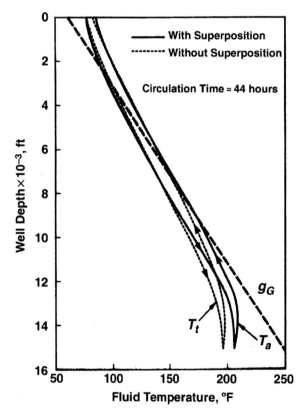

Fig. 8.13—Pronounced temperature-superposition effect during forward circulation.

totic value, T_{ae} = 46°C. A simple optimization procedure led to a Ω value of 0.025 for the second period. Because Ω is directly proportional to the circulation rate, w, one obtains Ω of 0.01071(= 0.025 × 3/7) for the first circulation period. In this way, we obtain the lumped parameters of the model, leading to a very satisfactory match, as shown in **Fig. 8.15.**

We did a similar analysis for Case Two. Here, we considered the late-time data only. The reported data show a con-

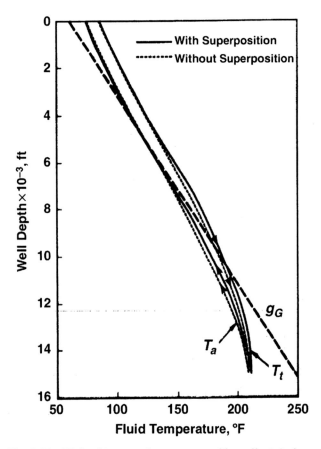

Fig. 8.14—Minimal temperature-superposition effect during reverse circulation.

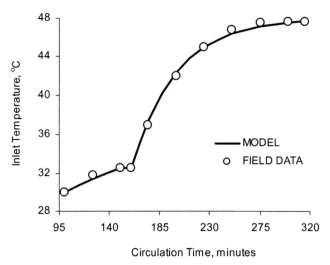

Fig. 8.15—Matching inlet-fluid temperature, Davies *et al.* Case One data.

stant value of 18°C at the inlet for about two hours before rising sharply to 40°C. This initial temperature transient reflects the travel time needed by the fluid to return to the surface in this 16,400-ft well. Because the model presupposes steady-state circulation rates, mismatch results at early times. However, good agreement results beyond one hour of circulation, as **Fig. 8.16** illustrates. **Fig. 8.17** exhibits the quality of match obtained in the entire borehole. Although the overall

trend has been captured by simulation, a more desirable agreement eludes us. This discrepancy is expected to occur because measurements were made after the cessation of circulation, while the model computes temperature during circulation. Consequently, we expected generally higher measured temperature, especially at shallower depths, as the wellbore-fluid gain heat from the formation. Note that good agreement of the inlet or tank temperature implies good agreement in the downhole dynamic temperature.

8.1.7 Discussion. A host of variables significantly impacts wellbore-temperature distribution during fluid circulation. These variables include fluid heat capacity and density, inlet temperature, geothermal gradient, formation thermal conductivity, well depth, circulation time and rate. In Sec. 8.1, we presented simple algebraic solutions, involving all these variables as input parameters, which are adaptable for simple spreadsheet calculations.

We also note that, from a heat-transfer viewpoint, a wellbore with a uniform hydraulic radius is quite adequate and that the allowance for multiple casing strings and a string of

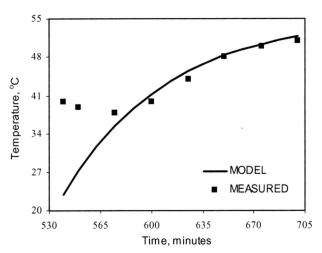

Fig. 8.16—Matching inlet-fluid temperature, Davies *et al.* Case Two data.

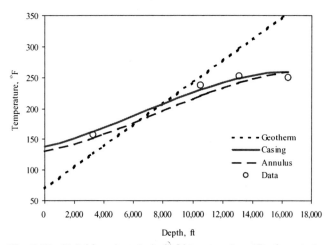

Fig. 8.17—Matching downhole-fluid temperature, Davies *et al.* Case Two data.

FLUID FLOW AND HEAT TRANSFER IN WELLBORES

drill collars is unnecessary. Thus, the inability to easily include multiple casing strings is not a limitation of the analytic approach presented here.

Although not discussed explicitly, various T_D models can be used (in Eq. 8.3) en route to solving the temperature equations. We favor the one presented in Ref. 8 because it encompasses the entire time domain of interest.

8.1.8 Fluid Circulation Temperature Summary.
In Sec. 8.1, we discussed two approaches for computing fluid-temperature profiles in both conduits as a function of time, during fluid circulation. Both the forward- and the reverse-circulation cases are considered in the formulations. In the first approach, we showed how the variable inlet fluid temperature could be modeled, and in the second, the variable heat flux is accounted for, leading to a fully transient model. Specifically, based on our computational results and field testing, we observed

- Increasing the inlet fluid temperature results in a much higher exit temperature than obtained for the constant-inlet temperature case.
- A cold tank gains considerable heat with increasing circulation time—heat transfer parameters, such as the tank's cross-sectional area, volume, and heat-transfer coefficient, appear to have a marginal impact on fluid temperature profiles, if we allow for a long circulation time.
- A somewhat higher temperature is attained at the bottomhole when the variable heat flux is accounted for throughout the wellbore for the forward circulation case; however, no significant temperature difference occurs for the reverse circulation situation—perhaps the variable heat flux boundary condition is of limited importance for the flow problem at hand.
- Field examples demonstrate the usefulness of the model, and in particular, we showed that both the tank fluid and downhole temperatures could be computed accurately even without the precise knowledge of various heat-transfer parameters.

8.2 Static Formation Temperature

8.2.1 Introduction.
An accurate estimation of the static formation temperature (T_{ei}) is required for a variety of applications. Some of these applications include: designing cementing programs, evaluating formation water resistivity for openhole log analysis, establishing geothermal gradients for exploration mapping and cased hole temperature logging, and estimating heat content in geothermal reservoirs. Formation temperature is also critically important when transient simulations are made using a coupled wellbore/reservoir simulator, as discussed in Chap. 7. Stakes increase when well tests are interpreted using both pressure and temperature transients.

These needs have prompted many to estimate T_{ei} during and after mud circulation. Mud circulated during drilling causes considerable cooling of the formation around the well. Therefore, temperatures recorded after the cessation of mud circulation are always lower than the static formation temperature. Depending on the contrast between the inlet mud and formation temperatures, circulation time, and thermal characteristics of the reservoir, several days or weeks

may be required to attain complete thermal equilibrium between the wellbore mud and formation. Such long waits are usually economically prohibitive. Therefore, practicality demands discerning T_{ei} from transient temperature data after the cessation of mud circulation. In this process, effects of thermal disturbances, introduced earlier by the circulating mud, must be addressed.

Two approaches have emerged for estimating T_{ei} in an openhole situation. In the first approach, forward simulation is attempted by accounting for changes in mud composition, inlet temperature of mud, circulation rate, and rock physical properties for the entire borehole. Methods of Edwardson et al.,[13] Holmes and Swift,[14] and Wooley,[15] among others, are cases in point.

In the second approach, inverse solution is sought of the measured mud-temperature data, gathered at the bottom section of the borehole, which is analogous to pressure-transient analysis. This approach is very convenient because of its simplicity and is rooted in the line-source solution proposed by Bullard.[16] In the petroleum literature, Dowdle and Cobb[17] popularized this method in an analogy to Horner's[18] method of analyzing transient pressure data. In this approach, the circulation time is presumed long enough for the logarithmic approximation of the EI (Exponential Integral) function to be valid. Unfortunately, the line-source assumption is usually much less appropriate for thermal transients than its pressure counterpart. In other words, this popular method has limitations. Solutions[19, 20] of different complexity are now available circumventing those limitations. We present some simplified approaches for evaluating T_{ei} in this section.

All these methods presuppose that the data are free of errors. Actually, a gauge carrier can store or release heat just as the tubulars and cement sheath do. This heat storage leads to distortion of early-time temperature data. Of course, this storage problem is far less in an openhole situation than in a cased hole. We will show that when temperature data are gathered during transient-pressure testing in a cased borehole, they lend themselves to proper analysis. A pragmatic approach of data gathering and its analysis, after the diagnosis and exclusion of storage-free data, will be presented.

8.2.2 Analysis of Openhole Data.
We[19] developed a simple model to use openhole temperature logs for estimating static formation temperature, T_{ei}. **Fig. 8.18** presents a schematic of the temperature measurements made in an openhole after mud circulation. This model, based on an unsteady-state energy balance, is given in Appendix D. The analysis leads to the following expression for the mud temperature, T_{ws}, in terms of the static formation temperature, T_{ei}, and a time function, $F(t_D)$.

$$T_{ws} = T_{ei} - C_o'' F(t_D), \qquad \ldots\ldots\ldots\ldots\ldots\ldots\ldots(8.17)$$

where C_o'' and $F(t_D)$ terms are presented in Appendix D, Sec. D.2.

Eq. 8.17 is only valid as long as t_D is less than 1.5, which corresponds to about six real hours for a typical formation. Note that both conductive and convective heat-transfer mechanisms are included in this formulation. Another assumption

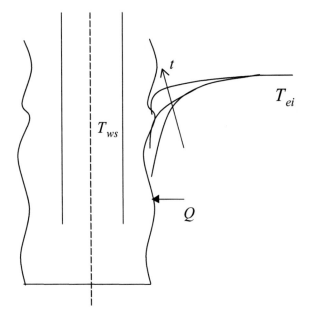

Fig. 8.18—Schematic presentation of temperature rise after mud circulation.

made in deriving Eq. 8.17 is that the formation temperature distribution remains undisturbed during mud circulation. In reality, however, mud circulation causes a general decrease in the formation temperature around the wellbore. Therefore, the assumption is untenable in general, and only approximately true if the mud circulation time is short.

Method One: Rigorous Approach. To account for the effect of mud circulation on the formation temperature distribution, we can apply the superposition principle. Here, for a total dimensionless mud circulation time t_{pD}, Eq. 8.18 applies with t_{pD} replacing t_D. We write the following expression for the mud temperature for a period of Δt_D because of the cessation of circulation.

$$T_{ws} = T_{ei} - C_o''\left[F\left(t_{pD} + \Delta t_D\right) - F\left(\Delta t_D\right)\right]. \quad\cdots\cdots (8.18)$$

The analysis just presented requires that the heat flow rate becomes zero immediately after the circulation has ceased. This condition of instantaneous cessation of heat flow is much more difficult to satisfy for heat transfer than the analogous requirement for mass flow rate for a pressure-buildup test. The continuous decay of heat gain (or loss) from the mud to the formation poses some theoretical problems with any method for estimating T_{ei}. However, note that the heat-transfer rate following mud circulation is negligible compared to that during mud circulation. Thus, Eq. 8.18 is likely to be quite sound for most practical cases.

Eq. 8.18 suggests that a plot of T_{ws} vs. $F(t_{pD}+\Delta t_D) - F(\Delta t_D)$ should result in a straight line with the intercept yielding the static formation temperature. To evaluate $F(t_{pD}+\Delta t_D)$ and $F(\Delta t_D)$ for use in Eq. 8.18, estimates of three constants—C_1, C_2, and a—are needed: these constants may be calculated with the equations from Appendix D, Eqs. D-21, D-22, and D-27, respectively, when appropriate property values for the mud and formation are known. The estimation of free convective heat-transfer coefficient U for

the wellbore mud presents a challenge. However, reasonably accurate values may be calculated from available correlations. When data are sketchy, Eq. D-26, in Appendix D, may still be applied with initial guesses for the constants, C_1 and C_2, and a regression analysis would yield values of T_{ei} and C_o''. Mud temperatures can then be computed with standard deviation. This procedure can be repeated for a set of values of the constants. The values of the constants, exhibiting the lowest standard deviation, are then selected as the final solution.

Method Two: Exponential Approach. One approximation results if we assume parameter A', given by Eq. D-14, is a constant. This would be true for a combination of small values of t_D and low heat transfer coefficient for the mud. In such a case, integrating Eq. D-13 between $t=0$ (T_{ei}) to $t=t(T_{ws})$ yields

$$T_{ws} = T_{ei} - \left(T_{ei} - T_{wso}\right)e^{-L_R't}. \quad\cdots\cdots\cdots (8.19)$$

Eq. 8.19 shows that a plot of mud temperature against $e^{-L'_R t}$ should result in a straight line with the intercept yielding the static formation temperature. Use of superposition to account for mud circulation before shut-in does not change the form of Eq. 8.19 because of the exponential nature of the equation. Therefore, with superposition,

$$T_{ws} = T_{ei} - \left(T_{ei} - T_{wso}\right)\left[e^{-\frac{tp}{A'}} - 1\right]e^{-L_R'\Delta t}. \quad\cdots\cdots (8.20)$$

Note that the initial mud temperature, T_{wso}, need not be known; it may be estimated from the slope of the curve. However, the procedure requires an estimate of L_R'. When data are unavailable, an optimization procedure may be used.

Method Three: Log-Linear Approximation. Noting the similarities between the differential equations for temperature and pressure distribution in the formation, Dowdle and Cobb[17] suggested that the transient response of fluid temperature in the wellbore may be used to estimate T_{ei}, analogous to estimating initial reservoir pressure from a pressure buildup analysis. If the mud has been circulating long enough, the logarithmic approximation to formation temperature distribution would apply, and Ramey's $f(t)$ function[11] and the dimensionless temperature function, T_D, are both approximated by Eq. D-16. If we further assume that $T_{wb}=T_{ws}$, the defining equation for T_D may then be written in terms of T_{ws} as

$$T_{ws} = T_{ei} - BT_D, \quad\cdots\cdots\cdots\cdots\cdots\cdots (8.21)$$

where $B = \dfrac{MQ}{2\pi k_e}. \quad\cdots\cdots\cdots\cdots\cdots\cdots (8.22)$

Therefore, for a total dimensionless mud circulation time, t_{pD}, we can combine Eqs. 8.22 and D-16 to write

$$T_{ws} = T_{ei} - B\left[0.406 + 0.5\ln t_D\right]. \quad\cdots\cdots\cdots (8.23)$$

			Methods		
TABLE 8.2—COMPARISON OF STATIC TEMPERATURE COMPUTATION: **SYNTHETIC DATA**					
Data Source	Time, hr	Mud Temperature, °C	Log-Linear Eq. 8.24	Rigorous Eq. 8.18	Exponential Eq. 8.20
Shen-Beck[21] synthetic data with $T_{ei}=80°C$	2.5	56.6	55.5	57.2	57.55
	5.0	61.3	62.4	61.0	60.85
	7.5	64.3	65.4	63.9	63.65
	10.0	66.6	67.2	66.2	66.01
	15.0	69.6	69.2	69.6	69.69
	20.0	71.7	70.3	72.2	73.32
Computed static temperature, °C			74.1	78.6	78.9

Note that the second bracketed term of Eq. D-16 has been omitted simply because the equation becomes the line-source approximation or the Ramey's $f(t)$ function[11] at large times as discussed in Ref. 19.

Applying the superposition principle, we may write the expression for the mud temperature for a period of Δt_D because the cessation of circulation is

$$T_{ws} - T_{ei} = -B(T_{pD} + \Delta T_D) + \Delta T_D$$

$$= -0.5B \ln\left(\frac{t_p + \Delta t}{\Delta t}\right) . \quad \ldots\ldots\ldots\ldots (8.24)$$

Therefore, a plot of the mud temperature against log of time ratio, $(t_p+\Delta t)/\Delta t$, should be linear. The intercept at $(t_p+\Delta t)/\Delta t = 1.0$; that is, very large Δt, of such a line should yield T_{ei}.

We note that this method presupposes that heat exchange between the formation and wellbore is zero after the mud circulation has ceased. While this assumption is reasonable at very long circulation times, it may be untenable at intermediate times when significant heat transfer may occur.

In addition to the assumption of instantaneous cessation of heat flow with mud circulation, the method uses the log-linear approximation of Ramey's $f(t)$ solution, which is only acceptable at long times. In most cases of newly drilled holes, mud circulation is discontinued almost immediately after drilling. The data reported by Dowdle and Cobb[17] show typical circulation time between one to ten hours. For typical formation and fluid properties, such circulation times are equivalent to the dimensionless production time, t_{pD}, between 0.25 to 2.5 hours. Unfortunately, the log-linear approximation is invalid for such short periods. In addition, note that we have assumed a very high heat-transfer coefficient for the mud so that the mud temperature at the wellbore center, T_w, may be assumed to be equal to the temperature at the interface of the wellbore and the formation, T_{wb}. This assumption is not robust for high-viscosity muds because of low-convective heat transfer.

Method Four: Square-Root Time Approximation. Another approach that relies on the superposition principle would be to use Eq. D-13, but instead of using the log-linear approximation for T_D, we use Eq. D-15. Assuming, as in the last case, $T_{wb}=T_{ws}$, we obtain

$$T_{ei} - T_{ws} = B\left[T_D(t_{pD} + \Delta T_D) - T_D(\Delta t_D)\right] . \quad \ldots\ldots (8.25)$$

Rewriting Eq. 8.25,

$$T_{ws} = T_{ei} - 1.1282BF'(t_D), \quad \ldots\ldots\ldots\ldots\ldots (8.26)$$

where $F'(t_D) = \left(\sqrt{t_{pD} + \Delta t_D}\right)\left(1 - 0.3\sqrt{t_{pD} + \Delta t_D}\right)$

$$-\sqrt{t_{pD}}\left(1 - 0.3\sqrt{t_{pD}}\right) . \quad \ldots\ldots\ldots\ldots (8.27)$$

A plot of T_{ws} against $F'(t_D)$, should yield a straight line with T_{ei} as the intercept and $-1.1282B$ as the slope. The major drawback of this approach is that it is only applicable to very early-time data. Application of this approach to the data reported in **Tables 8.2** and **8.3** resulted in unrealistic numbers, except for the first data point in each set. The method is only recommended for dimensionless time less than two, which translates to approximately eight hours in a typical system.

Although use of Eq. D-15 is inherent in formulation of both Eqs. D-18 and 8.26, there is an important difference between the two. The development of Eq. D-18 involved a treatment of the convolution integral, which is analogous to the pressure-rate problem solved in well testing. Thus, Eq. D-18 is rigorous for the heat flow problem in question. On the other hand, the formulation of Eq. 8.26 circumvents the convolution operation, thereby limiting its application to early-time data, $t_D < 1.5$.

Example Application 8.1. We used Shen and Beck's synthetic data[21] to verify the model just presented. Thereafter, oil well data of Dowdle and Cobb[17] and geothermal well data of Roux *et al.*[22] are used to illustrate applications of the recommended approach. Both exponential and log-linear approximations were also considered in these analyses.

Synthetic Example 8.1. To generate their data, Shen and Beck[21] used a constant-temperature wellbore model, without convective heat transfer. Most of the property values were available, which were used to calculate constants C_1 and C_2. The overall heat-transfer coefficient, U, in our model was approximated with $U=k_m/r_w$. The results are shown in Table 8.2 and **Fig. 8.19.** We must emphasize that the model used by Shen and Beck to generate the data in Table 8.2 assumes only conductive heat transfer in the

TABLE 8.3—COMPARISON OF STATIC TEMPERATURE COMPUTATION: FIELD DATA

Data Source	Time, hr	Mud Temperature, °F	Methods Log-Linear Eq. 8.24	Rigorous Eq. 8.18	Exponential Eq. 8.20
Dowdle and Cobb[17], Set I	5.10	99	98.9	99.4	99.4
	10.30	106	105.7	104.8	104.7
	14.48	107	108.0	107.9	107.8
	18.12	110	109.2	109.9	109.9
Computed static temperature, °F			114.8	117.2	117.4
Dowdle and Cobb[17], Set II	8.25	241	241.7	242.1	242.1
	11.00	257	255.2	254.4	254.2
	13.50	262	263.1	263.5	263.5
Computed static temperature, °F			303.4	315.1	313.9
Roux et al.[22], Set I	7.0	286	286.7	287.1	287.0
	11.0	308	305.6	304.8	304.9
	13.5	312	313.7	314.1	314.0
Computed static temperature, °F			364.0	382.0	363.2
Roux et al.[22], Set II	14.3	183	182.5	182.8	182.6
	22.3	194	195.2	194.6	194.9
	29.3	202	201.0	201.6	201.3
Computed static temperature, °F			221.6	213.2	212.1

mud. Therefore, Eq. 8.17 will not agree completely with these synthetic data. We think that convective heat transfer in mud is a more accurate representation of reality, especially when large temperature differentials exist between the inlet mud and the formation (e.g., geothermal, high-temperature reservoirs). However, the excellent agreement between the model and data, as shown in Table 8.2 and Fig. 8.18, indicates that differences in one particular aspect of modeling is not critical for this situation. **Figs. 8.20** and **8.21** show how T_{ei} values were obtained with the simple graphical technique.

Note that the exponential approximation performed very well in this case. The underlying assumption of the exponential approximation is that L_R' is time invariant, which is true if the $1/rU$ term dominates the T_D/k_e term. Because T_D increases slowly with t_D, the approximation works reasonably well, as it did in this case. A U value of 1 Btu-hr^{-1}-ft^{-2}-°F^{-1} was used along with an average value of T_D of 1 to compute L_R'. As expected, the log-linear approximation performed less satisfactorily because the early-time data were used for extrapolation. Indeed, the T_{ei} value was lower by as much as 6°C of the true solution.

About half the data in Table 8.2 involved dimensionless times larger than 1.5, for which the proposed solution is not strictly applicable. Nonetheless, the agreement of the method's predictions is very encouraging. The physical explanation lies in the convolution approach as used here at early times when most heat transfer occurs. At late times, the inaccuracy of Eq. D-15, in Appendix D, is not necessarily magnified because the heat transfer rate diminishes. The primary application of this model is to early-time data when other available methods are of doubtful validity.

Field Example 8.2. Field data reported by Dowdle and Cobb[17] and by Roux *et al.*[22] were used to verify the model and also to compare the results with other approximate solutions. Because of lack of various property values for the mud and formation, the mud was assumed to have the properties of water and a U of 1 Btu-hr^{-1}-ft^{-2}-°F^{-1}. The rock

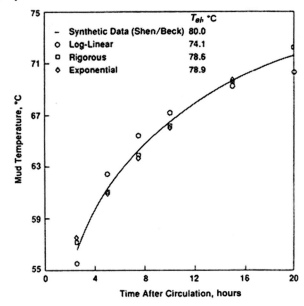

Fig. 8.19—Comparison of different methods with synthetic data.

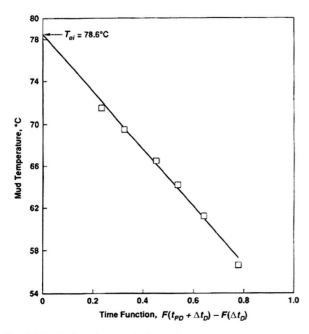

Fig. 8.20—Estimating static formation temperature (rigorous method).

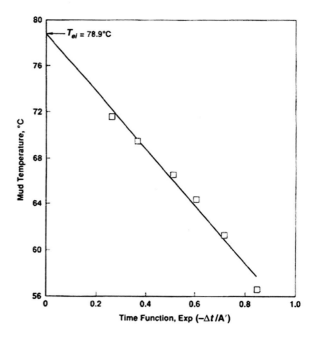

Fig. 8.21—Estimating static formation temperature (exponential method).

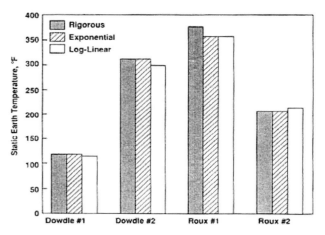

Fig. 8.22—Comparison of static formation temperature evaluated by various methods.

was assumed to have a conductivity of 1.4 Btu-hr^{-1}-ft^{-1}-°F^{-1} and a thermal diffusivity of 0.04 hr-ft^{-2}. The analysis was not very sensitive to these property values, the exception being k_e. The results, shown in Table 8.3 and **Fig. 8.22**, are in good agreement with the data.

Because the true formation temperatures are unknown in these field datasets, absolute accuracy of the rigorous approach (Eq. 8.17) cannot be attested. However, model validation suggests that Eq. 8.17 should yield results very close to the true values. Inspection of Table 8.3 suggests that the log-linear approximation underestimates the true solution, with the exception of the last dataset. This general underestimation of Eq. 8.24 was also noted by Roux *et al.*[22] and by Shen and Beck.[21] A similar trend also persists for the exponential approach as given by Eq. 8.20.

We point out that the results, obtained for the Dowdle/Cobb and exponential approximation methods, which are presented in both Tables 8.2 and 8.3, reflect the mud temperature values obtained following a regression analysis of the data. So, the reasonable agreement between these results is not very surprising. In contrast, the temperature values were computed with the appropriate values for the mud-formation systems in the case of the proposed methods, Eqs. 8.18 and 8.20.

8.2.3 Analysis of Cased-Hole Data. Problems common to application of all analytic methods previously discussed revolve around both the quality and the quantity of data collected in an openhole situation. In other words, sparse data gathering with each logging trip makes any method hard to apply. In contrast, when data are gathered in a cased hole environment, such as during pressure-transient testing, continuous data gathering over longer duration makes analysis less challenging.

Fig. 8.23 schematically illustrates how the temperature perturbation is related to gauge location during shut-in test in

an oil well. Shallower depths increase the temperature contrast between the fluid and its surroundings, leading to pronounced temperature excursions. Heating of liquid or cooling of gas, collectively known as Joule-Thompson (J-T) effects, can also lead to large temperature perturbations even if the probe is located at the producing interval. The severity of temperature contrast is dependent directly upon the degree of pressure drawdown involved. In this context, a damaged well in a very high-flow-capacity formation can induce a large pressure drop with attendant large temperature change.

In this section, we present the semi-analytic, rectangular hyperbola method for obtaining T_{ei}. The method is verified by using synthetic data, and its application is shown by using field data. We also illustrate how discrete T_{ei} data can be pieced together to obtain a region's geothermal gradient.

Hyperbola Method. As shown elsewhere,[23] the temperature decay equation during a pressure buildup test can be

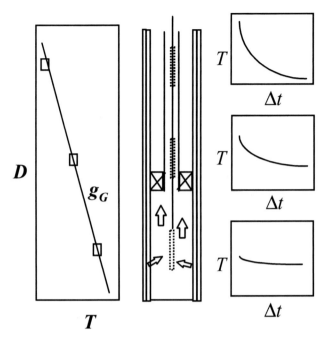

Fig. 8.23—Schematic presentation of temperature transients at various well depths.

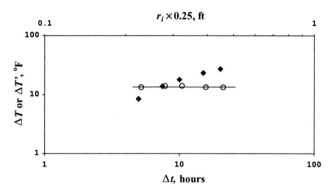

Fig. 8.24—Diagnosis of storage-free Shen/Beck synthetic data (from Ref. 21).

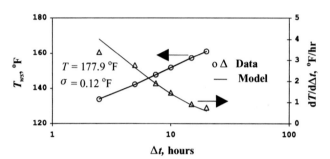

Fig. 8.25—Hyperbola analysis yields T_{ei} for synthetic data.

approximated by a rectangular hyperbola during the infinite-acting period. The hyperbola equation is given by

$$\left(T_{ws} - a'\right)\left(b' + \Delta t\right) = c' , \quad\dotfill (8.28)$$

where $a' = T_{ei} - \dfrac{m_t}{1.151}\left(\ln\alpha' - 2\right) , \quad\dotfill (8.29)$

$$b' = \frac{t_p}{\left(\alpha' + 1\right)} , \quad\dotfill (8.30)$$

$$c' = -\frac{4m_t t_p}{2.303\left(\alpha' + 1\right)} , \quad\dotfill (8.31)$$

$$m_t = C_J \frac{162.6qB\mu}{kh} , \quad\dotfill (8.32)$$

and $C_J = \left(\dfrac{\partial T}{\partial p}\right)_H = -\dfrac{0.185}{\rho c_h} ; \quad\dotfill (8.33)$

and α' is a system parameter. Eq. 8.28 representing infinite-acting reservoir behavior is always applicable when dealing with temperature transients because the radius of investigation is only about a few feet. We explore this point further while discussing field examples. Note that Eq. 8.28 may also be written as: $T_{ws} = a' + c'/(b' + \Delta t)$. Therefore, when Δt approaches infinity, T_{ws} approaches a', the hyperbola's asymptote. Therefore, the parameter a' represents the reservoir temperature at infinite shut-in time; that is, $a' = T_{ei}$, the static reservoir temperature.

Example Application 8.2. *Synthetic Example 8.2.* As shown in Table 8.2, we used synthetic data of Shen and Beck,[21] generated after mud circulation, to compute T_{ei}. Because the data contained no thermal storage, as exemplified by the plateau on the derivative graph of **Fig. 8.24,** all six data points were included in these analyses. **Fig. 8.25** presents the hyperbola and its derivative fitting the data. Although the results of the three methods used previously were close to the true value of 176°F (80°C), the hyperbola analysis gives an answer that is closest to the true value.

Also shown in Fig. 8.24 is the radius of investigation, r_i. We can write a relation for r_i by recognizing the analogy between pressure and thermal diffusion processes as

$$r_i = \sqrt{\frac{4k_e\Delta t}{\rho_e c_e}} \quad\dotfill (8.34)$$

Typical parameter values used for the r_i computation for all examples include: k_e=1.8 Btu/(ft-hr-°F), ρ_e=165 lbm/ft³, and c_e=0.22 Btu/(lbm-°F).

Field Example 8.3. **Fig. 8.26** presents the diagnostic graph of temperature data gathered some 2,500 ft above the midpoint of perforations in a 11,000-ft well. Just as the previous synthetic example, one observes the dominating influence of thermal storage here. A derivative plateau barely appears toward the end of the test. **Fig. 8.27** presents the semilog analysis yielding a T_{ei} value of 214.5°F with a least-squares coefficient of 0.94. In contrast, the hyperbola analysis shows a good fit beyond 15 hours, as **Fig. 8.28** shows. The hyperbola-derived value of 215.1°F is

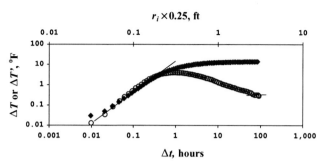

Fig. 8.26—Diagnosis shows storage domination in off-bottom measurements.

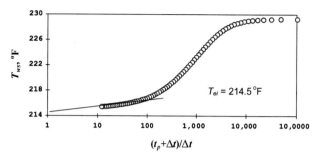

Fig. 8.27—Semilog analysis straightens a small data span.

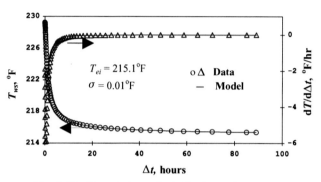

Fig. 8.28—Hyperbola analysis fits large data span.

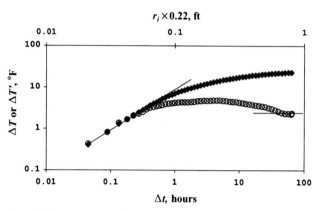

Fig. 8.29—Diagnosis of a test with large J-T heating effects.

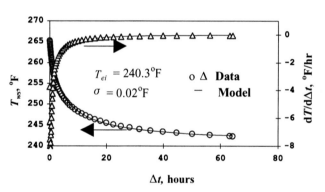

Fig. 8.30—Hyperbola analysis yields reliable T_{ei}.

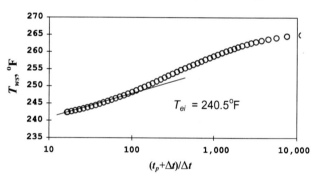

Fig. 8.31—Semilog analysis corroborates hyperbola-derived T_{ei}.

in good agreement with that of the semilog analysis. However, much greater confidence can be placed on the T_{ei} value computed by the hyperbola approach because of its ability to treat a much larger data span.

Joule-Thompson (J-T) heating of oil is associated with the degree of drawdown involved. In this example, where the test experienced some 5,800-psi drawdown at the sandface because of high skin damage, a large attendant temperature change also occurred. Here, **Fig. 8.29**, representing the diagnostic graph, shows a total temperature change of about 23°F, although the gauge was located at the perforations. In this case, thermal effects are caused by the J-T effects and not by the borehole gauge location. **Figs. 8.30** and **8.31** present the hyperbola and semilog analyses, respectively, showing good agreement with each other.

Establishing Regional Geothermal Gradient. Transient temperature data, collected during pressure-buildup tests in different producing horizons, can be used to con-

struct a region's geothermal gradient, g_G. Here, we present how Kuwait's geothermal gradient was established. The examples presented in the preceding section were two of the 52 tests that were analyzed for this purpose. **Fig. 8.32** presents the geothermal gradient obtained. As discussed by Kabir et al.,[23] the transient analysis approach is superior to those obtained by using the openhole and cased borehole data, gathered during various logging operations, unless enough time is allowed for thermal equilibration to occur between the borehole fluids and formation. We verified this geothermal gradient by measuring borehole temperatures in a well shut-in for nearly a year. Here, the measurements were made at each station stop for 15 minutes. **Fig. 8.33** presents this data, corroborating the g_G obtained by the transient method.

8.2.4 Discussion. The first approach for interpreting openhole data attempts to capture both the heat transfer mecha-

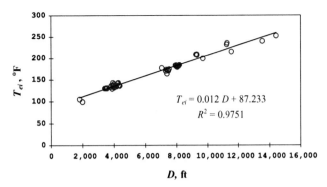

Fig. 8.32—Estimating g_G using transient-test data.

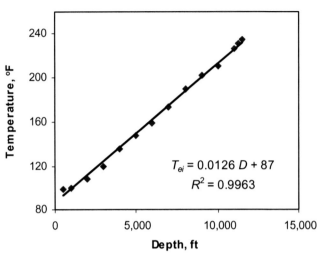

Fig. 8.33—Estimating g_G using static-test data.

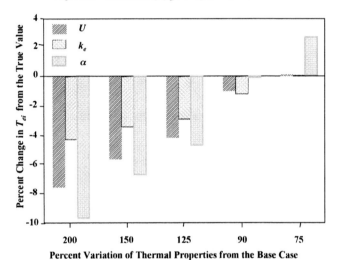

Fig. 8.34—Sensitivity of three parameters on T_{ei} estimation.

nisms—conduction and convection—while formulating the working equations for estimating T_{ei}. We note that convective heat transfer can play a significant role when large contrast exists between the inlet mud and formation temperatures. Both geothermal and high-temperature hydrocarbon reservoirs are cases in point. Previous studies in this area appear to have neglected this important heat-transfer mechanism.

If we were to consider the conductive heat-transfer mode alone, the formulation would be much simplified even when the superposition effects were considered, as shown by Shen and Beck.[21] In this context, theoretical difficulty of using the superposition principle is noteworthy. For example, from a heat-transfer viewpoint, the complex process of drilling and mud circulating is not analogous to that of fluid flow, wherein measurable quantities of fluid may be withdrawn or injected into the formation. Therefore, the superposition theorem, as used here, is approximate at best. Note also that the model considers conductive and convective heat transfer in the borehole only and that conductive heat transfer occurs in the formation. In other words, the filtrate that invades the formation is assumed not to carry any heat.

Despite these apparent restrictions, the first method presents a simple tool for analyzing field data even when mud and formation properties are not well defined. The method also avoids making some of the assumptions made in the existing techniques. For example, assumptions of a line-source well and its logarithmic approximation are not always tenable in a heat-transfer problem of this nature. Use of the cylindrical-source well avoids the problem of treating the early-time data. The algebraic simplifications, given in Appendix D, lead to solutions in different time domains.

The main advantage of the first method is that T_{ei} can be estimated reliably from very early-time data. Consequently, considerable rig time can be saved because waiting periods can be minimized to a large degree. We point out that the traditional practice of gathering transient-temperature data, during each discrete logging trip with different tools, is not conducive to ensuring the data quality because of the physical operation. Collection of continuous temperature data with minimal disturbances ensures unambiguous interpretation.

Methods based on sparse openhole data are still reliable even when questions arise about the availability or accuracy of values for various heat-transfer parameters. Experiences suggest that modeling of the physical process is far more important than the absolute values of these parameters. **Fig. 8.34** illustrates this point by showing large variations of the overall heat-transfer coefficient, U, formation thermal conductivity, k_e, and thermal diffusivity, α. We observe that the error in T_{ei} solution is no greater than 10% of the true value even under extreme circumstances.

In contrast to a drilling environment, continuous temperature data can be gathered routinely during a transient-pressure test. Thus, open- or cased-hole drillstem tests or production tests offer excellent opportunities to collect this information. Note that maximum perturbations are created when (1) large Joule-Thompson heating or cooling is associated with large pressure drawdowns, and (2) measurements are made away from the midpoint of a producing interval. In a cased borehole, the early-time data are generally distorted by thermal storage effects.

An important point to reiterate is the thermal storage phenomenon, first mentioned in Chap. 7. Thermal storage arises because tubulars, cement sheath, and the gauge carrier all have the ability to store or release heat, depending on the fluid type and well-operating condition. Slow thermal equilibrium at any depth of measurement raises questions about the validity of routine cased borehole-temperature surveys run to diagnose flow problems. For instance, attempting to

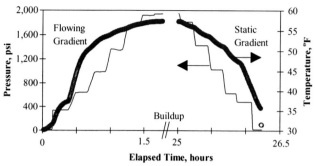

Fig. 8.35—Tool-induced temperature distortion in gradient surveys.

diagnose tubular leaks by temperature logs may run into serious problems unless large volumes of flow are associated with them. That is because significant cooling or heating is required to monitor measurable temperature difference. For the same reason, subtle problems may remain clouded by a probe's inability to respond to the temperature change, given the time allowed at each station stop or when the tool is run at a certain speed.

We illustrate this point by presenting **Fig. 8.35,** which shows both temperature and pressure data measured before and after a pressure-buildup test. While pressure attains rapid equilibrium at each station, shown by solid stair-steps, the same is not true for temperature during both the flowing and static gradient surveys. Smearing of the temperature profile, regardless of the wellbore flow condition, is a direct consequence of the tool-induced thermal storage. The probe's casing sheath largely contributes to this measurement distortion. In other words, true fluid temperature at a given depth cannot be discerned directly from raw measurements; clearly, interpretation is required. One way of reducing thermal storage distortion is to use probes that are in direct contact with wellbore fluids.

8.2.5 Static Formation Temperature Summary. In Sec. 8.2, we presented two approaches, reflecting open- and cased-hole data source, for estimating the undisturbed formation temperature, T_{ei}. In the first approach, an algebraic equivalence of cylindrical-source well solution at early times ($t_D < 1.5$) is used. Both conductive and convective heat-transfer mechanisms are considered in this formulation. Also in the first approach, a rigorous method and its various simplifications, representing different time domains, are presented. In all cases, a simple graphical analysis is possible. The first approach is validated by using synthetic data and verified by using published field data obtained from both oil and geothermal wells.

In the second approach, a semitheoretical method is shown to yield reliable T_{ei} when temperature data are collected with pressure data during a transient test in a cased-borehole environment. Here, we identified thermal storage as exhibited by the gauge carrier, tubulars, and cement sheath. Despite this storage, the data are amenable to the rectangular hyperbola analysis, aided by its derivative counterpart. Finally, we show how discrete T_{ei} values, collected from different horizons, can be used to develop a region's geothermal gradient.

8.3 Oil Well Blowout

8.3.1 Introduction. Unrestricted or uncontrolled flow of pressurized fluids from a pipe or a well is commonly termed a blowout. The main concerns with blowout of an oil well are the danger of gas/oil combustion, leading to possible damages to equipment and wellhead, jeopardizing personnel safety, and the serious environmental effects of the expelled fluids. In addition, loss of reserves can have significant economic implications in certain cases.

Most relevant studies address kick detection and blowout control; a few deal with dynamic-kill operations to regain well control. Clark and Perkins[24] presented a comprehensive study on blowout, based on steady-state two-phase flow calculations. Unsteady-state modeling for well control was reported by Fan et al.,[25] whereas, Hasan et al.[26] addressed the dynamic aspects of blowout.

The primary mechanism governing a blowout well is the rapid, near-surface liberation and subsequent expansion of large amounts of dissolved gas. Increased free gas results in higher mixture velocity with consequent increase in the total pressure gradient owing to higher friction and kinetic energy losses. The reduced fluid pressure leads to lower fluid density and further increase in velocity and pressure loss. As the fluids accelerate to the surface, the available flowing pressure limits their speeds and corresponding flow rates. If fluid pressure becomes sufficiently low, the velocities of the fluids will reach the critical (sonic, choking) velocity of the mixture. Under this condition, the pressure at the wellhead is termed the critical discharge pressure.

For a number of reasons, the blowout rate can be less than the critical value. For example, surface restrictions at the wellhead or relatively low-reservoir potential can lead to a blowout where the fluid velocity is below its critical value. In this case, the wellhead pressure will stabilize at a value higher than the critical pressure and the sonic discharge velocity will not be reached. Computation of fluid flow and pressure profile in such cases must account for the interaction between the expelled-wellbore two-phase fluids and the atmosphere. In this section, we will concern ourselves only with cases where two-phase flow will stabilize at the critical condition while discussing the study reported by Hasan et al.[26]

8.3.2 Analysis of a Blowout. The critical (sonic) velocity represents the maximum speed fluids may attain. The reason for this limitation lies in the inability of rarefaction wavefronts, which is the pulse traveling down the wellbore, to propagate in a direction counter to that of the flow. In other words, the sonic velocity of these downstream-traveling pressure pulses is balanced exactly by that of the upstream-traveling fluids. If critical flow is reached, it must stabilize such that the sonic condition is established at the wellhead while subsonic flow occurs below in the wellbore.

Analysis of oil well blowout is complicated by the need to consider sonic velocity of a two-phase mixture. Sonic velocities in two-phase systems are typically much less than those in single-phase flows of the individual components. Wallis[27] developed a model for two-phase sonic velocity in one-dimensional steady-state homogeneous equilibrium flow.

In this text, we adopt the model proposed by Wallis,[27] based on the analysis of one-dimensional (1D) steady homogeneous flow. According to this model, the critical or sonic velocity, v_c, for a two-phase system, depends on the sonic velocities of the two phases, v_{cL} and v_{cg}, and their in-situ volume fractions, f_L and f_g, as

$$\frac{1}{v_c^2} = \left[f_L \rho_L + (1 - f_L) \rho_g \right] \left(\frac{f_L}{\rho_L v_{cL}^2} + \frac{1 - f_L}{\rho_g v_{cg}^2} \right) . \quad \ldots \ldots (8.35)$$

The sonic velocities of the individual phases can be estimated from the partial derivative of pressure with respect to density at constant entropy with the expressions,

$$v_{cL}^2 = \left(\frac{\partial p}{\partial \rho_L} \right)_S \text{ and } v_{cg}^2 = \left(\frac{\partial p}{\partial \rho_g} \right)_S \ldots \ldots \ldots (8.36)$$

Expressions for these partial derivatives depend on the pressure/volume/temperature (PVT) behavior of the fluids and are available in many thermodynamics texts.

During critical flow in an oil well, there may be a two-phase supersonic flow above the wellhead. To analyze the interaction between discharge jet and atmosphere, the flow conditions at the end of the supersonic jet must be determined. We will not present any such analysis; the interested reader is referred to the work of Shirie and Seubold.[28]

8.3.3 Computation of Blowout Rate.

When control of a well is lost leading to blowout, critical flow is generally established at the wellhead at near-atmospheric pressure. With the reservoir properties and the wellhead pressures known, the problem boils down to computing a flow rate for which the total pressure-drop in the formation and the wellbore equals reservoir pressure minus the wellhead pressure. Transient pressure loss in the wellbore and in the formation depends on the complex manner of the flow rate. Therefore, estimating the flow rate at which a blowout well discharges fluids to the environment requires an iterative approach.

The transient transport model for two-phase flow,[29] also discussed in Chap. 7, can be used to do the trial-and-error calculations for estimating the blowout rate from a well. As we noted earlier, the simulator uses a finite-difference method to solve the mass, momentum, and energy equations for the wellbore, while an analytic approach is used for the reservoir. Let us recall some of the basic equations used earlier in Chap. 7.

Mass and momentum balances for a differential length, dz, of the pipe in terms of the mixture density, ρ_m, and velocity, v_m, are written as (similar to Eqs. 7.1 and 7.2)

$$\frac{\partial}{\partial t} (A \rho_m) = -\frac{\partial}{\partial z} (A \rho_m v_m) \quad \ldots \ldots \ldots \ldots (8.37)$$

and $$\frac{1}{\rho_m} \frac{\partial p}{\partial z} = -\frac{\partial v_m}{\partial t} - v_m \frac{\partial v_m}{\partial z} - g \sin\alpha - \frac{2 f_m v_m^2}{d} ,$$
$$\ldots \ldots \ldots \ldots (8.38)$$

where $\rho_m = f_g \rho_g + (1 - f_g) \rho_L$ · $\ldots \ldots \ldots \ldots (8.39)$

The energy balance equation in terms of energy entering the control volume, q, flow rate, $w(= \rho_m v_m)$, control volume mass per unit length, m, enthalpy, H, and internal energy, E, follows the form used in standard thermodynamics texts, which is

$$q = \frac{d}{dz} \left[m \left(H + \frac{1}{2} v^2 + gz \right) \right] + \frac{d(wU)_{cv}}{dt} \cdot \quad \ldots \ldots \ldots (8.40)$$

The control volume includes both the fluid (indicated by subscript m) and the tubing/casing material (indicated by subscript w). Thus, the energy accumulation term (the last term in Eq. 8.40) is separated into two components, resulting in the expression,

$$Q = \frac{d}{dz} \left[m \left(H + \frac{1}{2} v^2 + gz \right) \right] + \frac{\pi d^2}{4} \frac{d}{dt} (\rho_m c_m T_m)_{cv}$$

$$+ \frac{\pi (d_o^2 - d_i^2) \rho_w c_w}{4} \frac{dT_w}{dt} \cdot \quad \ldots \ldots \ldots \ldots (8.41)$$

Heat transfer between the formation and wellbore fluid was discussed in Chap. 5, Sec. 5.3. Heat entering the fluid from the formation is given in terms of formation and fluid thermal properties and formation and fluid temperatures (T_{ei} and T_m) by Eqs. 5.19 and 5.20.

$$Q \equiv L_R w c_p (T_{ei} - T_m) , \quad \ldots \ldots \ldots \ldots \ldots (5.19)$$

where $$L_R \equiv \frac{2\pi}{c_p w} \left[\frac{r_{to} U_{to} k_e}{k_e + (r_{to} U_{to} T_D)} \right] . \quad \ldots \ldots \ldots \ldots (5.20)$$

We initiate computation with an assumed flow rate of q STB/D. This flow rate, along with the producing gas/oil ratio (GOR) are used to compute gas and liquid phase velocities. The simulator then calculates wellbore pressure, temperature, and velocity iteratively for the entire production period, using the set of equations presented (Eqs. 8.37 through 8.41, and Eqs. 5.19 and 5.20). If the computed wellhead pressure is higher than ambient (atmospheric), the program restarts the calculation with a higher flow rate. However, if the assumed flow rate is actually higher than the critical flow rate, the computed pressure will become negative somewhere along the wellbore because the rate is too high for the reservoir/wellbore system to support. When the calculated pressure becomes negative, the calculation sequence terminates. Thereafter, we restart the whole iterative sequence using a lower flow rate. This procedure is repeated until the two-phase pressure drop limitation is established at the surface. The flow rate, at which this limitation is established, is the blowout rate.

8.3.4 Example Application.

We present an example of a blowout oil well. This synthetic data, originally published by Clark and Perkins,[24] are listed in **Table 8.4.** The pertinent data

TABLE 8.4—WELL, RESERVOIR, AND FLUID DATA FOR THE EXAMPLE PROBLEM	
Reservoir pressure, psia	4,300
Bottomhole pressure, psia	1,420
Well depth, ft	8,800
Tubing ID, in.	5.5
Gas/Oil ratio (GOR), scf/STB	800
Productivity index, STB/D-psi	3.5
Critical flow rate, STB/D	10,000
Critical wellhead pressure, psia	29

TABLE 8.5—ADDITIONAL DATA USED IN TWO-PHASE FLOW SIMULATION	
Pipe roughness, ft	0.00002
Formation permeability, md	212
Formation thickness, ft	100
Formation porosity, fraction	0.26
Skin factor	21.1
Oil gravity, °API	30
Reservoir temperature, °F	138.7
Geothermal gradient, °F/ft	0.015
Formation thermal conductivity, Btu/(ft-°F-hr)	3.33
Formation density, lbm/ft^3	135
Formation heat capacity, Btu/(lbm-°F)	0.625
Tubing/Casing material thermal conductivity, Btu/(ft-°F-hr)	30
Annular fluid thermal conductivity, Btu/(ft-°F-hr)	0.2
Annulus fluid thermal conductivity, Btu/(ft-°F-hr)	0.1
Cement thermal conductivity, Btu/(ft-°F-hr)	0.38

TABLE 8.6—MAJOR SIMULATION RESULTS		
	Hasan et al.[22]	Clark and Perkins[24]
Possible lowest bottomhole pressure, psia	1,480.5	1,420
Possible lowest wellhead pressure, psia	28.5	29
Terminal blowout rate, STB/D	10,000	10,000

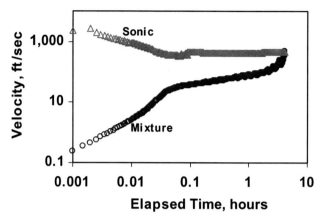

Fig. 8.36—Evolution of sonic and mixture velocities during blowout (example problem).

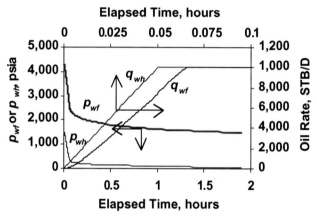

Fig. 8.37—Evolution of blowout (example problem).

405 ft/sec. Because the theoretical sonic velocity is still higher than the calculated mixture velocity, we continued computation with a slightly higher production rate. However, near the wellhead, the program computed negative pressure at this flow rate, and the computation was terminated. Thus, the simulator calculates a blowout rate of about 10,000 STB/D. **Fig. 8.36** presents the evolution of sonic and mixture velocities at the wellhead condition of one of the cases we considered here.

We expect the theoretical sonic velocity to be higher than the actual maximum velocity attainable in the well because the sonic velocity is computed assuming isentropic expansion. One issue with the assumption of isentropic expansion is that all mechanical losses, such as frictional, are negligible, which is untenable in practice. For instance, with increases in GOR, the isentropic-expansion assumption becomes progressively worse because of higher expected frictional loss. Our simulations at various GOR values clearly bear out this fact; that is, the higher the GOR, the greater is the difference between the sonic velocity and computed maximum attainable velocity.

Fig. 8.37 captures the unsteady-state process that leads to blowout. In this base-case simulation, the blowout or terminal rate is reached very rapidly, in 1.89 hours. The rate difference at the wellhead (q_{wh}) and sandface (q_{wf}) is a reflection of the wellbore storage arising from fluid compressibility. However, after the attainment of terminal rate, the wellhead rate will

and parameters used in our simulator are listed in **Table 8.5** and the final calculated results are reported in **Table 8.6.**

Our computed mixture velocity at the wellhead condition is 396.5 ft/sec, quite close to the theoretical sonic velocity of

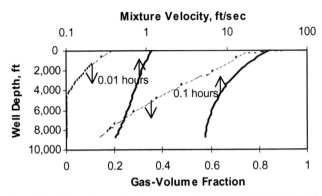

Fig. 8.38—Time-dependent f_g and v_m profiles (example problem).

continue to decline because of constant-pressure production. We explore this point further in the next section while addressing the cumulative-fluid-loss question.

Note that the results of unsteady-state simulations and those done by Clark and Perkins[24] using the steady-state approach are very similar. Nonetheless, time-dependent nature of the process cannot be captured with a steady-state model. For instance, if one wishes to learn the time to reach the terminal rate in a given system, one must do unsteady-state calculations. Obviously, the element of time is crucial when intervention is sought.

To gain insights into wellbore dynamics, we examined wellbore profiles of the two-phase mixture velocity (v_m) and gas-volume fraction (f_g). As **Fig. 8.38** shows, at 0.01 hr into the blowout process, bubbly flow starts at about 4,500 ft with a v_m about 1.2 ft/sec at the wellhead. Corresponding pressure (p) and temperature (T) profiles are shown in **Fig. 8.39**. The mixture velocity grows very rapidly and attains a value of 35 ft/sec in 0.1 hr. At this time, the wellbore experiences bubbly flow starting at the well bottom, while slug flow occurs above 5,000 ft.

8.3.5 Sensitivity Studies. In the preceding example, we discussed wellbore dynamics leading to blowout. Naturally, questions arise concerning which parameters govern a blowout. We examined four major parameters, such as formation

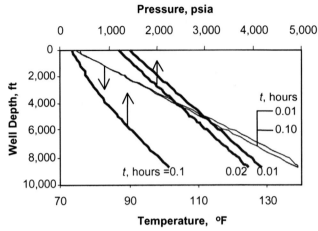

Fig. 8.39—Time-dependent p and T profiles (example problem).

permeability or well index, flow-string diameter, GOR, and reservoir pressure. We used the same example problem discussed earlier to amplify certain points.

Fig. 8.40 presents the effect of permeability on blowout rate. Also shown is the time to attain blowout, which grows significantly with permeability. Perhaps an explanation is in order. As expected, the blowout rate is strongly dependent upon permeability or well index. Unless limited by the flow-string diameter, a larger rate is associated with higher inflow at the sandface. Time to reach the blowout rate grows after the initial decline. That is because high permeability causes higher flowing bottomhole pressure (BHP) or lower pressure drawdown, as shown in **Fig. 8.41**. In other words, in a high-PI case, the time to attain the blowout rate increases significantly, thereby allowing intervention time. The early decline in the blowout time is explained by noting that excessive drawdown causes the low-p_{wf} value to be attained rapidly in a low-PI case.

The notion of tubing controlling the blowout rate is exemplified by **Fig. 8.42**. The results shown in the figure are quite intuitive for the 40-md case. In fact, if a choke is present in the system, at either subsurface or surface, that will dictate the ultimate rate. In other words, a conduit with minimum diameter in the wellbore/wellhead system becomes the controlling variable in an uncontrolled flow situation.

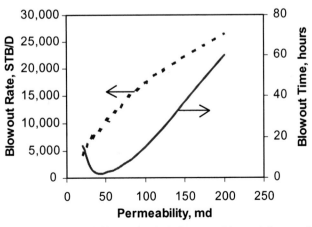

Fig. 8.40—Permeability strongly influences blowout time and rate.

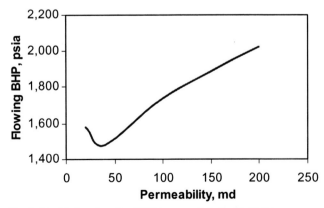

Fig. 8.41—Higher flowing BHP is associated with higher permeability.

TABLE 8.7—RESERVOIR SIMULATION INPUT PARAMETERS			
	P-10	*P*-50	*P*-90
Drainage area, acres	500	1,000	2,000
Initial reservoir pressure, psia	4,000	4,300	4,600
Flowing bottomhole pressure, psia	1,350	1,444	1,550
Decline coefficient, dimensionless	0	0.1	0.2
Formation volume factor, RB/STB		1.15	
Total system compressibility, 1/psi		1E–5	
Oil viscosity, cp		1.33	

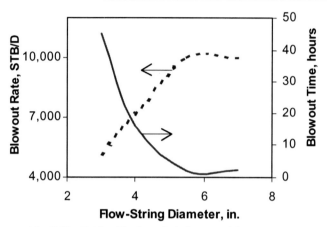

Fig. 8.42—Tubing ID strongly influences blowout rate.

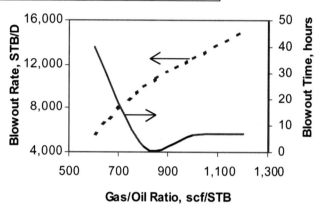

Fig. 8.43—Blowout rate increases with solution-GOR.

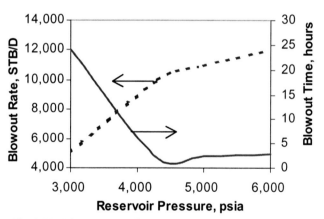

Fig. 8.44—Higher reservoir pressure increases blowout rate.

As stated earlier, increasing solution-GOR will increase blowout rate. As **Fig. 8.43** shows, this trend is monotonic for the range of GOR investigated. Note that at low-solution GOR's, the total pressure drop in the string is dominated by the hydrostatic head because of the presence of essentially single-phase oil in 5.5-in. tubing. However, with increases in solution-GOR, two-phase flow starts to become important, leading to increases in pressure drop. Therefore, until the rate becomes tubing limited owing to excessive pressure drop, the system will exhibit increasing blowout rate with increasing GOR because of an increasingly lighter fluid column. With further increases in GOR, excessive gas will probably cause higher pressure drop, leading to a plateau in the blowout rate. At low-GOR's, decline in the blowout time occurs because of lower pressure drop at the sandface. Obviously, a heavier liquid column associated with low-GOR oil causes reduced drawdown.

Increasing reservoir pressure has similar effects on the blowout rate as increasing GOR. That is, in both cases the hydrostatic head is influenced the same way because of the pressure gradient, as shown in **Fig. 8.44.** In other words, the blowout rate will be higher in an overpressured reservoir than in its depleted counterpart.

8.3.6 Cumulative Fluid Loss. Any blowout presents a significant challenge for well control and the consequent environmental hazards. Equally important, reservoir engineers are faced with a daunting task to estimate the lost volume. We will now address ways to estimate this lost volume in an uncontrolled flow situation using a probabilistic approach.

To simulate the post-blowout well performance, we used an analytic unsteady-state reservoir simulator described elsewhere.[30] This simulator is independent of wellbore, however. Nonetheless, we used a p_{wf} value of 1,444 psia (from Table 8.6) corresponding to the critical rate to predict the future behavior. Other input parameters for the 50% probability (*P*-50) case are given in **Table 8.7.**

Fig. 8.45 shows that the wellhead rate continues to decline with the attendant decrease in reservoir pressure. Rate decline is expected to occur because the well is being pro-

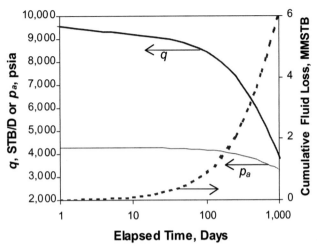

Fig. 8.45—Post-blowout well performance for the base case.

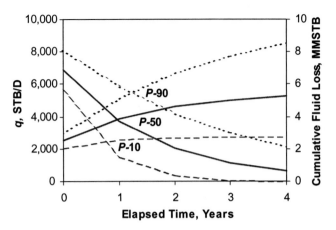

Fig. 8.46—Probabilistic well performance in the post-blowout period.

duced at near-constant wellhead pressure. This inner-boundary condition is fully met when critical flow sets in. Field observations[31] of declining plume height support the notion of decreasing rate with time. Note that a blowout period of 1,000 days is unrealistic but is shown here merely to complete a time decade.

Fig. 8.45 presents the results of a deterministic case. In practice, however, many of the reservoir parameters may have large uncertainties, especially for an exploratory well. To obtain a better idea of the fluid loss, we resorted to probabilistic simulations. As Table 8.7 shows, four parameters have uncertainties within certain bounds. Although permeability may have large uncertainty, we presumed that the flow would be tubing-limited.

Using uncertainties of the four selected parameters, **Fig. 8.46** synthesized results of all simulations, reflecting 10, 50, and 90% probability cases. Rates are averaged over one year, which clarifies the low initial rate for the P-50 case. Note that rapid rate decline occurs, thereby explaining an instantaneous rate of 9,600 STB/D and not 10,000 STB/D, at the start of first day, as shown in Fig. 8.46.

Of the four parameters, drainage area had the greatest impact on fluid loss. That is, larger fluid loss is associated with a larger drainage area within a given time span. Therefore, to minimize fluid loss, offset wells should be produced at maximum rates to shrink the drainage boundary of the blowout well.

8.3.7 Oil Well Blowout Summary. Blowout is an unsteady-state, uncontrolled flow process. In general terms, the maximum or critical rate is reached after the initiation of blowout. Thereafter, rate decline occurs owing to constant-pressure production. Several wellbore/reservoir parameters govern the magnitude of blowout rate and the time to reach this maximum rate. Among these, diameter of the flow conduit has the maximum impact on the blowout rate. Low-GOR oil will mean a lower blowout rate if the condition for tubing-limited flow is not met. Formation permeability or well productivity index appears to have minimal impact on the blowout rate. We recommend probabilistic reservoir simulations, encompassing uncertainties in reservoir parameters, to obtain clues about the volume of oil lost in a given situation.

Summary

This chapter deals with issues that pertain to drilling operations. The first two sections discuss unsteady-state heat transfer models that are associated with steady fluid circulation. Borehole-temperature measurements made after the cessation of circulation lead to estimating the undisturbed formation temperature. We also showed how the temperature data, collected in conjunction with pressure-buildup tests in cased boreholes, can yield formation temperature, en route to establishing a region's geothermal gradient.

On the other hand, in the last section, the application of unsteady-state fluid and heat flows, discussed earlier in Chap. 7, is shown while probing the blowout problem of an oil well. Use of a coupled wellbore/reservoir model help to understand the issues surrounding the loss of reservoir fluids, so that appropriate steps can be taken to minimize fluid loss in the event of such occurrence.

Nomenclature

a = length of mud tank, ft

a' = asymptote of rectangular hyperbola, °F

A = cross-sectional area for heat flow, ft²

b = width of mud tank, ft

b' = parameter of rectangular hyperbola, °F

B = parameter defined by Eq. 8.4, ft

c' = parameter of rectangular hyperbola, °F-hr

c_e = specific heat of earth or formation, Btu/(lbm-°F)

c_{fl} = specific heat of fluid, Btu/(lbm-°F)

c_h = specific heat of fluid, Btu/(lbm-°F)

c_{pm} = specific heat of mud, Btu/(lbm-°F)

C_o = constant defined by Eq. D-23, dimensionless

C_o = constant defined by Eq. D-17, dimensionless

C_1 = constant defined by Eq. D-20, dimensionless

C_2 = constant defined by Eq. D-21, dimensionless

C_3 = constant defined by Eq. D-22, dimensionless

C_J = Joule-Thompson coefficient, °F/psi

d = diameter, ft

$f_1(t_D)$ = function defined by Eq. D-24, dimensionless

$f_2(t_D)$ = function defined by Eq. D-25, dimensionless

$f_3(t_D)$ = function defined by Eq. D-26, dimensionless

f_g = volumetric in-situ gas fraction

f_L = volumetric in-situ liquid fraction

F = function used in Eq. 8.18, defined by Eq. D-23, dimensionless

F' = function used in Eq. 8.26, defined by Eq. 8.27, dimensionless

$F(t_D)$ = function defined by Eq. D-23, dimensionless

g_G = geothermal gradient, °F/ft

h = mud tank height, ft

k = formation permeability, md

k_e = earth or formation thermal conductivity, Btu/(hr-ft-°F)

k_h = formation thermal conductivity, Btu/(hr-ft-°F)

k_m = thermal conductivity of mud, Btu/(hr-ft-°F)

L = total vertical well depth, ft

L'_R = parameter used in Eqs. 8.19 and 8.20, 1/hr

L_R = relaxation length, ft^{-1}

L_{Rn} = relaxation length with superposition taken into account, ft^{-1}

m_t = semilog slope, °F/~

M = mass of fluid in a one-foot length of well, lbm

p = pressure at any point in the well, psia

p_{wf} = flowing bottomhole pressure, psia

p_{wh} = flowing wellhead pressure, psia

q = liquid flow rate, STB/D

q_{bo} = blowout rate, STB/D

q_{wf} = flow rate at sandface, STB/D

q_{wh} = flow rate at wellhead, STB/D

Q = heat flow rate per unit well length, Btu/(hr-ft)

Q_a = convective heat flow in the annulus, Btu/hr

Q_t = convective heat flow in the tubing, Btu/hr

Q_{ta} = rate of heat flow from the annulus to the tubing per unit depth, Btu/(hr-ft)

r, r_c, r_w = wellbore radius, ft

r_i = radius of investigation, ft

t, t_p = fluid circulation or production time, hr

t_D = dimensionless circulation time ($=k_h t_p/\rho c_h r_w^2$)

T = fluid temperature at any point in the well, °F

T_a = annular-fluid temperature, °F

T_{ae} = annular-fluid exit temperature, °F

T_{ai} = annular-fluid inlet temperature, °F

T_{air} = air temperature, °F

T_{as} = annular-fluid temperature at surface, °F

T_D = dimensionless temperature [$=2\pi k_e(T_{wb}-T_{ei})/q_F$]

T_{ei} = formation static temperature at bottomhole, °F

T_{es} = formation static temperature at surface, °F

T_o = initial fluid temperature, °F

T_t = tubing/drillpipe fluid temperature, °F

T_{ti} = fluid temperature entering the wellbore, °F

T_w, T_{wb} = wellbore temperature, °F

T_{ws} = sandface shut-in temperature, °F

T_{wso} = initial wellbore temperature, °F

Δt = shut-in time, hr

Δt_D = dimensionless shut-in time

ΔT = shut-in temperature difference, °F

$\Delta T'$ = superposition-time derivative of ΔT, °F

U = overall heat-transfer coefficient, Btu/(hr-ft^2-°F)

U_a = overall heat-transfer coefficient for annulus, Btu/(hr-ft^2-°F)

v_c = critical velocity of two-phase mixture, ft/sec

v_{cg} = critical velocity of gas, ft/sec

v_{cL} = critical velocity of liquid, ft/sec

v_m = velocity of the gas/oil mixture, ft/sec

w = mass flow rate of fluid, lbm/hr

x = mass fraction of gas, dimensionless

Y = parameter defined by Eq. 8.9, °F

z = any vertical depth, ft

z_{Tmax} = depth at which maximum temperature occurs, ft

α = heat diffusivity of formation [$=k_e/c_e\rho_e$], ft^2/hr

α' = constant used in Eqs. 8.5 and 8.6, °F

β = constant used in Eqs. 8.5 and 8.6, °F

λ_1, λ_2 = exponents used in Eqs. 8.5 and 8.6, ft^{-1}

Λ = parameter used in Eqs. 8.13 and 8.14, °F/ft

μ = fluid viscosity, cp

ρ, ρ_e = bulk density of earth or formation, lbm/ft^3

ρ_{fl} = density of fluid, lbm/ft^3

ρ_g = gas density, lbm/ft^3

ρ_L = liquid density, lbm/ft^3

σ = standard deviation, °F

ω_1, ω_2 = lumped parameters used in Eqs. 8.13 and 8.14, °F

Ω = parameter defined by Eq. 8.8, dimensionless

Subscripts

c = casing

m = fluid mixture

S = entropy

t = tubing

w = wall of tubulars

References

1. Edwardson, M.J. *et al.:* "Calculation of Formation Temperature Disturbances Caused by Mud Circulation," *JPT* (April 1962) 416; *Trans.*, AIME, 225.

2. Tragesser, A.F., Crawford, P.B., and Crawford, H.R.: "A Method for Calculating Circulating Temperatures," *JPT* (November 1967) 1507.

3. Raymond, L.R.: "Temperature Distribution in a Circulating Drilling Fluid," *JPT* (March 1969) 333.

4. Keller, H.H., Couch, E.J., and Berry, P.M.: "Temperature Distribution in Circulating Mud Columns," *SPEJ* (February 1973) 23.

5. Wooley, G.R.: "Computing Downhole Temperatures in Circulation, Injection, and Production Wells," *JPT* (September 1980) 1509.

6. Beirute, R.M.: "A Circulating and Shut-in Well Temperature Profile Simulator," *JPT* (September 1991) 1140.

7. Holmes, C.S. and Swift, S.C.: "Calculations of Circulating Mud Temperatures," *JPT* (June 1970) 670.

8. Kabir, C.S. *et al.:* "Determining Circulating Fluid Temperature in Drilling, Workover, and Well Control Operations," *SPEDC* (June 1996) 74.

9. Hasan, A.R. *et al.:* "A Mechanistic Model for Circulating Fluid Temperature," *SPEJ* (June 1996) 133.

10. Hasan, A.R. and Kabir, C.S.: "Aspects of Wellbore Heat Transfer During Two-Phase Flow," *SPEPF* (August 1994) 211.

11. Ramey, H.J., Jr.: "Wellbore Heat Transmission," *JPT* (April 1962) 427; *Trans.*, AIME, **225**.

12. Davies, S.N. *et al.*: "Field Studies of Circulating Temperatures Under Cementing Conditions," *SPEDC* (March 1994) 12.

13. Edwardson, M. J. *et al.*: "Calculation of Formation Temperature Disturbances Caused by Mud Circulation," *JPT* (April 1962) 416; *Trans.*, AIME, **225**.

14. Holmes, C.S. and Swift, S.C.: "Calculations of Circulating Mud Temperatures," *JPT* (June 1970) 670.

15. Wooley, G.R.: "Computing Downhole Temperatures in Circulation, Injection, and Production Wells," *JPT* (September 1980) 1509.

16. Bullard, E.C.: "The Time Necessary for a Bore Hole to Attain Temperature Equilibrium," *Monthly Not. Roy. Astr. Soc., Geophys. Suppl.* (1947) **5**, No. 5, 127.

17. Dowdle, W. L. and Cobb, W. M.: "Static Formation Temperature From Well Logs–An Empirical Method," *JPT* (November 1975) 1326.

18. Horner, D.R.: "Pressure Build-Up in Wells," *Proc.*, Third World Pet. Cong., The Hague (1951) Sec. II, 503; *Pressure Analysis Methods*, Reprint Series, SPE, Richardson, Texas (1967) **9**, 25.

19. Hasan, A.R. and Kabir, C.S.: "Static Reservoir Temperature Determination From Transient Data After Mud Circulation," *SPEDC* (March 1994) 17.

20. Cao, S., Lerche, I., and Hermanrud, C.: "Formation Temperature Estimation by Inversion of Borehole Measurements," *Geophysics* (July 1988) **53**, No. 7, 979.

21. Shen, P. Y. and Beck, A. E.: "Stabilization of Bottomhole Temperature With Finite Circulation Time and Fluid Flow," *Geophys. J. R. Astr. Soc.* (1986) **86**, No. 1, 63.

22. Roux, B., Sanyal, S. K., and Brown, S. L.: "An Improved Approach to Estimating True Reservoir Temperature From Transient Temperature Data," paper SPE 8888 presented at the 1980 SPE California Regional Meeting, Los Angeles, 9–11 April.

23. Kabir, C.S. *et al.*: "Establishing Geothermal Gradient Using a New Static-Temperature Analysis Method," paper SPE 38667 presented at the 1997 SPE Annual Technical Conference and Exhibition, San Antonio, Texas, 5–8 October.

24. Clark, A.R. and Perkins, T.K.: "Wellbore and Near-Surface Hydraulics of a Blown-Out Oil Well," *JPT* (November 1981) 2181.

25. Fan, J., Shi, Tai-He, and Lian, Zhang-Gui: "A Dynamic Model and Simulation for Killing of Empty Hole Blowout," paper SPE 49963 presented at the 1996 Asia Pacific Oil and Gas Conference and Exhibition, Perth, Australia, 12–14 October.

26. Hasan, A.R., Kabir, C.S., and Lin, D.: "Modeling Wellbore Dynamics During Oil Well Blowout," paper SPE 64644 presented at the 2000 SPE International Oil and Gas Conference and Exhibition, Beijing, 7–10 November.

27. Wallis, G.B.: *One-Dimensional Two-Phase Flow*, McGraw-Hill Book Co. Inc., New York City (1969) 25.

28. Shirie, J.W. and Seubold, J.G.: "Length of Supersonic Core in High-Speed Jets," *AIAA J.* (November 1967) **5**, No. 11, 2062.

29. Hasan, A.R., Kabir, C.S., and Wang, X: "Wellbore Two-Phase Flow and Heat Transfer During Transient Testing," *SPEJ* (June 1998) 174.

30. Kabir, C.S., Ainley, C.M., and Brown, D.R.: "An Analytic Simulator for Rapid Forecasting Rate Behavior of Oil Wells," paper SPE 36725 presented at the 1996 SPE Annual Technical Conference and Exhibition, Denver, 6–9 October.

31. Oudeman, P.: "Analysis of Surface and Wellbore Hydraulics Provides Key to Efficient Blowout Control," paper SPE 36485 presented at the 1996 SPE Annual Technical Conference and Exhibition, Denver, 6–9 October.

SI Metric Conversion Factors

acre $\times$ 4.046 873	E + 03	= m^2
°API	141.5/(131.5 + °API)	= g/cm^3
bbl $\times$ 1.589 873	E $-$ 01	= m^3
Btu $\times$ 1.055 056	E + 00	= kJ
Btu/(hr-ft^2-°F) $\times$ 5.678 263	E + 00	= W/(m$^2\cdot$K)
Btu/lbm $\times$ 2.326*	E + 03	= J/kg
Btu/(lbm-°F) $\times$ 4.186 8*	E + 03	= J/(kg·K)
cp $\times$ 1.0*	E $-$ 03	= Pa s
ft $\times$ 3.048*	E $-$ 01	= m
ft^2 $\times$ 9.290 304*	E $-$ 02	= m^2
ft^3 $\times$ 2.831 685	E $-$ 02	= m^3
ft/sec^2 $\times$ 3.048*	E $-$ 01	= m/s^2
°F	(°F $-$ 32)/1.8	= °C
in. $\times$ 2.54*	E + 00	= cm
lbf $\times$ 4.448 222	E + 00	= N
lbm $\times$ 4.535 924	E $-$ 01	= kg
lbm/ft^3 $\times$ 1.601 846	E + 01	= kg/m^3
lbm/ft-hr $\times$ 4.133 789	E $-$ 04	= Pa·s
lbm/hr $\times$ 1.259 979	E $-$ 04	= kg/s
psi $\times$ 6.894 757	E + 00	= kPa

* Conversion factor is exact.

Chapter 9
Production Operations

9.1 Systems Analysis

9.1.1 Introduction. The systems or nodal analysis as practiced today is rooted in Gilbert's[1] pioneering work of 1954. Studies[2-4] done in the 1980's laid the foundation of the modern systems analysis. In a conventional systems analysis, a steady-state two-phase model is used to simulate the wellbore flow behavior and an empirical correlation,[5] which based on Darcy flow, describes the reservoir's inflow performance. This approach has served the industry quite well. Many texts[6-8] have elucidated this item; therefore, we will not repeat here. Rather, we provide some insights that will improve flow simulation in both the reservoir and wellbore.

This section also explores how surface and downhole data gathering can be coordinated and the systems analysis be performed at the same time, leading to superior understanding of the behavior of a coupled wellbore-reservoir system. Finally, we introduce the concept of seamless-systems analysis, which allows one to model elements of the wellbore and reservoir as an integrated system, rather than in discrete nodes.

9.1.2 Conventional Systems Analysis. Ordinarily, systems analysis relies on forward steady-state, two-phase flow calculation from such input parameters as wellhead pressure and temperature, tubular ID, flow rates of each phase, and the like. If measured downhole pressure and/or rate data are available, the pressure traverse is matched before projecting well behavior at other wellhead choke settings. While this approach is practiced routinely, attention to details often reveal some of the uncertainties associated with the analysis and the potential pitfalls. Problems compound in systems where pressure drops in the reservoir and wellbore are in the same order of magnitude.

Let us examine some of the uncertainties associated with any systems analysis. While matching performance of a production test, changes in gas/oil ratio (GOR) is perhaps the most popular of them all. Modest changes in GOR are often justified because of the inherent errors associated with rate measurements, gas in particular. Use of a standard pressure/volume/temperature (PVT) correlation is another source of error. In particular, if the oil's bubblepoint pressure occurs in the wellbore, matching this pressure is of great significance before successfully mimicking the entire pressure profile. Other sources of error stem from unstable wellhead

rates, assumptions of linear wellbore fluid-temperature profiles, computations from top down rather than bottom up, among others. Besides wellbore flow simulation, flow in the reservoir can introduce a great deal of uncertainty. Presence of non-Darcy flow, flow contributions from other layers at larger drawdowns, and disproportionate volumes of gas or water at larger drawdowns are some of the problems one may encounter.

What is disconcerting is that matching wellhead pressure or a wellbore-pressure profile for a given rate is no guarantee that the well will behave any better at other rates. In other words, calibration does not assure superior performance projection, which runs counter to conventional wisdom. This point is made amply clear when we examine **Fig. 9.1.** Here, a match was obtained at a p_{wh} of 529 psia with the Hagedorn-Brown[9] correlation. With decreased p_{wh} or increased choke settings, the mismatch becomes quite apparent.

This mismatch problem is further highlighted by **Fig. 9.2,** showing another field example. In these two figures, the equations describing flow in the reservoir have the following forms:

Forchheimer equation:

$$\Delta p = \bar{p} - p_{wf} = a_t q + b q^2 , \quad\quad\quad\quad (9.1)$$

and Backpressure/Fetkovich equation:

$$q = C(\Delta p)^n \quad\quad\quad\quad\quad\quad (9.2)$$

The Darcy equation has the same form as Eq. 9.2, with the exponent, n, set at 1.0. Note that in the examples shown, we used Δp instead of Δp^2 because of single-phase flow in the reservoir.

We surmise that the logical explanation for seemingly unpredictable behavior, with different choke settings, is rooted in two-phase flow modeling in the wellbore. That is, a correlation may represent a given flow condition better than others yet may do an unsatisfactory job in mimicking the pressure behavior when flow patterns change under different choke settings. Let us explore practical implications of the uncertainty of the p_{wf} calculation from wellhead data.

Often, engineers estimate p_{wf} en route to computing inflow performance relationship when direct measurements are unavailable. While this practice is acceptable in systems

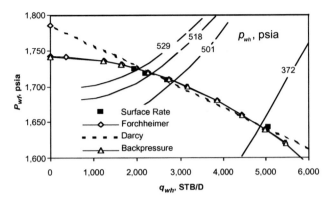

Fig. 9.1—Systems analysis for Well B-OF8.

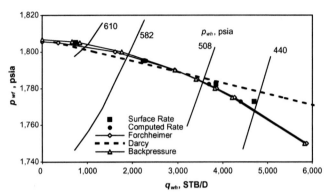

Fig. 9.2—Systems analysis for Well B-FN9.

where large reservoir pressure-drop occurs because of unfavorable reservoir flow characteristics,[10] problems arise for systems where pressure drops in the formation and wellbore are comparable. Let us illustrate this point with a case study. Wellbore pressure-drop calculations on some 109 wells in a multidarcy reservoir show that, among other correlations, the widely used Hagedorn-Brown correlation[9] yields the lowest average error of 3.17%. **Fig. 9.3** compares the measured p_{wf} with those calculated. By all measures this error is very low. Yet, its implication may be quite serious. For instance, **Table 9.1** exemplifies the problem by showing the error analysis for a single well, assuming just 3% error. For wells not conforming to the 3% error band, the absolute error in the productivity index, J_p, will be much higher. The main problem stems from the error in the p_{wf} calculation (± 50 psi), which is in the same order as the Δp (~91 psi) itself. Uncertainty in $\bar{p}$ is, of course, another source for error.

9.1.3 Establishing Reservoir Flow Behavior With Pressure-Rate Data.
As we stated earlier, the conventional systems analysis relies on the use of Vogel's method[5] for computing a well's inflow performance relationship (IPR). Once the bubblepoint pressure is established, the method requires measuring or inferring flowing bottomhole pressure for the corresponding wellhead rate to establish IPR during pseudo- or steady-state flow in the reservoir. Below the bubblepoint pressure, the Vogel-type expression is given by

$$\frac{q}{q_m} = 1 - 0.2\frac{p_{wf}}{\bar{p}} - 0.8\left(\frac{p_{wf}}{\bar{p}}\right)^2 . \quad \ldots\ldots\ldots\ldots (9.3)$$

Ordinarily, one rate suffices to describe the IPR, once q_m is evaluated from Eq. 9.3 for a corresponding p_{wf}-q data set, with known system $\bar{p}$. However, this method presupposes that flow in the reservoir obeys Darcy's law. In other words, presence of non-Darcy flow can potentially introduce large errors in systems analysis.

Historically, non-Darcy flow has been associated with gas wells. However, a number of studies has shown that non-Darcy flow can occur in oil reservoirs. We will now explore the approach that establishes the Darcy or non-Darcy characteristic of the reservoir flow behavior using transient testing. Although a multirate transient test can be conducted in a stand-alone mode, data gathering can often occur in conjunction with production logging (PL).

Conventional practices of systems analysis, transient testing, and flow profiling generally lack coordination to maximize information gathering. Although PL's are run routinely to diagnose wellbore flow problems, their full potentials often go unexplored. Ordinarily, flow and shut-in passes are recorded to discern flow contributions from completion intervals. Because various choke settings cause changes in rates, stationary measurements of transient pressure and rate data have the potential for yielding reservoir parameters for a single zone or a layered-reservoir system. Tests can be conducted so that flow profiling and transient downhole pressure-rate data gathering is done in a single operation. Ref. 11 presents details of the test procedure.

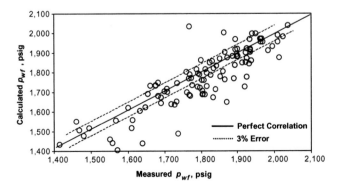

Fig. 9.3—Comparison of measured and computed p_{wf}.

TABLE 9.1—ERROR ANALYSIS OF J_p, WELL D-78			
	Measured	p_{wf} Error, −3%	p_{wf} Error, 3%
$\bar{p}$, psig	1,841	1,841	1,841
p_{wf}, psig	1,738	1,685.86	1,790.14
Δp, psi	103	155.14	50.86
q, STB/D	4,956	4,956	4,956
J_p, STB/D-psi	48.12	31.945	97.44
Error in J_p, %	0	−33.6	102.5

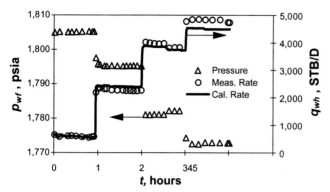

Fig. 9.4—Test history, Well B-148.

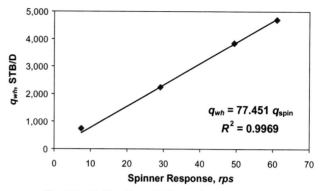

Fig. 9.5—Calibration of inline spinner response.

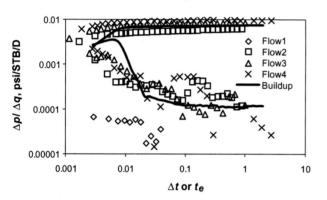

Fig. 9.6—Log/log diagnosis of all transients.

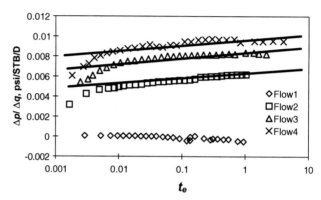

Fig. 9.7—Semilog analysis separates skin components.

Field Example 9.1. This example is abstracted from Ref. 11. The well was flowing on a 36/64-in. choke, and the test was carefully done to avoid altering the pseudosteady-state flow condition. Flowing gradient data were gathered en route to reaching the desired depth by running flowing passes across perforations at various tool speeds. Thereafter, the tool string was set within the tubing, and all transient-test data were gathered by keeping the entire PL tool string within the tubing.

Fig. 9.4 presents the test history without the two-hour buildup at the end of the four-hour flow-after-flow (FAF) period for clarity. Also shown in Fig. 9.4 is the computed rate history, generated after diagnosing the model and estimating its parameters. Measurements of both surface and sandface rates allowed calibration of inline spinner, used for collecting sandface rates. **Fig. 9.5** presents a calibration curve reflecting the expected linear trend of two independent measurements. This calibration line was used to convert the spinner response to volumetric surface rate recorded at discrete time intervals, shown in Fig. 9.4.

Model diagnosis entails constructing the log/log pressure/convolution-derivative graph of all transients, shown in **Fig. 9.6.** Despite the use of quality spinner data, scatter is quite evident. However, the buildup signature, shown by the solid line, presents the customary radial-flow response. Separation of pressure curves is a strong indication of rate-dependent skin, however.

Fig. 9.7, presenting the same data on a semilog graph, clearly indicates separation of various flow period data with progressively higher rates. Data for the first flow period do

not conform to the expected positive-slope trend. Scrutiny of absolute rates suggests that the well was not in a very stable-flowing condition at the 24/64-in. choke setting, thereby explaining the discrepancy.

The analysis of individual transients, shown in Fig. 9.7, allowed separation of static from dynamic or non-Darcy skin. **Fig. 9.8** presents the total skin-rate analysis. Interestingly enough, the conventional buildup analysis estimates the total composite skin, shown in **Fig. 9.9.** In absence of multirate tests, diagnosing non-Darcy skin becomes a nearly impossible proposition.

To check the results of the multirate analysis, we constructed a graph in accord with Eq. E-4 in Appendix E. Appendix E presents the details of both pressure and rate superposition equations used in this example. **Fig. 9.10** corroborates the quality of computed rates. We estimated that at

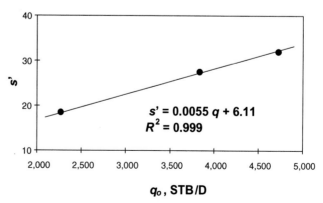

Fig. 9.8—Skin analysis shows significant non-Darcy effect.

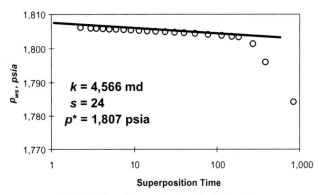

Fig. 9.9—Semilog analysis of buildup data.

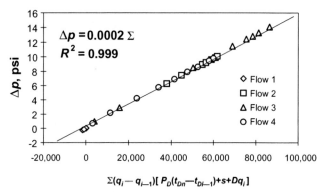

Fig. 9.10—Validation of computed rates.

the highest drawdown, corresponding to the fourth flow period, additional production of about 300 STB/D occurred from the upper completion interval, shown in **Fig. 9.11**. Actually, there was evidence of some flow from the upper interval, which has inferior flow characteristics than the main interval, even at 2,811 STB/D of total production. With this body of information, one can attempt to get flow properties of the tighter upper layer by using the layered-reservoir analysis.

This example demonstrates how transient data can be collected and analyzed for estimating reservoir parameters. Once parameters are estimated, characterizing a reservoir's inflow performance becomes the next logical step. As shown in Fig. 9.1, the IPR can be generated using three methods: the straight-line method, assuming Darcy flow above the bubble-point, and the Forchheimer and backpressure analyses for non-Darcy flow. Note that the average pressure calculation of 1,807 psia from the non-Darcy analysis corroborates that estimated from the semilog (Fig. 9.9) analysis, thereby lending credence to the non-Darcy flow parameter estimation.

9.1.4 Seamless Systems Analysis. As shown in Figs. 9.1 and 9.2, individual nodes (across which pressure drop occurs), such as the reservoir and wellbore, require separate analysis in a conventional systems analysis. That is, the final output at

the wellhead is determined by the intersection of the IPR with the tubing performance curve at a given wellhead pressure. Other nodes, such as completion, surface and downhole chokes, may be added to the analysis, if desired. In other words, various nodes can be pieced together to make up the complete system. Note that because of steady-state flow simulation at each node, rate instability or any transient process cannot be captured. We now present the notion of seamless systems analysis.

In this systems-analysis approach, various nodes of reservoir, completion, and wellbore are treated as parts of a contiguous unit. This treatment is possible when we use a coupled transient wellbore-reservoir simulator, such as those discussed in Chap. 7. The advantage of this approach is that various everyday unsteady-state flow situations can be addressed to obtain a realistic picture of the well's ability to handle a given situation. Some of these examples include, among others, flow instability, triggered by reduced choke size; complex heat flow problems, induced by simultaneous flow in both tubing and annulus or in offshore wells; and wellbore unloading upon well shut-in. Conventional systems analysis is clearly not designed to handle these and other transient problems.

Field Example 9.2. The advantages of the seamless systems analysis is emphasized by the following field example involving the reservoir and wellbore described earlier. Forward simulations were performed using the estimated reservoir parameters (k, s, $\bar{p}$, D) and the well description to match the observed wellbore data, collected during flow and shut-in conditions. **Fig. 9.12** shows the

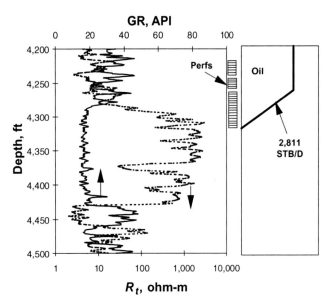

Fig. 9.11—Openhole and production log traces, Well B-OF8.

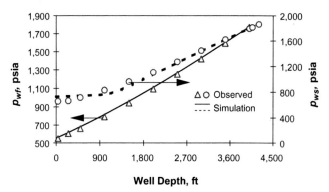

Fig. 9.12—Matching pressure profiles during flow and shut-in cases.

FLUID FLOW AND HEAT TRANSFER IN WELLBORES

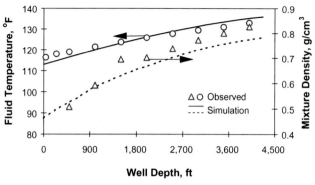

Fig. 9.13—Matching fluid temperature and density profiles.

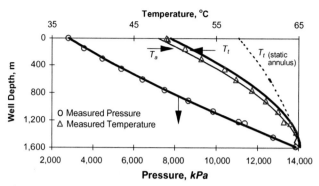

Fig. 9.14—Matching wellbore temperature and pressure data, Well A28.

match of wellbore pressure profiles during both flow and shut-in conditions. On the other hand, **Fig. 9.13** presents the fluid temperature and density profiles during the flowing condition. No adjustments of input parameters were made to achieve the matches.

In these transient simulations, we observed dominating influence of bubbly and slug flows. To do these simulations, we modified the simulator,[12] as discussed earlier in Chap. 7, to include non-Darcy flow effects. Because data from only one flow period were available, we were able to match data from that flow period. However, the ability to reproduce the pressure behavior during shut-in condition lends confidence in the modeling approach.

We present one other field example where complex heat transfer occurs because of simultaneous production in the tubing and in tubing-casing annulus. In this case, we present just the steady-state flow simulation in the wellbore to underscore the need for an appropriate heat-transfer model to solve a given problem.

This well produces up the tubing and annulus. Field measurements were made in the tubing string during flowing condition at various depths, called stations. At each station, 15 minutes were allowed for thermal equilibration to occur between the external temperature probe with its surrounding fluids.

Fig. 9.14 shows that the model, discussed earlier in Chap. 6 and represented by the solid line, successfully reproduces the measured tubing fluid temperature within engineering accuracy. The temperature difference between the tubing and annulus is small because flow in both strings promotes heat transfer. Note that the production of annular fluid causes higher dissipation of heat because of forced convection than would be the case had the annular fluid been stationary. The dotted line captures the trend for this hypothetical case of no production through the annulus. Also shown in Fig. 9.14 is the match of pressure data with the two-phase flow models of Ansari *et al.*[13] and Hasan and Kabir.[14]

As Fig. 9.14 shows, both the Hasan-Kabir and Ansari *et al.* models performed well in reproducing the field data. In fact, these two models produced indistinguishable traces. That is because most of the string is dominated by the bubbly flow pattern, straddled by single-phase flow toward the bottom and slug flow at the top. As shown by Ansari *et al.*, these two models perform very similarly in the bubbly flow regime.

9.1.5 Systems Analysis Summary.
Conventional systems analysis as practiced today is intended for steady-state flow. Although it works well for common usage, problems arise when heat flow becomes complex owing to completion and/or when non-Darcy flow occurs in the reservoir. In Sec. 9.1, we discuss a method for collecting and analyzing transient data for generating an appropriate IPR for a well. Thereafter, we present the notion of seamless systems analysis that requires the use of a transient wellbore-reservoir simulator. In this approach, complex fluid and heat flow situations can be handled for either unsteady-state or steady-state flow in a rigorous fashion.

9.2 Temperature Profiles in Gas-Lift Wells

9.2.1 Introduction. In a continuous-flow gas-lift operation, gas is injected down the annulus into the tubing near the top of perforations to aerate the liquid column, thereby providing the necessary stimulus for fluid flow. Because the volumetric gas rate is dependent on both the pressure and temperature at the depth of injection, accurate knowledge of these entities cannot be overemphasized for an efficient lift. In particular, the behavior of the nitrogen gas, charged in the dome, is critically dependent on the temperature estimation for the optimal performance of the bellows-charged gas-lift valves.

Gas-lift technology has evolved and matured over the years since the pioneering works of Poettmann-Carpenter[15] and Bertuzzi *et al.*[16] in the early 1950's. This lift technique ranks second to sucker-rod pumping based on the number of installations around the world. Although the main design criterion revolves around minimizing the energy; that is, compressor horsepower, for gas injection at a certain depth for the maximum lift, systematic approaches have emerged[17-19] for optimizing gas-lift design. Rapid development has also been made in the design of various types of gas-lift valves,[4,20] such as pressure-controlled, fluid-controlled, and throttled. In particular, wireline-retrievability of these valves has made this lift technique very attractive, especially in offshore wells.

To design a gas-lift system from the viewpoints of both fluid flow and valve mechanics, an accurate knowledge of fluid temperature in both strings is very desirable. Empirical methods[21,22] are available for computing temperature profiles in the tubing, while assuming a linear temperature profile in the annulus experiencing gas injection. Ordinarily, these methods are not always reliable because of their empirical basis. Methods discussed earlier in Chap. 5, Sec. 5.4 apply to self-flowing wells and are not directly applicable because the gas temperature in the annulus needs estimating.

In this section, we present a mechanistic model to compute temperature profiles for fluids in both conduits of a vertical or a deviated well. The coupled tubing/annulus/formation heat flow problem is solved so that simultaneous solutions are obtained as a function of elapsed time and well depth. Unsteady heat transfer is considered in the formation, while steady heat transfer is assumed in the conduits. This material is abstracted from Ref. 23.

9.2.2 Mathematical Model. During a continuous-flow gas-lift operation, the gas is injected down the annulus to aerate the liquid to be lifted up the tubing. The physical situation, as shown schematically in **Fig. 9.15**, is very similar to the case of production through tubing and annulus described in Chap. 6, Sec. 6.2.1. We may write energy balance[23] for the annular gas contained in a differential element, dz, in terms of heat transferred from the formation to the fluid, Q, from the annulus fluid to the tubing fluid, Q_{ta}, fluid enthalpy, H, and its potential and kinetic energies as

$$H_a(z) + \frac{zg\sin\theta}{g_cJ} + \frac{v^2(z)}{g_cJ} + \frac{Q}{w_a}dz$$

$$= H_a(z+dz) + \frac{(z+dz)g\sin\theta}{g_cJ} + \frac{v^2(z+dz)}{g_cJ} + \frac{Q_{ta}}{w_a}dz \cdot$$

$$\dots\dots\dots\dots\dots\dots (9.4)$$

Rewriting Eq. 9.4,

$$\frac{dH_a}{dz} + \frac{g\sin\theta}{g_cJ} + \frac{v_a}{g_cJ}\frac{dv_a}{dz} = \frac{Q-Q_{ta}}{w} \cdot \dots\dots\dots\dots (9.5)$$

In Eq. 9.5, Q is the heat transferred from the formation to the annular fluid given by (see Eq. 5.20)

$$Q = w_a c_{pa} L_R (T_{ei} - T_a) \cdot \dots\dots\dots\dots\dots (9.6)$$

Heat transferred from the annular fluid to that in the tubing, Q_{ta}, is given by (see Eq. 6.2)

$$Q_{ta} = \frac{w_a c_{pa}}{B}(T_a - T_t) , \dots\dots\dots\dots\dots (9.7)$$

where $B = \frac{w_a c_{pa}}{2\pi r_t U_t} \cdot \dots\dots\dots\dots\dots\dots (9.8)$

Combining Eqs. 9.5 through 9.8 and expressing enthalpy change in terms of changes in temperature and pressure, $dH = c_p dT - C_J c_p dp$ (Eq. 5.14 where C_J is the Joule-Thompson coefficient), we obtain

$$c_{pa}\frac{dT_a}{dz} - \frac{C_J c_{ga}}{J}\frac{dp}{dz} + \frac{g\sin\theta}{g_cJ} + \frac{v_a}{g_cJ}\frac{dv_a}{dz}$$

$$= c_{pa}L_R(T_{ei} - T_a) + \frac{c_{pa}}{B}(T_t - T_a) \cdot \dots\dots (9.9)$$

Following the arguments we made in Chap. 6, Sec.6.2.1, we combine the insignificant terms as D_a and obtain

$$c_{pa}\frac{dT_a}{dz} + D_a = L_R c_{pa}(T_{ei} - T_a) + \frac{c_{pa}}{B}(T_t - T_a) ,$$

$$\dots\dots\dots\dots\dots\dots (9.10)$$

where $D_a = -\frac{C_J c_{pa}}{J}\frac{dp_a}{dz} + \frac{g\sin\theta}{g_cJ} + \frac{v_a}{g_cJ}\frac{dv_a}{dz} \cdot \dots (9.11)$

An energy balance for the tubular two-phase mixture yields[23]

$$c_{pt}\frac{dT_t}{dz} - \frac{C_J c_{pt}}{J}\frac{dp}{dz} + \frac{g\sin\theta}{g_cJ}$$

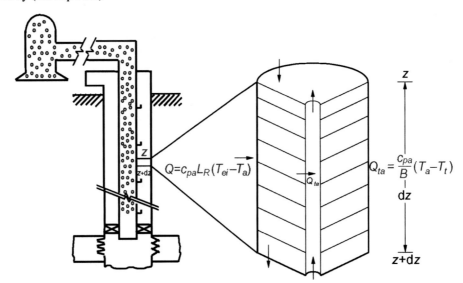

Fig. 9.15—Schematic of heat balance for tubulars and formation in a gas-lift well.

TABLE 9.2—WELL, FORMATION, AND FLUID DATA OF SYNTHETIC EXAMPLES

Parameters	Examples 1 & 2	Example 3
Total well depth, ft	15,000	4,500
Casing diameter, ft	0.35	0.35
Tubing diameter, ft	0.23	0.23
Mass fraction of gas in the tubing	0.10	0.676
Formation density, lbm/ft³	165	165
Formation heat capacity, Btu/(lbm-°F)	0.20	0.20
Producing time, hr	44	44
Specific heat of oil, Btu/(lbm-°F)	0.4	1.0
Specific heat of gas, Btu/(lbm-°F)	0.25	0.25
Tubing overall heat-transfer coefficient, Btu/(hr-°F-ft)	10.0	5.0
Annular overall heat-transfer coefficient, Btu/(hr-°F-ft)	4.0	2.0
Earth thermal conductivity, Btu/(hr-°F-ft)	1.3	1.3
Geothermal gradient, °F/ft	0.0127	0.012
Bottomhole earth temperature, °F	250	124
Surface earth temperature, °F	59.5	60
Surface gas inlet temperature, °F	75	75

$$+\frac{v_t}{g_c J}\frac{dv_t}{dz}=\frac{w_a c_{pa}}{w_t B}\left(T_t-T_a\right). \qquad \dots\dots\dots (9.12)$$

In other words,

$$c_{pt}\frac{dT_t}{dz}+D_t=\frac{w_a c_{pa}}{w_t B}\left(T_t-T_a\right), \qquad \dots\dots\dots (9.13)$$

where D_t is the term analogous to D_a for the tubing fluid. Combining Eqs. 9.10 and 9.13 and simplifying and defining $B'=\dfrac{c_{pt}}{c_{pa}}\dfrac{Bw_t}{w_a}$, as detailed in Ref. 23, we obtain

$$\frac{B'}{L_R}\frac{d^2T_t}{dz^2}+B''\frac{dT_t}{dz}-T_t+T_{es}+g_G z\sin\theta+D'=0,$$
$$\dots\dots\dots (9.14)$$

where $B''=B'+\dfrac{B'}{L_R B}-\dfrac{1}{L_R}, \qquad \dots\dots\dots (9.15)$

and $D'=B'\dfrac{D_t}{c_{pt}}+\dfrac{D_t}{c_{pt}}\dfrac{B'}{L_R B}-\dfrac{D_a}{L_R c_{pa}} \qquad \dots\dots\dots (9.16)$

The term D', comprised of D_a, D_t, and other terms, is quite small and may be neglected. For example, in D_a, the second term with (dp/dz) of the annular gas, is usually very small in all cases. The kinetic term in the high-annulus-pressure environment turns out to be negative and tends to balance the potential-energy term. For instance, for injection of methane at surface conditions of 100°F and 1,000 psi, the sum of the kinetic and potential energy terms amount to 0.001496 Btu/lbm-ft. By contrast, the first term ($c_{pa}dT_a/dz$) has a value of 0.221 Btu/lbm-ft. Similar arguments for simplification also apply to Eq. 9.12. The final solutions of Eq. 9.14 are presented here, and some of the details are shown in Appendix E.

$$T_t=\alpha e^{\lambda_1 z}+\beta e^{\lambda_2 z}+g_G z\sin\theta+B''g_G\sin\theta+T_{es}+D',$$
$$\dots\dots\dots (9.17)$$

and $T_a=T_t-B'\dfrac{dT_t}{dz}=\left(1-\lambda_1 B'\right)\alpha e^{\lambda_1 z}$

$$+\left(1-\lambda_2 B'\right)\beta e^{\lambda_2 z}+g_G\sin\theta\left(B''-B'\right)+g_G z\sin\theta+T_{es}+D'.$$
$$\dots\dots\dots (9.18)$$

These expressions for the annular- and tubing-fluid temperatures are exactly the same as those for the case of production through the annulus and tubing, as shown in Chap. 6 (Eqs. 6.12 and 6.13). However, because the annular-fluid flows in a direction opposite to that in the tubing, unlike the case shown in Chap. 6, the expressions for the various parameters are different. Careful examination of the equations for these parameters, presented in Appendices B and E, is worthwhile.

9.2.3 Factors Affecting Temperature Profiles. In this section, we explore the sensitivity of overall-heat-transfer coefficients and production/injection rates on fluid temperature profiles during steady-state gas-lift operation in vertical wells.

Heat-Transfer Coefficient—Example One. Consider a vertical well with an oil rate of 9,286 STB/D and a gas injection of 10% of the total mass in the tubing string. To reflect the low-heat-transfer coefficient for flowing gas in the annulus, let us assign a value of 4 Btu/(hr⁻¹-ft⁻¹-°F⁻¹) for U_a (for heat transfer between formation and annulus) and 10 Btu/(hr⁻¹-ft⁻¹-°F⁻¹) for U_t (for heat transfer between the annulus and the tubing). **Table 9.2** presents all the relevant data for this example and the two other examples that we discuss.

Temperature profiles so calculated are shown in **Fig. 9.16.** The figure shows that the fluid temperature remains high throughout the length of the tubing. This high-tubing-fluid temperature (T_t) is precipitated by the annular gas, which reduces the overall-heat-transfer coefficient, thereby permitting the produced fluid mixture to retain most of its high entering enthalpy. As a consequence of high T_t and low overall-heat-transfer rate, the annular gas also is generally at a high temperature, except in the area close to the wellhead.

Figs. 9.16 and **9.17** show the effect of changing heat-transfer coefficients for the annulus and tubing. As expected, Fig. 9.17 shows that when both U_a and U_t are reduced by

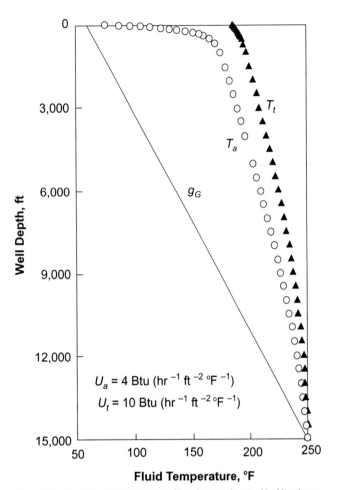

Fig. 9.16—Fluid temperature profiles for moderate U_a, U_t values.

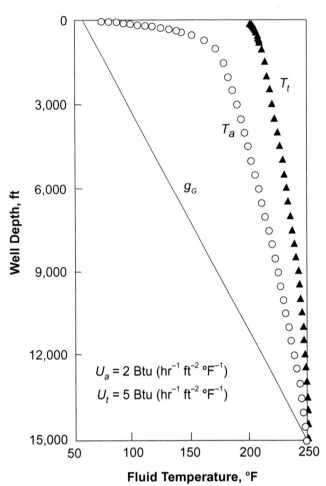

Fig. 9.17—Fluid temperature profiles for low U_a, U_t values.

50%, the tubing fluid temperature, and to some extent, the annular gas temperature (T_a) becomes somewhat higher than they were in Fig. 9.16. However, the U_t value also makes the temperature difference between the tubing and annulus larger. In **Fig. 9.18**, we have $U_a=4$ and $U_t=20$ Btu/(hr^{-1}-ft^{-1}-°F^{-1}). The higher value of U_t causes T_a to approach T_t more closely.

The impact of low-gas-injection rate on temperature profiles is explored by keeping the same production rate of 9,286 STB/D but with a gas injection rate of only 5% of the total mass. **Fig. 9.19** shows that the temperature profiles are similar to those shown in Fig. 9.16 except that they are slightly higher. The T_a is now closer to T_t because of a lower mass rate in the annulus, leading to a sharper rise near the wellhead because of increased heat transfer from the tubing fluid.

Flow Rate. Conduit fluid temperatures, given by Eq. 9.17 and 9.18, are influenced by flow rate because the parameters L_R, B, B', B'', λ_1, and λ_2 used in these expressions, are strong functions of rate. This influence of flow rate is apparent in **Fig. 9.20**, which shows that a decrease in annular-injection rate results in an increase in both T_a and T_t. In particular, the values of λ_1 and λ_2 (Eqs. E-11 and E-12, in Appendix E) are much smaller at low rates than at higher rates. Because $e^{\lambda z}$ may be expressed as $1+\lambda z$ for low values of λz, expressions

for the tubing- and annular-fluid temperatures may be simplified to the form,

$$T_t = \alpha + B'' g_G \sin\theta + T_{es} + (\alpha\lambda_1 + g_G)z\sin\theta \, , \tag{9.19}$$

and
$$T_a = (1-\lambda_1 B')\alpha + (B''-B')g_T \sin\theta + T_{ew}$$
$$+\left[(1-\lambda_1 B')\alpha\lambda_1 + g_G\right]z\sin\theta . \tag{9.20}$$

Thus, T_t and T_a become linear with z with slopes represented by the terms in the parentheses of Eqs. 9.19 and 9.20. Because λ_1 and λ_2 are small, the values of these slopes are very close to g_G, and T_t and T_a are lines parallel to the geothermal gradient.

Example Two. Fig. 9.20 shows the temperature profile for a gas-lift operation with 431 STB/D of oil-production rate. The gas-injection rate was kept at 10% of the total mass produced. Table 9.2 presents the pertinent parameters. Both T_t and T_a profiles in Fig. 9.20 appear to be parallel to the geothermal temperature for the entire well. Exception occurs at very close to the bottomhole, where λz is no longer small because of large z. Small values of α, β, λ_1, and λ_2 cause the slopes of these lines to be approxi-

FLUID FLOW AND HEAT TRANSFER IN WELLBORES

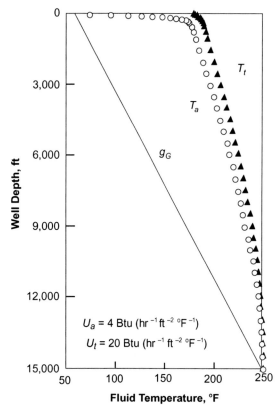

Fig. 9.18—Fluid temperature profiles for high U_t values.

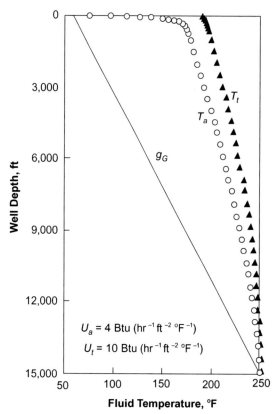

Fig. 9.19—Influence of low-mass fraction of gas on fluid-temperature profiles.

mately equal to the geothermal gradient and ultimately T_a and T_t profiles become close to each other.

Example Three. No field data of T_a profiles have been reported because of the obvious difficulty of such measure-ments. Nonetheless, we selected a case reported in Ref. 16 to capture the essence of a field example. While the flow rates and tubular dimensions are used verbatim, the heat-transfer coefficients are assumed values. Again, Table 9.2 presents all the pertinent data.

The sensitivity of different T_D models[24,25] on fluid tem-perature profiles is shown in **Fig. 9.21**. As discussed else-

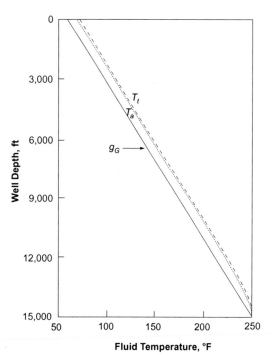

Fig. 9.20—Influence of low-oil rate upon fluid-temperature pro-files.

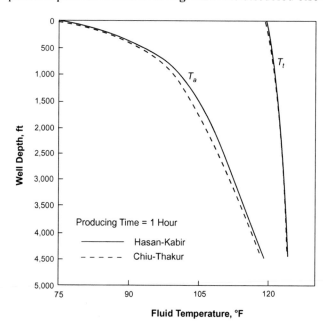

Fig. 9.21—Impact of T_D models on fluid-temperature profiles.

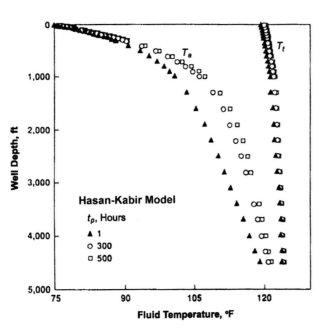

Fig. 9.22—Influence of producing time on fluid-temperature profiles.

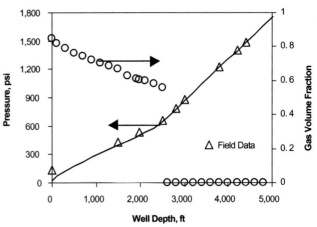

Fig. 9.23—Matching tubing pressure with two-phase model, Thompson well.

where,[26] different inner-boundary conditions of the two models results in some difference in the T_a profile where the maximum temperature change is experienced. However, no perceptible difference exists for the T_t profile because the wellhead and bottomhole temperature difference is minimal. Although this figure is generated for only after one hour into the injection period, a similar trend persists for larger times.

Fig. 9.22 illustrates that the temperature profiles do change with injection time, particularly in the annulus. The significance of the highly nonlinear $T_a(t)$ profile is that the characteristics of the transfer valves, located at shallower depths, can be fine tuned for the optimal performance. Therefore, the model allows one to take advantage of annular temperature computation, both as a function of time and depth.

One readily observes that the temperature profiles have different starting points at the well bottom, unlike those

shown earlier. Both larger gas mass and shorter well depth translate into a cooler annular fluid than the previous cases when heat-transfer characteristics remain unchanged.

Field Examples 9.3 and 9.4. We present two field examples to show application of the model discussed here. These examples are taken from the published work of Kanu.[27] The pressure-traverse match is shown in **Fig. 9.23** for the Thompson well. This match was obtained by using the Hasan-Kabir two-phase model discussed earlier in Chap. 3. As shown, large discontinuity in the in-situ gas volume-fraction occurs at 2,500 ft, where the lift gas is introduced through the annulus. Predictably, the high producing gas/liquid ratio (GLR) of 550 scf/STB caused excessive pressure drop toward the wellhead. As Kanu reported, when the GLR was reduced to 221 scf/STB, a 58% gain in total liquid productivity was realized.

The corresponding tubing-temperature profile, both measured and computed, are shown in **Fig. 9.24**. Results of the Shiu-Beggs (SB) correlation[22] are also included in this figure. Both the measured pressure and temperature profiles are in good agreement with the model presented here. However, the same is not true for the SB correlation. As expected, the computed temperature profile, obtained from the proposed model, is quite different at shallower depths in the annulus. **Table 9.3** presents all the parameters used to compute the pressure and temperature traverses.

For the O'Connor well, we reproduced the flowing tubing pressure traverse quite well, as **Fig. 9.25** suggests. **Fig. 9.26** shows that good agreement in temperature occurs at shallower depths, where two-phase flow is prevalent. However, the match suffers below the point of gas injection. Two possible reasons exist for this mismatch. Either the geothermal gradient is different below the point of gas injection, or short-duration station stops did not allow the thermometer to equilibrate with the fluid temperature. Despite this difficulty, both pressure and temperature profiles were reproduced with acceptable accuracy above the point of gas injection, which leads one to do proper design or adjustments of gas-lift valves for optimal performance. Again, we observe large discrepancy between the SB correlation with the measured values.

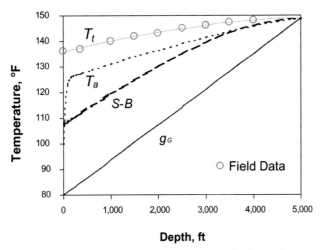

Fig. 9.24—Matching tubing temperature with Eq. 9.17, Thompson well.

TABLE 9.3—WELL, FORMATION, AND FLUID DATA OF FIELD EXAMPLES		
Parameters	O'Connor Well	Thompson Well
Total well depth, ft	4,979	5,019
Depth of gas injection, ft	2,209	2,400
Casing ID, in.	5.0	7.0
Tubing OD, in.	2.5	2.875
Oil + water flow rate, STB/D	3,660	2,080
Mass fraction of gas in the tubing	0.0225	0.0681
Gas/liquid ratio, scf/STB	158	550
Oil + water API gravity	26	10.3
Gas gravity (air=1)	0.60	0.61
Specific heat of liquid, Btu/(lbm-°F)	1.0	1.0
Specific heat of gas, Btu/(lbm-°F)	0.25	0.25
Tubing overall heat-transfer coefficient, Btu/(hr-°F-ft)	10.0	10.0
Annular overall heat-transfer coefficient, Btu/(hr-°F-ft)	1.0	4.0
Earth thermal conductivity, Btu/(hr-°F-ft)	1.30	1.30
Geothermal gradient, °F/ft	0.0159	0.0137
Bottomhole earth temperature, °F	161	149
Surface earth temperature, °F	82	80
Surface gas inlet temperature, °F	100	100

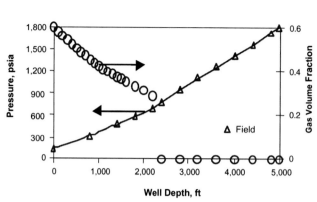

Fig. 9.25—Matching tubing pressure with two-phase model, O'Connor well.

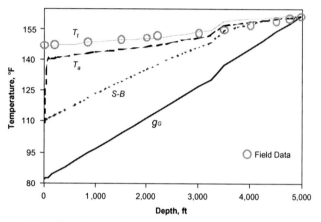

Fig. 9.26—Matching tubing temperature with Eq. 9.17, O'Connor well.

All the parameters used to compute the pressure and temperature profiles are presented in Table 9.3.

We note that low-GLR situations in both cases do not result in large separation of the two temperature profiles at the existing conditions. As Kanu noted, adjustments in the GLR were required to improve the gas-lift performance in both wells. Thus, one must redo the temperature and pressure analysis with the new GLR values to ensure that valve adjustments are made for the revised operating conditions.

Discussion. The intent of this section is to introduce the reader to a mechanistic approach for computing fluid temperature profiles in both conduits. Therefore, by definition, we addressed a very narrow issue that pertains to the design and operation of a gas-lift operation. We hope that this piece of technology can be plugged into a comprehensive software package to facilitate design calculations.

Knowledge of accurate fluid temperature profiles in both flow conduits is critical for gas-lift operations. With the introduction of mechanistic models[28,29] for both valve mechanics and flow through such valves, the importance of fluid temperature modeling has become more relevant than

gas injection at the lowermost valve; that is, the transfer valves required for flow initiation are not considered in this analysis. However, the model presented by Tang *et al.*[30] shows how the dynamic unloading process can be modeled rigorously. Their model adapts many elements of the heat-transfer model discussed here and also the countercurrent flow model discussed in Chap. 4.

In this section, we presented expressions for fluid temperature in both tubing and annulus by analyzing energy transport between the tubular fluids and the formation. Note that the final form of the fluid temperature expressions (Eqs. 9.14 and 9.15) do not contain the well deviation term in an explicit fashion; rather, it manifests itself in terms of geothermal gradient, g_G.

Pressure profile calculations in the annulus, although not shown, indicate that the pressure gradient, dp/dz, is essentially linear although we are dealing with highly nonlinear temperature profiles. Only density inversion will cause a nonlinear pressure profile. Thus, the current practice for calculating the annular gas pressure remains unchanged. However, the pressure gradient will be much different for a deviated wellbore compared to its vertical counterpart.

9.2.4 Temperature Profiles In Gas-Lift Wells Summary. Sec. 9.2 discusses a mechanistic approach to compute flowing fluid temperature profiles in both conduits simultaneously for a continuous-flow gas-lift operation. While formulating, we assumed unsteady heat flow in the formation, but steady heat flow in the conduits. This model can treat either a vertical or a deviated wellbore. The solution is presented in simplified algebraic form for easy implementation in any existing computer model handling gas-lift issues. A limited sensitivity study shows that nonlinearity in the annular-gas-temperature profile is dependent on the mass fraction of gas (GOR) injected into the tubing, well depth, heat-transfer coefficients, and the magnitudes of flow rates in both conduits.

9.3 Wellbore Steam/Water Flow and Surface Metering

9.3.1 Steam Injection.
Previous discussion on heat transfer in Chaps. 5 and 6 pertains to flow of noncondensable fluids in wellbores, which was pioneered by Ramey.[24] In a steamflood project, superheated or saturated steam is injected into oil-bearing formations to reduce oil viscosity, thereby improving the recovery. Injection of condensable steam into a single horizon[31-34] is a common occurrence. Concentric injection down the common wellbore can also occur in more than one sand interval[35] for efficient heat management. **Fig. 9.27** schematically shows the two injection schemes.

As steam travels downward in the wellbore, it loses energy to the surrounding formation. This heat loss may result in condensation with consequent reduction in steam quality and enthalpy. During phase change the temperature of a single-component fluid depends solely on its pressure. Increases in pressure with depth occur owing to the static head of steam. This increased steam pressure will result in rise of temperature, although heat is lost to the formation.

In this section, we present a computational scheme for steady-state flow. For simplicity, we treat the traditional single-string injection scheme, based on the material presented in Chap. 5. Although not shown, one can easily adapt the model presented in Chap. 6 to deal with the concentric injection case.

Mathematical Model. Unlike the earlier treatment of heat-transfer problems in Chaps. 5 and 6, which did not involve occurrence of phase change, simultaneous solution of both the momentum balance and energy balance equations is required for the problem at hand. For convenience, we reproduce the energy-balance equation, Eq. 5.13 from Chap. 5 as

$$\frac{dH}{dz} + \frac{g\sin\theta}{g_c J} + \frac{v}{g_c J}\frac{dv}{dz} = \mp\frac{Q}{w} \ . \ \ldots\ldots\ldots\ldots (9.21)$$

For steady flow systems, the pressure gradient, dp/dz, is balanced by the static head, $\rho g\sin\theta$, the friction head, $\rho f v^2/2d$, and the kinetic head, $(\rho v)(dv/dz)$. Therefore, the momentum balance equation becomes

$$-\frac{dp}{dz} = \rho g\sin\theta + \frac{f\rho v^2}{2d} + \rho v\frac{dv}{dz} \ . \ \ldots\ldots\ldots\ldots (9.22)$$

Here, the friction factor, f, must account for flow of a two-phase mixture. For mixture density, we need to use the appropriate expression given by

$$\rho_m = f_L\rho_L + (1-f_L)\rho_g \ . \ \ldots\ldots\ldots\ldots\ldots (9.23)$$

One can use either the Hasan model,[36] discussed in Chap. 4, Sec. 4.4.2, or the Beggs and Brill correlation[37] for the computation of liquid holdup and pressure drop in downward two-phase flow. Note that the Griston-Willhite model[35] for concentric steam injection involves simultaneous solution of four partial differential equations, two each for two conduits, using a numerical scheme.

Example Application. Superheated steam at the rate of 120,000 STB/D, (1331.4 lbm/hr) at 1,000°F and 500 psia is being injected into a 6,000-ft vertical well. The pertinent data are:

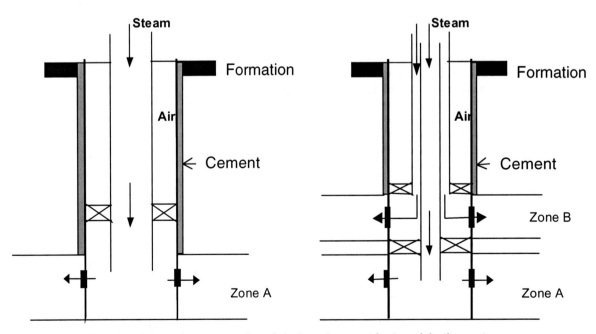

Fig. 9.27—Schematic representation of single and concentric steam injection systems.

$$q_t = 120{,}000 \text{ STB/D}$$
$$T_{ts} = 1{,}000°\text{F}$$
$$p_{ts} = 500 \text{ psia}$$
$$H = 1520.3 \text{ Btu/lbm}$$
$$d_{ti} = 2.441 \text{ in.}$$
$$d_{to} = 2.875 \text{ in.}$$
$$d_{ins} = 3.5 \text{ in.}$$
$$d_{ci} = 5.989 \text{ in.}$$
$$d_{co} = 6.625 \text{ in.}$$
$$t_p = 8.75 \text{ hr}$$
$$T_{es} = 75°\text{F}$$
$$T_{eb} = 141°\text{F}$$
$$\alpha_h = 0.0458 \text{ ft}^2/\text{hr}$$
$$k_e = 1 \text{ Btu/(hr-ft-°F)}$$
$$k_{cem} = 4.021 \text{ Btu/(hr-ft-°F)}$$
$$k_a = 0.1 \text{ Btu/(hr-ft-°F)}$$
$$k_t = 26 \text{ Btu/(hr-ft-°F)}$$
$$k_c = 26 \text{ Btu/(hr-ft-°F)}$$
$$k_{ins} = 0.135 \text{ Btu/(hr-ft-°F)}$$

Using these data, we calculate an overall-heat-transfer coefficient, U, of 0.80 Btu/(hr-ft²-°F) and a relaxation parameter, L_R of 3.45×10^{-4} ft⁻¹ at the wellhead. Note that because of high temperature involved in this case, we have allowed for radiative heat transport. Additionally, for this case, values of both U and L_R vary significantly with well depth. Therefore, the problem demands a solution using a numerical scheme.

Accordingly, we divided the wellbore into 100 parts, each 60-ft long. Computation was initiated at the wellhead. Assuming that steam temperature and the value of L_R remain the same for the 60-ft interval, we calculated that the steam will lose 26,122 Btu/hr of heat in this section. Use of the energy balance equation then gives a steam enthalpy of 1,500.7 Btu/lbm at 60 ft below the wellhead. At 500 psia, with this value of enthalpy, the steam is still superheated, and we estimated its temperature at 981°F.

Next, we use the momentum balance equation (Eq. 9.21) to estimate a pressure of 500.3 psi for the steam at this point. Because steam enthalpy depends slightly on pressure as well as temperature, we recalculate the steam temperature at this point. This value then allows us to estimate an average temperature for this section, and we refine our heat loss estimate based on that value. Usually, a single iteration suffices.

Repeating this calculation procedure by traversing the well in the downward direction, we found that at a depth of 1,440 ft, the steam enthalpy becomes 1,199.4 Btu/lbm, and its pressure is 507.64 psia. Steam quality of 0.991 at this condition indicated slight condensation and the start of two-phase flow. While calculations involving the energy-balance equation hereafter remains the same, the pressure-drop estimation procedure must account for a two-phase mixture flowing in the downward direction. As mentioned earlier, we used the Hasan model[36] discussed earlier in Chap. 4, Sec. 4.4 to estimate the pressure drop.

The iterative procedure becomes somewhat more complicated in the remaining wellbore owing to two-phase flow. As long as both the vapor and liquid phases coexist, the fluid temperature depends only on its pressure and not on the extent of heat loss or its enthalpy. However, the mass fraction

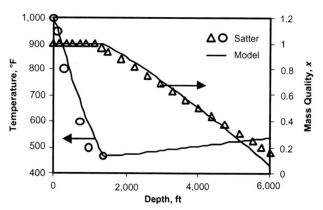

Fig. 9.28—Comparison of temperature and mass quality of steam with those reported by Satter.

of steam (quality) depends on its enthalpy, H, the saturation liquid enthalpy, H_l^{sat}, and the heat of vaporization, H_{lg}, as shown in Eq. 9.24.

$$x = \frac{H - H_l^{sat}}{H_{lg}} . \quad\quad\quad\quad\quad\quad\quad (9.24)$$

The saturation enthalpy and heat of vaporization depend on the system pressure. Therefore, the calculation procedure involves first estimating the fluid pressure using the momentum-balance equation. This step requires an estimated average value for quality to allow computation of fluid density and frictional loss. The estimated pressure is used to calculate the fluid temperature and steam/water property values. Thereafter, the energy-balance equation is used to estimate heat loss, fluid enthalpy, and quality. With the new value of quality, the interval (60 ft, in this case) pressure drop is recalculated. Usually, two iterations lead to good estimates of fluid temperature, pressure, and quality.

Fig. 9.28 shows the calculated values of temperature and steam quality along with those reported by Satter.[31] We note a very good agreement between the two methods.

9.3.2 Geothermal Production.
Geothermal energy is a widespread resource that has been used directly and indirectly since the early 1900's. In the United States, California and Nevada have been making significant use of this energy source. Although hot (~250°C) dry rock and superhot (~500°C) magma systems are possible geothermal energy sources, hydrothermal systems—providing pressurized hot water and steam/water mixtures—are the most prevailing. Direct application of geothermal energy includes use of hot water for space heating, evaporation, crystallization, drying, etc. Indirect use of wet steam from geothermal wells is generally for power generation in boilers.

The mathematical model for the transport processes occurring in a geothermal well is same as the one we presented for steam injection. We need to simultaneously solve for both the momentum balance and energy balance equations; that is, solution of Eqs. 9.21 through 9.23.

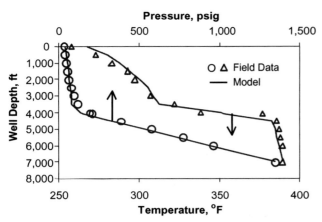

Fig. 9.29—Matching pressure and temperature profiles in a geo-thermal well.

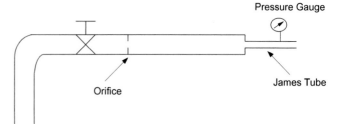

Fig. 9.30—Schematic of a combination of an orifice-meter and James tube for metering steam flow in geothermal wells.

Fig. 9.29 compares the results of computations performed for a geothermal well (East Mesa 6-1) with pressure and temperature data. This 7,000-ft vertical well was producing from a hot-water reservoir at 389°F and 1,330 psig.

Single-phase flow of water occurs up to a depth of 4,200 ft. The change in the slopes of pressure and temperature profiles clearly indicates the commencement of two-phase flow at this depth. From 4,200 ft up to the wellhead, the flow experiences all four regimes. The Hasan-Kabir model, as discussed in Chap. 3 and used in the computation of pressure profile, indicates that the last 3,550 ft of the well experiences annular two-phase flow of steam and water. The agreement between computed values of pressure and temperature with the reported data appear very good. Note that the author[38] of the study points out the difficulties in relating temperature values to the fluid enthalpy because of the presence of dissolved solids and gases.

9.3.3 Metering Steam Flow Rate and Quality. Steam injection often requires steam flow rate and quality measurements. These measurements are also critical in producing hot water and wet steam from geothermal wells. Metering two-phase flow is complicated by the necessity of obtaining at least an additional data set, because of an extra phase, compared to that for single-phase flow. In addition, the interaction and slip between the two phases may have to be accounted for through modeling or empiricism.

In single-phase flow, the pressure loss across a flow restriction, such as a venturi or an orifice, can be related to the mass flow rate through the channel. A similar relation also exists for flow of two-phase mixtures, provided some simplifying assumptions regarding the mixture density at the constriction are made. The pressure drop is then related to the total flow rate and the quality (gas mass fraction). However, we must obtain another independent expression relating rate and phase fraction.

Critical flow of steam and water yields the desired relation between flow rate and quality. An expression for the maximum (critical or sonic) velocity attainable in pipe flow can be derived from thermodynamic considerations of isentropic expansion of single-phase systems with uniform density. However, for two-phase systems, some assumptions

regarding the flowing density and its rate of change is needed to obtain a critical flow relationship. A number of theoretical models have been proposed relating steam-water critical flow with system variables. These models usually involve writing the momentum and energy balance equations for each phase and making an assumption regarding the rate of change of pressure or slip ratio of the phases at the critical flow. Usually, however, the assumptions made in these models cannot be verified and the resulting expressions are quite complicated.

James[39,40] proposed an empirical equation relating the combined mass flux of steam and water at critical flow conditions to the lip (critical) pressure and stagnation enthalpy. He validated his equation using a large set of data with a wide range of parameters. Subsequently, Hasan[41] developed modifications of the James equation, allowing the critical flow correlation to be used for geothermal wells containing dissolved substances, such as CO_2 and salts.

Because of its simplicity, James' equation for critical flow of wet steam has become very popular in the geothermal industry. In conjunction with his correlation for flow through orifices, James' critical flow correlation is often used for computing geothermal wellbore discharge characteristics. The industry practice is to use an orifice at the well's upstream and attach a James tube, which has a smaller diameter than the well itself, to obtain critical flow. Such a combination of an orifice-meter and James tube is schematically shown in **Fig. 9.30.** Data gathered are the pressure drop across the orifice and the pressure at the lip of the James tube. Because pressure changes rapidly during critical flow, positioning the pressure tap is critical. The standard location is ¼-in. from the exit of the tube, as suggested by James. The two equations, one for flow through orifices and the other for critical flow, are solved simultaneously for mass flux and quality, using an iterative procedure.

We will first present theory of two-phase flow through orifices and then discuss the James equation for critical flow. The sensitivity analysis will be presented thereafter, followed by suggestions for using other metering devices.

Two-Phase Flow Through Orifices. Pressure drop caused by the passage of gas/liquid mixtures through a sharp-edged orifice is of great interest in the area of metering, for the design of steam and refrigeration plants, and in analyzing the failure of high-pressure circuits. Derivation of an expression for the pressure differential across an orifice is possible by extending the treatment for single-phase flow; that is, the homogeneous model, or by setting up the

FLUID FLOW AND HEAT TRANSFER IN WELLBORES

momentum balance separately for individual phases using the separated-flow model.[42,43]

Assuming the fluid to be homogeneous results in an expression for mass flux at the orifice throat, G_o, in terms of the density, ρ, pressure drop across the orifice, Δp ($=p_2-p_1$), and the throat to pipe diameter ratio, β, which is written as

$$G_o = YC_D \frac{\sqrt{2g_c\Delta p\rho}}{\sqrt{\left(1-\beta^4\right)}} \cdot \quad \dots\dots\dots\dots\dots (9.25)$$

At high Reynolds numbers, typical of these applications, the value of the orifice discharge coefficient, C_D, is usually 0.61. Note that the expansion factor, Y, has a value of unity for single-phase liquid flow. For two-phase flow, the expression developed for single-phase gases may be used without sacrificing much accuracy.

Attempts to use homogeneous mixture density, given by

$$\frac{1}{\rho_m} = \frac{x}{\rho_g} + \frac{1-x}{\rho_L} \quad \dots\dots\dots\dots\dots (9.26)$$

in Eq. 9.26, has not been very successful in correlating two-phase orifice-meter data. This experience led James to propose the following expression for calculating the throat mixture density for use in Eq. 9.26.

$$\frac{1}{\rho_m} = \frac{x^{1.5}}{\rho_g} + \frac{1-x^{1.5}}{\rho_L} \cdot \quad \dots\dots\dots\dots\dots (9.27)$$

Two-Phase Critical Flow Relationship. As mentioned earlier, theoretical relationships for critical flow are quite complicated and are not necessarily very accurate for steam/water flow. The empirical correlation proposed by James[38,39] shows excellent agreement with available steam/water data and has become the industry standard for geothermal wells. The correlation relates the lip critical pressure, p_c, and stagnation enthalpy, H_c, to the critical mass-flow rate at the exit of the James tube, G_c, as

$$G_c = 11,400 p_c^{0.96} / H_c^{1.102} \cdot \quad \dots\dots\dots\dots (9.28)$$

The critical-mass flux at the exit of the James tube of diameter D_c is related to the mass flux at the orifice throat of diameter D_o, through the continuity equation,

$$G_o = G_c \left(d_c / d_o\right)^2 \cdot \quad \dots\dots\dots\dots\dots (9.29)$$

Eq. 9.28 is dimensional with units of pressure p_c, in psia, enthalpy H_c, in Btu/lbm, and mass flux G_c, in lbm/ft²sec. The stagnation enthalpy, H_c, refers to the enthalpy at the critical condition plus the kinetic energy of the fluid. However, if the process is assumed adiabatic and enthalpy is evaluated at the upstream pressure tap of the orifice-meter where pressure is high and kinetic energy is low, the kinetic energy may be neglected. This simplification allows the stagnation enthalpy to be related to the steam quality at the throat by the expression,

$$H_c = xH_L + (1-x)H_L \cdot \quad \dots\dots\dots\dots (9.30)$$

The liquid and vapor enthalpies, H_L and H_g, are saturation enthalpies corresponding to the pressure at the orifice throat.

James[38] showed excellent agreement between Eq. 9.28 and field data when steam quality was known. When both flow rate and quality are unknowns, Eqs. 9.25 and 9.28 (in conjunction with Eqs. 9.27 and 9.29) can be solved simultaneously for G_o and x, when data for the pressure drop across the orifice and the critical lip pressure are available. However, when both G_o and x must be computed from these equations, solution accuracy deteriorates significantly for high quality ($x > 40\%$) systems. Hasan[42] noted that the use of a rigorous model for Δp across the orifice, rather than Eqs. 9.25 and 9.26, does not improve accuracy significantly. Reasons for this inaccuracy at high quality is related to the coupled nature of data gathering; that is, orifice-meter and critical flow, rather than the uncertainty stemming from individual correlations themselves.

Chien and Schrodt[44] developed a similar method of using orifice in series with a critical flow meter to measure steam flow rate. They used the James correlation (Eq. 9.27) for flow through orifice and the King and Crocker[45] equation for critical flow. They reported excellent agreement between their estimates and model. The model's superior performance owes largely to the optimized parameters that they had developed using field data in both the orifice and critical flow correlations. However, for making *a priori* estimates, the method proposed by James appears preferable.

9.3.4 Pressure Drop in Fittings. Pressure change, occurring when two-phase fluid flows through sudden enlargements and contractions, such as expanders, reducers, and orifices, depends on the area ratio, R_A (=final area/initial area=A_2/A_1), as well as other parameters. We recommend the following expression for estimating permanent pressure gain during two-phase flow through *a sudden enlargement.*

$$p_2 - p_1 = \frac{G_1^2(1-x)^2}{R_A\rho_L}\left(1-\frac{1}{R_A}\right)\left(1+\frac{C}{X}+\frac{1}{X^2}\right), \quad \dots (9.31)$$

where C and X are given by

$$C = \left[\lambda + (C_2-\lambda)\sqrt{\rho_g/(\rho_L-\rho_g)}\right]\left[\sqrt{\rho_g/\rho_L}+\sqrt{\rho_L/\rho_g}\right]$$
$$\dots\dots\dots\dots\dots (9.32)$$

and $X = \frac{1-x}{x}\sqrt{\rho_g/\rho_L}, \quad \dots\dots\dots\dots\dots (9.33)$

with $\lambda=1.0$ and $C_2=0.5$, as suggested by Chisholm.[46] Note that the area ratio, $R_A=A_2/A_1$, is greater than one in this case.

For *sudden contraction*, we recommend a homogeneous flow approach, as suggested by Collier,[47] for estimating two-phase pressure loss, which is written as

TABLE 9.4—EQUIVALENT LENGTH AND OTHER FACTORS FOR PIPES AND FITTINGS

	C_2	$L_e = L/d$	X	Pressure Drop
Straight pipe	G/G^*	1	Eq. 9.33	Eq. 9.36
45° elbow/bend	3	15	Eq. 9.37	Eq. 9.36
90° elbow/bend	3	32	Eq. 9.37	Eq. 9.36
180° elbow	3	75	Eq. 9.37	Eq. 9.36
Tee	1.75	90	Eq. 9.37	Eq. 9.36
Gate valve (open)	1.2	7	Eq. 9.37	Eq. 9.36
Globe valve (open)	2.3	300	Eq. 9.37	Eq. 9.36
Disk water meter	1	400	Eq. 9.37	Eq. 9.36
Reducer/Contraction	0.5		Eq. 9.37	Eq. 9.34
Expander	0.5		Eq. 9.37	Eq. 9.31

$$p_1 - p_2 = \frac{G_2^2}{\rho_L}\left[\left(1 - R_A^2\right) + \left(\frac{1}{C_c} - 1\right)^2\right]\left[1 + \frac{x(\rho_L - \rho_g)}{\rho_g}\right].$$
$$\dots\dots\dots\dots\dots (9.34)$$

The value of C_c, which depends on the area ratio, R_A ($R_A < 1$ for contractions), can be approximated by $0.598 + 0.13 (R_A - 0.2)$ using the data given by Collier.[47]

In single-phase flow, the pressure loss in valves is generally expressed as the loss that would be experienced in an equivalent length of the straight pipe.[48] For example, for a globe valve, the pressure drop is that which would occur in the straight pipe of length $300d$, where d is the pipe diameter. Chisholm[44] suggested that the equivalent pipe-length approach be used for estimating two-phase pressure loss in valves and bends. Thus, for any such fitting, the pressure loss is given by

$$(\Delta p)_{\text{fit}} = d(L_e)_{\text{fit}}(dp/dz), \quad \dots\dots\dots\dots (9.35)$$

where the equivalent length $(L_e)_{\text{fit}}$ is the emperically determined value for the particular fitting. We recommend the Lockhart-Martinelli method for calculating the two-phase pressure gradient, (dp/dz), in Eq. 9.3.15 because the L_e values recommended by Chisholm[15] for various fittings were developed using the same method of (dp/dz) calculation. Thus, following the method outlined in Chap. 2,

$$(\Delta p)_{\text{fit}} = d(L_e)_{\text{fit}}\left(\frac{fG_2(1-x)}{2\rho_L d}\right)\left(1 + \frac{C}{X} + \frac{1}{X_2}\right).$$
$$\dots\dots\dots\dots\dots (9.36)$$

Eq. 2.26, which is repeated next and slightly different from Eq. 9.33, is used for calculating the Lockhart-Martinelli parameter, X.

$$X = \frac{1-x}{x}\sqrt{\rho_g/\rho_L}\left(\frac{\mu_L}{\mu_g}\right)^{0.1}. \quad \dots\dots\dots\dots (9.37)$$

Chisholm[15] also suggested that for high-pressure systems ($p > 30$ atm), the parameter C in Eq. 9.35 be calculated with Eq. 9.32. To account for the effect of mass flux on the parameter C in straight pipes, he suggested that in Eq. 9.32, the value of λ is 1.0 and that $C_2 = G/G^*$, where the reference mass flux G^* is 307 lbm/ft²sec (=1,500 kg/m²s). For all fittings, he recommends λ is 1.0. The value of C_2 varies with the fitting; in **Table 9.4**, we reproduce the recommended values of these parameters for various fittings.

Field Example 9.5. Here we present a calculation procedure for various fittings using a simplified version of an actual field problem. Note that the flowlines are all horizontal.

A 10-in. line supplies steam to a system of six steam-injection wells, as shown in **Fig. 9.31**. The flow rate is 660,790 lbm/day/well water equivalent or 45.89 lbm/sec. The steam pressure at the main is 1,500 psia and the quality is 80%. There is a 90° bend in the 10-in. line, which is 20 ft from the boiler and another 90° bend after five feet. At this point, the 10-in. line connects to an 8-in. line with a 10×8 reducer. This 8-in. line continues for 100 ft, at which point there is a fully open globe valve. After the valve, there are four 45° elbows. The 8-in. line continues after that for another 100 ft.

The 8-in. line then gets connected to a 6-in. manifold via a T-joint and an 8×6 reducer. The 6-in. manifold supplies the wet steam to six 3-in. lines, connected via 6×3 reducers. These 3-in. lines are 10-ft long and are each connected to a vertical injection well.

Calculate the pressure and quality at the wellhead and at various points in the network. The following values of saturated steam properties are available from any steam table:

$$p = 1,500 \text{ psia,}$$
$$T^{\text{sat}} = 596.2°\text{F,}$$
$$x = 0.80,$$
and $d_{\text{main}} = 0.8233$ ft.

The values for enthalpies, Btu/lbm, are

$$H_g = 1169.2,$$
$$H_L = 611.7,$$
$$H_m = xH_g + (1-x),$$
and $H_L = 1057.7.$

For densities, lbm/ft³, the values are

$$\rho_g = 3.6137,$$
and $\rho_L = 42.6.$

The values for viscosities, cp, are

$$\mu_g = 0.02052,$$
and $\mu_L = 0.08589.$

The friction factor specific to the flowlines is

$$f_L/4 = 0.0035 + 0.264/\text{Re}_L^{0.42}.$$

Solution.

For a 10-in. line (20-ft long), the values are

$$G_{mi} = (\text{mass flow rate/area}) = 84.135 \text{ lbm/ft}^2\text{sec,}$$

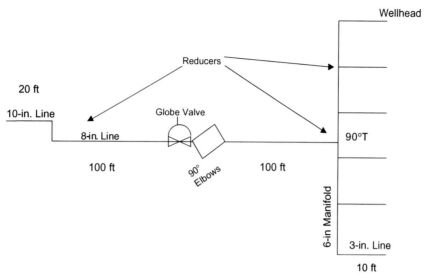

Fig. 9.31—A schematic representation of a steam-injection manifold.

$X = [(1-x)/x] (\rho_g/\rho_l)^{0.5} (\mu_L/\mu_g)^{0.1} = 0.0965,$

$C = [\lambda+(C_2-\lambda)\{(\rho_L-\rho_g)/\rho_L\}^{1/2}],$

$[(\rho_g/\rho_L)^{1/2}+(\rho_L/\rho_g)^{1/2}] = 13.1608,$

$\phi_L^2 = 1+C/X+1/X^2 = 244.71,$

$Re_L = (dG/\mu_L) = 1.216*10^6$ and $f_L/4 = 0.0035$
$+0.264/Re_L^{0.42} = 0.0042,$

$(dp/dz)_L = f_L G_m^2(1-x)^2/[2(\rho_L)(g_c)(d)] = 2.0984 \times 10^{-3}$ psf/ft,

and $-(\Delta p)_F = (dp/dz)_L L\phi_L^2 = 20(2.0984 \times 10^{-3})(244.71)$
$= 10.27$ psf $= 0.071$ psi.

For a 90° bend, we obtain

$X = [(1-x)/x](\rho_g/\rho_l)^{0.5} = 0.0729,$

$C = [1+(3-1)\{(\rho_L-\rho_g)/\rho_L^{1/2}]$
$[(\rho_g/\rho_L)^{1/2}+(\rho_L/\rho_g)^{1/2}] = 10.851,$

$\phi_L^2 = 1+C/X+1/X^2 = 337.9,$

and $-(\Delta p) = (dp/dz)_L \phi_L^2(L_e)d = (2.0984 \times 10^{-3})(337.9)$
$(32 \times 0.8233) = 18.96$ psf $= 0.1317$ psi.

For a 10 × 8 contraction, the solution is

$R_A = (8/10)^2 = 0.64$ and $G_2 = G_{mi}/0.64 = 84.135/0.64$
$= 131.46$ lbm/ft²sec,

$C_c = 0.598+0.13(R_A-0.2) = 0.655$ and $1/C_c = 1.526,$

(Eq. 9.34, first term)$(131.46)^2[(1-0.64)^2+(1.526-1)^2]/$
$(2 \times 42.6)/(32.2) = 5.468$ psf,

(Eq. 9.34, second term)$1+[0.7999(42.6-3.613)]/3.613$
$= 9.633,$

and $-(\Delta p) = 5.468 \times 9.633 = 52.67$ psf $= 0.366$ psi.

For a globe valve on the 8-in. line, the values are

$G_2 = 131.46$ lbm/ft²sec,

$Re_L = (dG/\mu_L) = 1.519 \times 10^6$ and $f_L/4 = 0.0035$
$+0.264/Re_L^{0.42} = 0.00417,$

$(dp/dz)_L = f_L G_2^2(1-x)^2/[2(\rho_L)(g_c)(d)] = 6.384 \times 10^{-3}$ psf/ft

$X = [(1-x)/x](\rho_g/\rho_l)^{0.5} = 0.0733,$

$C = [1+(2.3-1)\{(\rho_L-\rho_g)/\rho_L\}^{1/2}][(\rho_g/\rho_L)^{1/2}$
$+(\rho_L/\rho_g)^{1/2}] = 8.362,$

$\phi_L^2 = 1+C/X+1/X^2 = 301.2,$

and $-(\Delta p) = (dp/dz)_L \phi_L^2(L_e)d = (6.384 \times 10^{-3})(301.2)(300)$
$(8/12) = 384.3$ psf $= 2.669$ psi.

For a 45° elbow on the 8-in. line, we have

$Re_L = (dG/\mu_L) = 1.518 \times 10^6$ and $f_L/4 = 0.0035$
$+0.264/Re_L^{0.42} = 0.00417,$

$(dp/dz)_L = f_L G_2^2(1-x)^2/[2(\rho_L)(g_c)(d)] = 6.377 \times 10^{-3}$ psf/ft

$X = [(1-x)/x](\rho_g/\rho_l)^{0.5} = 0.0732,$

$C = [1+(3-1)\{(\rho_L-\rho_g)/\rho_L\}^{1/2}][(\rho_g/\rho_L)^{1/2}$
$+(\rho_L/\rho_g)^{1/2}] = 10.871,$

$\phi_L^2 = 1+C/X+1/X^2 = 336.2,$

and $-(\Delta p) = (dp/dz)_L \phi_L^2(L_e)d = (6.377 \times 10^{-3})(336.2)(15)$
$(8/12) = 21.441$ psf $= 0.1489$ psi.

For t on the 8-in. line, the values are

$Re_L = (dG/\mu_L) = 1.518 \times 10^6$ and $f_L/4 = 0.0035$
$+0.264/Re_L^{0.42} = 0.00417,$

$(dp/dz)_L = f_L G_2^2(1-x)^2/[2(\rho_L)(g_c)(d)] = 6.387 \times 10^{-3}$ psf/ft,

$X = [(1-x)/x] (\rho_g/\rho_l)^{0.5} = 0.0732,$

$C = [1+(1.75-1)\{(\rho_L-\rho_g)/\rho_L\}^{1/2}][(\rho_g/\rho_L)^{1/2}$
$+(\rho_L/\rho_g)^{1/2}] = 6.4123,$

$\phi_L^2 = 1+C/X+1/X^2 = 275,$

and $-(\Delta p) = (dp/dz)_L \phi_L^2(L_e)d = (6.387 \times 10^{-3})(275)(90)(8/12)$
$= 105.4$ psf $= 0.7321$ psi.

For a 6 × 8 expansion,

$R_A = (8/6)^2 = 1.7778$ and $G_2 = 131.46$ lbm/ft²sec,

$X = [(1-x)/x](\rho_g/\rho_l)^{0.5} = 0.0731,$

$C = [1+(0.5-1)\{(\rho_L-\rho_g)/\rho_L\}^{1/2}][(\rho_g/\rho_L)^{1/2}$
$+(\rho_L/\rho_g)^{1/2}] = 1.9487,$

(Eq. 9.31, first term)$(131.46)^2(1-0.7987)^2(1-0.5625)/$
$1.7778/42.6/32.2 = 0.3972$ psf,

(Eq. 9.31, second term)$1+C/X+1/X^2 = 214.5,$

and $(\Delta p) = 0.3972 \times 214.5 = 85.1929$ psf $= 0.592$ psi increase
in pressure.

Table 9.5 shows calculated pressure drop for the particular fitting/segment as well as cumulative pressure drop up to the point. The cumulative distance is shown from the steam entrance point at the boiler. Note the significant pressure drop caused by the globe valve, when it is open. The next highest single-item pressure drop, 1.487 psi, occurs in the 8 × 6 reducer. The pressure drop at this reducer is much higher than

TABLE 9.5—PRESSURE DROP IN VARIOUS ITEMS OF THE EXAMPLE PROBLEM						
Description	Segment Length, ft	Number of Items	Cumulative Distance, ft	Pressure, psia	Item Δp, psi	Cumulative Δp, psi
p_L			0	1,500.00	0	0
10-in. pipe	20		20	1,499.93	0.0692	0.0692
90° bend		2	20	1,499.67	0.2634	0.33255
10-in. pipe	5		25	1,499.65	0.0173	0.34985
10 × 8 reducer		1	25	1,499.28	0.3658	0.71563
8-in. pipe	100		125	1,498.61	0.6781	1.39372
Globe valve		1	125	1,495.94	2.6694	4.06311
45° elbow		4	125	1,495.34	0.5956	4.65867
8-in. pipe	100		225	1,494.66	0.6804	5.33905
Tee		1	225	1,493.93	0.7321	5.47949
8 × 6 reducer		1	225	1,492.44	1.4866	6.96611
6 × 8 expander		1	225	1,493.03	−0.5916	4.74743
6 × 3 reducer		1	225	1,492.78	0.8122	7.77835
3-in. pipe	10		235	1,492.75	0.0961	7.87449
p_{wh}				1,492.75		

that in the 10 × 8 reducer because the mass flux in the 6-in. line is almost twice as much as that in the 10-in. line. A reduced cross-sectional area causes this high-pressure loss as the pressure drop varies directly as the square of the mass flux. The pressure loss in the 6 × 3 reducer is also high but not as high as the loss in the 8 × 6 reducer. That is because even though the flow area is lower in the 3-in. line, the total rate of fluid flow, which is distributed over the six wells, is also lower.

9.3.5 Wellbore Steam/Water Flow and Surface Metering Summary.
In Sec. 9.3, we present some elements of steam/water, two-phase flow during saturated steam injection, geothermal production, and surface metering. The intrinsic idea is to show application of fluid and heat flow principles developed in earlier chapters to areas where heat transfer is accompanied by phase change. Results show that the fundamental principles hold in any combined fluid- and heat-flow situation.

9.4 Combating Wellbore Solids Deposition

9.4.1 Introduction.
In oilfield operations, unwanted flow restrictions frequently occur in the fluid production chain, from perforations to a gathering center. Potential causes for the development of these restrictions are numerous, including thermal stress, mechanical failures, stuck pigs, and vapor locks. However, most blockage-related damage is caused by the formation of compounds that adhere to the walls of the production string. Asphaltene and paraffin deposition and

hydrate formation are primary examples of such sticky problems that cost the industry millions of dollars in lost production and cleaning operations. Ref. 50 presents a com-i prehensive review of various field experiences arising from asphaltenes. **Fig. 9.32** presents a field example of asphaltene deposition onto a 2.992-in. ID tubing wall. Besides experencing declining productivity with increasing deposition thickness, assigning a friction factor becomes a daunting task.

Some recent works show novel ways of locating and characterizing wellbore blockages.[51,52] Unfortunately, treating problems arising from paraffin, asphaltene, or hydrate deposition still relies largely on pumping aromatic solvents to the suspected location in a flow string. Asphaltenes are ordinarily treated with aromatic solvents, such as toluene or

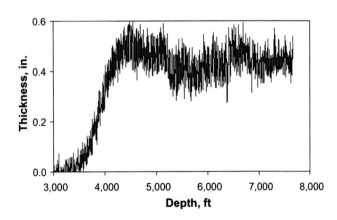

Fig. 9.32 —Asphaltene deposition in a producing well.

FLUID FLOW AND HEAT TRANSFER IN WELLBORES

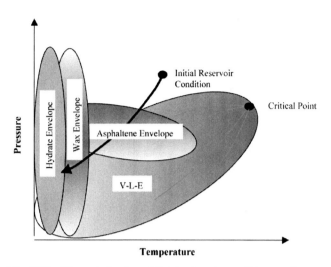

Fig. 9.33—Phase behavior of fluids showing solids envelopes (from Ref. 54).

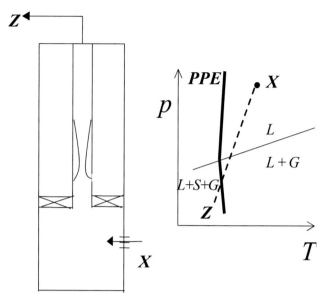

Fig. 9.34—Paraffin phase envelope offers the possibility of profile alteration.

xylene, or deasphalted oil. As the name implies, deasphalted oil is devoid of asphaltenes and, therefore, acts as a potent solvent. On the other hand, remedial measures for paraffins involve hot-oil treatment, mechanical scrapers, injection of chemical inhibitors and microbes.

Regardless of the method used, these measures are expensive and are undertaken usually after the problem surfaces. In this section, we focus on preventive or proactive measures by examining the phase behavior, and fluid and heat flow characteristics in a producing string. In other words, we examine the viability of measures, such as well design and altering flow characteristics, by exploring the underlying physics. Here, we address issues pertaining to asphaltenes and paraffins; hydrates are not considered explicitly. Much of the material discussed earlier in Chap. 8, Sec. 8.2 and Chap. 9, Sec. 9.1 will be used to tackle this problem. Ref. 53 forms the backbone of this section.

9.4.2 Fluid/Solid Thermodynamic Behavior. Understanding thermodynamic behavior of fluids forms the basis for most remedial measures. This element is particularly true for the solution approach discussed here. Most investigators focused on separate studies of each solid component; that is, asphaltene, wax or paraffin, and hydrate. However, in many oils, all of these solids can potentially occur and may present problems depending on the fluids' state (pressure and temperature) in the flow string. Jamaluddin *et al.*[54] presented a unified approach to combining all three solids envelopes, as shown in **Fig. 9.33.**

Paraffins. Paraffins or waxes are high molecular weight, high carbon number (30 to 75) *n*-paraffins that can present significant challenges when transported from reservoir conditions to any other condition. Wax crystallizes at a higher temperature (WCT) than its deposition temperature. WCT is also known as the cloudpoint. Comparison of extensive laboratory measurements with field data showed that the WCT values obtained from dead oils were in good agreement with those measured in flowing wellbores. Hammami *et al.*[55] speculated that the laminar or transitional

flow was probably conducive to crystallization of wax and its subsequent deposition.

Testing[56] of thermodynamic models to estimate the cloudpoint temperature and subsequent deposition suggest moderate success in modeling wax deposition. However, over the years, significant progress has been made in understanding deposition kinetics[57-61] of paraffins, unlike asphaltenes. In particular, Singh *et al.*[61] provided insights into deposition mechanism and subsequent growth of wax deposit with time. They showed that deposition growth is a result of counterdiffusion, wherein the wax molecules diffuse into the deposit, while oil molecules diffuse out.

Fig. 9.34 shows a qualitative paraffin phase envelope (PPE) and a well sketch. Our approach of addressing this issue is to avoid crossing the PPE, while expanding the fluid from downhole, *X*, to surface, *Z*, as shown in Fig. 9.34. As the oil expands up the wellbore to reach point *Z* at the wellhead, it experiences decline in pressure and temperature. In so doing, the liquid, *L*, oil phase gets in the liquid/gas ($L+G$) region before crossing the solid(s) envelope ($L+S+G$), thereby triggering flocculation of paraffins. The proposed treatment involves circulating a hot fluid in the annulus and/or insulating the production string. Thermodynamically speaking, paraffins are strongly temperature dependent; consequently, they are amenable to thermal treatment.

Asphaltenes. Asphaltenes, defined as n-pentane insoluble fraction of crude oil, are polar molecules, which aggregate through orbital association, hydrogen bonding, and acid-based interactions. The growth of aggregates is limited by the presence of resins in solution. Various asphaltene-solubility studies have been reported and a number of models to compute asphaltene flocculation or onset condition are available.[62-65]

In general, asphaltene onset depends on the existing pressure and temperature at any point in the wellbore. Asphaltene onset condition does not imply deposition onto the wall, however. Unlike paraffins, deposition kinetics for asphaltenes is

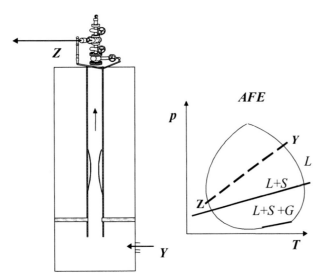

Fig. 9.35—Flocculation envelope provides clues about asphaltene deposition.

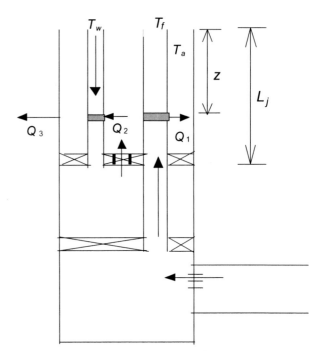

Fig. 9.36—Schematic representation of the fluid circulation system.

not well understood. Nonetheless, variation of oil composition in the wellbore requires that asphaltene flocculation envelope (AFE) be established for a given oil before solution is sought. Note that we prefer the term AFE over ADE, which implies asphaltene deposition enevelope, simply because flocculation is not necessarily deposition.

Fig. 9.35 shows a qualitative AFE diagram and a well schematic. Unlike Fig. 9.34, the liquid, L, oil phase gets in the liquid/solid (L+S) region within the phase envelope, thereby triggering flocculation of asphaltenes. Below the saturation line (in solid), gas evolution will occur, either near the wellhead or in the flowline. At very low pressure and temperature; that is, outside the AFE, asphaltenes are resolubilized in the liquid. Notwithstanding our lack of understanding of kinetics of deposition, we will presuppose that deposition occurs when the oil attains condition within the phase envelope.

Our approach to mitigating the asphaltene deposition problem is to inject solvent directly at the suspected depth of deposition. When the asphaltene phase envelope was originally advanced,[62] occurrence of oil to the left side of he phase envelope, the same side of Z was thought to be a possibility. However, experimental studies tend to show the occurrence of asphaltic oil to the right side of AFE; that is, Y is more common than thought previously. Ref. 54 is a case in point.

9.4.3 Fluid Circulation Model. Fig. 9.36 shows a schematic of the physical model. Either single-phase oil or a two-phase mixture of oil and gas is produced up the tubing. The circulating string carrying a cooling fluid is injected into the annulus at a depth, L_j. This string may have insulation to minimize energy exchange prior to actual injection.

Developing expressions for fluid temperature in the tubing, the annulus, and the circulating string requires setting up balances for heat transfer amongst these fluids. The energy balances are set up for the fluids in the control volume as shown in Fig. 9.36. Note that the z-coordinate represents well length, not depth, and that z is positive in the downward direction. We let subscript f denote the fluid in the production

string; whereas, subscripts w and a stand for the circulating and annular fluid, respectively.

We derived the differential equations for the tubing fluid, circulating fluid, and annular fluid, respectively, as shown in Appendix E, Sec. E.3.1, which are written as

$$\frac{dT_f}{dz} = L_{R1}\left(T_f - T_a\right) + \phi_f, \quad \cdots\cdots\cdots\cdots\cdots(9.38)$$

$$\frac{dT_w}{dz} = L_{R2}\left(T_a - T_w\right) + \phi_w, \quad \cdots\cdots\cdots\cdots\cdots(9.39)$$

$$\text{and } \frac{dT_a}{dz} = L_{R1}\left(T_f - T_a\right)\frac{c_f}{c_a} - L_{R2}\left(T_a - T_w\right)\frac{c_w}{c_a}$$

$$- L_{R3}\left(T_a - T_{ei}\right) + \phi_a. \quad \cdots\cdots\cdots\cdots\cdots(9.40)$$

Simultaneous solutions of Eqs. 9.38, 9.39, and 9.40 should give the expressions for fluid temperatures in the three conduits of the system. Unfortunately, combining these three equations results in a third-order-differential equation, which does not lend itself to analytic treatment. Therefore, we offer a numerical solution to this problem in Appendix E.

9.4.4 Solvent Injection Model. Fig. 9.37 presents a schematic of the model when a solvent is injected directly into the producing string at a distance L_j from the surface, after being conveyed through a chemical-injection line. We wish to compute temperature profiles in all three conduits so that the solvent's potency at a given pressure and temperature can be aligned with the asphaltene or paraffin deposits within the tubing. In other words, the knowledge of temperature profiles at the well operating condition leads us to optimal design of the injection line.

FLUID FLOW AND HEAT TRANSFER IN WELLBORES

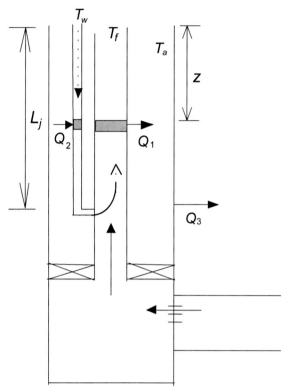

Fig. 9.37—Schematic representation of the solvent injection system.

Energy balances for the fluids in the three conduits in this case are very similar to that of fluid circulation in the annulus. For both produced and injected fluids, Eqs. 9.38 and 9.39 from the previous case apply here. However, direct injection increases the fluid rate in the tubing above the point of injection, thereby requiring a slight modification in the definition of the relaxation parameters, L_{R1}, as

$$L_{R1} = \frac{2\pi r_{to} U_1}{c_w w_w + c_f w_f} . \qquad (9.41)$$

The relaxation parameters, L_{R2} and L_{R3}, are the same as those defined in Eqs. E-31 and E-34. Another difference in this case is that the annular fluid is not subjected to forced convection. For annulus, the heat gain from the tubing fluid equals the heat loss to the injection string and the formation. In other words,

$$L_{R1}(T_f - T_a)(w_f c_f) = L_{R2}(T_a - T_w)(w_w c_w)$$

$$+ L_{R3}(T_a - T_{ei})(w_a c_a) \cdot \qquad (9.42)$$

The overall-heat-transfer coefficient, U_{to}, needed to compute L_{R3} in Eq. E-34, is slightly different in this case because of lack of forced convection in the annulus. U_{to} should be calculated from the expression,

$$\frac{1}{U_{to}} = \frac{r_{to}\ln(r_{co}/r_{ci})}{k_c} + \frac{r_{to}\ln(r_{cmo}/r_{cmi})}{k_{cm}} + \frac{r_{to}}{r_{ci}h_a} . \quad (9.43)$$

The annular fluid may experience natural convective heat transport because of the temperature difference between the

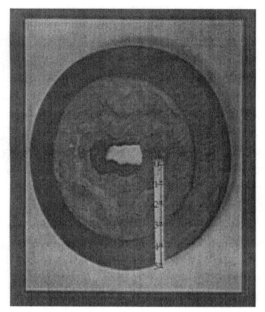

Fig. 9.38—Paraffin-plugged flowline (from Ref. 61).

inner and outer wall of the annulus. The estimation procedure for the heat-transfer coefficient for the annular fluid, h_a, may be made using the procedure discussed in Appendix A.

This model is robust enough for applications in offshore environments. In an offshore riser, direct heat transfer occurs between the production string and the seawater. We modified the expression for U_{to} to account for this altered heat-transfer scenario. Appendix A captures this modification.

Eqs. 9.38, 9.39, and 9.42 may be combined to form a second-order linear differential equation, which can be solved analytically for the three unknowns: T_f, T_w, and T_a. We present the solutions by omitting the tedious derivation.

$$T_f = \alpha_1 e^{\lambda_1 z} + \alpha_2 e^{\lambda_2 z} + (\beta_4/\beta_3)z + \beta_5/\beta_3 - (\beta_2\beta_4/\beta_3^2),$$
$$(9.44)$$

$$T_a = \omega_1 \alpha_1 e^{\lambda_1 z}(1 - A_2\lambda_1) + \omega_2 \alpha_2 e^{\lambda_2 z}(1 - A_2\lambda_2)$$

$$+ \omega_3 z + \omega_4 - A_2(\phi_w + \omega_3), \qquad (9.45)$$

and $T_w = \omega_1 \alpha_1 e^{\lambda_1 z} + \omega_2 \alpha_2 e^{\lambda_2 z} + \omega_3 z + \omega_4 \cdot \qquad (9.46)$

Constants of Eqs. 9.44 through 9.46 are given in Appendix E, Sec. E.3.3.

9.4.5 Application of Models.

Paraffin Control Using Fluid Circulation. As discussed earlier, paraffin-induced plugging can occur in wellbores or flowlines. **Fig. 9.38** shows significant plugging in a flowline. Hot-oil treatment is a popular way of addressing wellbore paraffin problems, despite its potential for formation damage.[66,67] Let us explore the feasibility of mitigating the same in a deepwater environment where well intervention is prohibitive. Cooling of fluids in the riser simply adds another dimension to the deposition problem. The measures studied include retaining fluids' energy by insulating the flow string and supplementing energy at the seafloor by circulating a fluid.

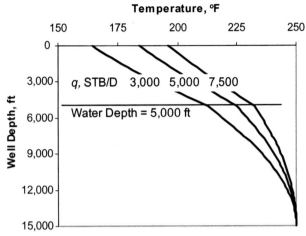

Fig. 9.39—Higher rate retains higher fluid temperature at the wellhead.

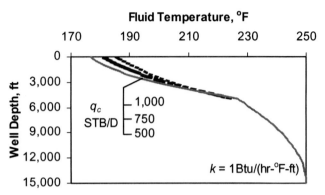

Fig. 9.40—Increasing circulation rate helps retain the fluids' energy.

Let us probe the underlying issue at hand. **Fig. 9.39** shows that higher temperature at the wellhead is tied to higher rates. The rationale is rather straightforward—fluids will retain higher energy at higher rates, a point made earlier in Chap. 7. In addition, the residence time in the riser declines with higher rates, thereby augmenting energy conservation. Economics dictate high-rate production in any offshore environment, let alone in deepwater. Fig. 9.39 shows that rates must be maintained above 5,000 STB/D to avoid potential wax precipitation at 190°F in this example.

When fluid is circulated down to the seafloor of a riser's annulus, the fluids' energy retention is enhanced but only in presence of insulation. As **Fig. 9.40** shows, an increasing fluid circulation rate helps retain increased energy in presence of insulation. In this case, the energy retention plateaus at a circulation rate of about 1,000 STB/D when production occurs at 5,000 STB/D. However, **Fig. 9.41** suggests that heat retention is quite efficient when fluid (preferably produced oil) is circulated down to the seafloor for augmenting energy retention. In absence of insulation and/or fluid circulation, heat transfer is dominated by the temperature gradient of the seawater. As **Fig. 9.42** shows, excessive heat loss in a bare riser will be very conducive to solids deposition because of

significant lowering of fluid temperature. At low temperatures, hydrates add further woe to the solids problem.

To explore the question of well intervention, we used a transient simulator[12] to study the time taken for temperature to decay at the wellhead. **Fig. 9.43** exhibits the decay trends with and without insulating the flow string. Insulation does help at the shallowest water depth of 2,500 ft. However, at greater depths, no advantage can be realized simply because the seawater acts as an overwhelming heat sink. Both Figs. 9.41 and 9.42 suggest that any notion of seafloor processing of fluids must consider heated pipelines for flow-assurance.

Asphaltene Control Using Fluid Injection. As stated before, multitudes of aromatic solvents can be injected into tubing to remove asphaltene plugs. Ordinarily, the solvent is banked by spacer fluids, such as diesel, and pumped directly into the tubing, thereby displacing the produced fluid back into the formation. This form of displacement is known as bull heading. Use of deasphalted oil[68,69] (DAO) has shown promise in mitigating asphaltene deposition, as illustrated by **Fig. 9.44**. A soak period of over 24 hours was used in this case. Note that several months had elapsed between the two measurements during which production continued to occur. This operating condition explains further deposition higher up (<4,000 ft) in the string, which remained untreated. The appeal for deasphalted oil stems from the fact that it is less

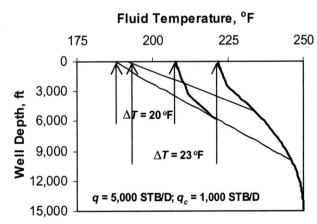

Fig. 9.41—Both fluid circulation and tubing insulation retain high WHT.

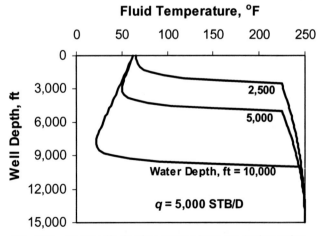

Fig. 9.42—Energy dissipation along a bare producing string.

FLUID FLOW AND HEAT TRANSFER IN WELLBORES

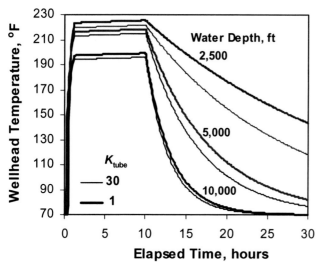

Fig. 9.43—Effect of insulation diminishes with increasing water depth.

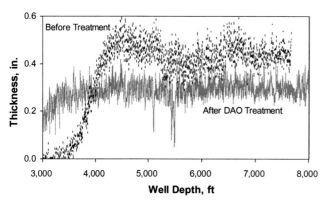

Fig. 9.44—Caliper measurements show effectiveness of DAO treatment.

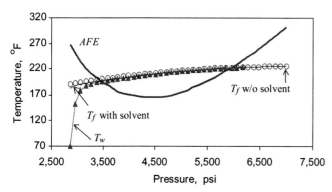

Fig. 9.45—Fluid temperature profiles with or without solvent injection.

TABLE 9.6—WELL, FLUID, AND TRANSPORT PROPERTY DATA	
Well depth, ft	10,000
Production string ID, in.	2.75
Production string OD, in.	3.25
Circulating string ID, in.	2.75
Circulating string OD, in.	3.25
Production casing ID, in.	10
Production casing OD, in.	11.5
Pipe roughness, in.	1.8×10^{-5}
Production rate, STB/D	2,000
Circulating fluid (water) rate, STB/D	200
Formation permeability, md	25
Formation thickness, ft	50
Formation porosity	0.293
Bottomhole temperature, °F	225
Geothermal gradient, °F/ft	0.0155
Formation thermal conductivity, Btu/(ft-°F-hr)	3.33
Formation density, lbm/ft³	135
Formation heat capacity, Btu/(lbm-°F)	0.625
Production tubing/casing material thermal conductivity, Btu/(lbm-°F)	30
Circulating string thermal conductivity (with insulation)	0.1
Circulating fluid inlet (wellhead) temperature, °F	70
Annular fluid thermal conductivity, Btu/(ft-°F-hr)	0.3
Cement thermal conductivity, Btu/(ft-°F-hr)	0.38
Cement diameter to 500 ft, in.	30
Cement diameter from 500 ft to bottomhole, in.	24

well shut-in is required, and this measure can be undertaken proactively. Let us now discuss some results of the model presented earlier.

Fig. 9.45 presents the pressure-temperature trace for direct injection of 200 STB/D of deasphalted oil into the tubing that is producing at 5,000 STB/D. The solvent is transported to a depth of 8,000 ft from the wellhead using a 0.5-in. ID and a 0.75-in. OD string. Other well and fluid property data are the same as those shown in **Table 9.6.**

Fig. 9.45 shows that the temperature of the solvent quickly approaches that of the produced fluid as it is transported down the circulation string. Note that the addition of the solvent reduces the temperature of the produced fluid somewhat. The main purpose of this model is to have the ability to compute the p-T trace and observe how the addition of solvent can help mitigate the problem at hand. For instance, to ensure efficient treatment, the flow rate may be reduced significantly. This action, in turn, will reduce the temperature profile itself, leading to a favorable condition during treatment.

expensive than other solvents and is not harmful to the environment, unlike those routinely used.

One problem with the traditional bull-heading treatment is that well intervention is required, which implies loss of production. In the novel approach discussed earlier, we wish to inject either deasphalted oil or a suitable solvent into theproduction string through a chemical injection line, as shown in Fig. 9.37. This approach is intrinsically different in that no

9.4.6 Combating Wellbore Solids Summary.

Sec. 9.4 presents proactive approaches to mitigating paraffin and asphaltene deposition in production strings. The first approach involves fluid circulation, leading to alteration of the p-T trace of the produced fluid to avoid intersecting the solid envelope. Specifically, mitigation of paraffins in deepwater situations was attempted. As exploration of deepwater prospects matures, flow assurance becomes cornerstone to their development. For instance, seafloor processing of all fluid streams is being actively investigated. As the results of this study show, ever increasing riser length will pose considerable challenges to conventional production systems. Electrical heating of flowlines and riser is another option that is factored in while designing flow assurance. Nonetheless, models presented here may be used as the starting point for designing both conventional and deepwater production strings.

For remediation of asphaltenes, practical solutions involve direct solvent injection into the production string when the reservoir fluid is in an unfavorable state relative to the AFE. Computational results shed light on temperature profiles of both the injection and production fluids. The model also allows one to adjust production rate, thereby permitting optimization of the solvent injection rate in relation to AFE. Both approaches are conceptual and, therefore, need field verification. Highlights of this section are outlined.

- Flowing temperature profile of a producing fluid may be altered by circulating a fluid in the annulus. When the altered temperature profile avoids intersecting the equilibrium solid envelope, deposition of solids is minimized. Low-circulation rates are efficient for heat removal, while mitigating asphaltene deposition.
- Intermittent or continuous injection of chemicals, such as deasphalted oil, may provide the desired result, when alteration of the fluid-temperature profile becomes infeasible.
- High-rate production coupled with fluid circulation and/or tubing insulation appears attractive for controlling wax deposition.

Summary

This chapter treats applications of four elements of production operations, as practiced in the field. Our main objective is to show how the principles learned earlier are used to solve everyday field problems. That is why complete treatment of any element is not attempted.

As expected, many problems are intertwined. For instance, transient fluid and heat flow simulator, discussed in Chap. 7, became useful in dealing with seamless systems analysis. Similarly, principles of heat flow, discussed in Chap. 5, were instrumental in developing working models for fluid temperatures in gas-lift operation, geothermal production, steam injection, and combating the solids problem. We also demonstrate that the drift-flux approach, used successfully in modeling gas/oil flow, is equally applicable to flow of steam and water in both upward and downward directions.

Nomenclature

a_t = linear coefficient in the Forchheimer deliverability equation, STB/D-psi

A = cross-sectional area for flow, ft^2

b = nonlinear coefficient in deliverability equation, (STB/D)^2-psi

B = constant defined by Eq. 9.8, ft

B' = constant ($=Bw_t/w_a$) used in Eq. 9.14, ft

B'' = constant defined by Eq. 9.15, ft

c_a = annular-fluid heat capacity, Btu/(lbm-°F)

c_e = formation heat capacity, Btu/(lbm-°F)

c_f, c_{flt} = specific heat of tubing fluid, Btu/(lbm-°F)

c_{ga} = specific heat of annular gas, Btu/(lbm-°F)

c_p = specific heat of fluid, Btu/(lbm-°F)

c_{pa} = specific heat of annular gas, Btu/(lbm-°F)

c_{pt} = specific heat of tubing fluid, Btu/(lbm-°F)

c_w = circulating-fluid heat capacity, Btu/(lbm-°F)

C = coefficient in backpressure deliverability equation, STB/D-psi

C_c = contraction coefficient used in Eq. 9.34, dimensionless

C_f = Joule-Thompson coefficient of fluid, lbm/(ft-°F-sec^2)

C_J = Joule-Thompson coefficient, °F/psi

d = diameter, ft

D = non-Darcy flow coefficient, STB/D

D' = constant defined by Eq. 9.16, °F

D_a = constant defined by Eq. 9.11, Btu/lbm-ft

D_t = constant analogous to D_a for tubing fluid, Btu/(lbm-ft)

f = friction factor, dimensionless

f_L = liquid holdup, dimensionless

g = gravitational acceleration, ft/sec^2

g_c = conversion factor, dimensionless

g_G = geothermal gradient, °F/ft

G = mass flux (mass flow rate/unit area), lbm/(hr-ft^2)

G^* = reference mass flux (=307), lbm/(hr-ft^2)

h = formation thickness, ft

h_a = forced-convection-heat-transfer coefficient, Btu/(°F-hr-ft)

h_c = natural-convection-heat-transfer coefficient, Btu/(°F-hr-ft)

H, H_f = fluid enthalpy, Btu/lbm

J = conversion factor, dimensionless

J_p = productivity index, STB/D-psi

k = formation permeability, md

k_c = casing material conductivity, Btu/(hr-ft-°F)

k_{cm} = cement conductivity, Btu/(hr-ft-°F)

k_e = earth or formation thermal conductivity, Btu/(hr-ft-°F)

L = pipe length, ft

L_e = equivalent length factor, dimensionless

L_R = relaxation length parameter, ft^{-1}

$m^* = kh/(141.2\mu B)$, md-ft/cp

p = pressure, psi

p^* = Horner's extrapolated pressure, psia

p_D = dimensionless pressure ($=\Delta p/141.2qB\mu$)

p_{ws} = shut-in bottomhole pressure, psia

p_{wf} = flowing bottomhole pressure, psia/flowing wellhead pressure, psia

q, q_{wh} = oil rate at wellhead, STB/D

q_c = liquid circulation rate, STB/D

q_m = maximum or open-flow potential, STB/D

q_{sf} = sandface oil rate, STB/D

q_t = total (gas+liquid) volumetric fluid flow rate, STB/D

Q = heat flow from formation to annular fluid per unit well length, Btu/(hr-ft)

Q_{ta} = heat flow from annular to tubing fluid per unit well length, Btu/(hr-ft)

r_c, r_w = wellbore radius, ft

r_{co} = outside casing radius, in.

r_{jo} = outside injection-tubular radius, in.

r_t = tubing radius, ft

r_{ti} = inside tubing radius, in.

r_{to} = outside tubing radius, in.

R_A = area ratio ($=A_2/A_1$), dimensionless

R_t = formation resistivity, ohm-m

s = damaged or static skin, dimensionless

s' = total skin ($=s+Dq$), dimensionless

t = producing time, hr

t_D = dimensionless production or injection time ($=2.64 \times 10^{-4} kt/\phi\mu c_t r_w^2$)

t_e = effective superposition time, hr

t_p = production time, hr

T = temperature, °F

T_a = annular-fluid temperature, °F

T_{ai} = annular-fluid temperature at surface, °F

T_D = dimensionless temperature [$=2\pi k_e(T_{wb}-T_{ei})/q_F$]

T_{ei} = formation static temperature at bottomhole, °F

T_{es} = formation static temperature at surface, °F

T_f = tubing-fluid temperature, °F

T_t = tubing fluid temperature, °F

T_w = circulating water or fluid temperature, °F

T_{wb} = wellbore/formation interface temperature, °F

U = overall-heat-transfer coefficient, Btu/(hr-ft²-°F)

U_1 = overall-heat-transfer coefficient for tubing fluid, Btu/(hr-°F-ft)

U_{tc} = overall-heat-transfer coefficient for tubular in seawater, Btu/(hr-°F-ft)

U_{to} = overall-heat-transfer coefficient for annular fluid, Btu/(hr-°F-ft)

v, v_f = fluid velocity, ft/sec

w, w_f = mass rate of tubing fluid, lbm/hr

w_w = mass rate of circulating fluid, lbm/hr

x = mass fraction of gas in the tubing-fluid mixture, dimensionless

X = Lockhart/Martinelli parameter, dimensionless

z = vertical well depth, ft

Z = gas-law deviation factor, dimensionless

α = constant used in Eq. 9.17, defined by Eq. E-17, °F

α_h = heat diffusivity of formation [$=k_e/c_e\rho_e$], ft²/hr

β = constant used in Eq. 9.18, defined by Eq. E-18, °F

Δp = pressure drop, psi

Δq = rate change, STB/D

Δt = shut-in time, hr

λ_1, λ_2 = constants used in Eq. 9.18, defined by Eqs. E-11 and E-12, °F

μ = oil viscosity, cp

ρ = density, lbm/ft³

ρ_e = bulk density of earth or formation, lbm/ft³

ϕ = porosity, fraction

Subscripts

1 = inlet state

2 = outlet state

a = annulus

bh = bottomhole

c = casing

cem = cement

ci = casing inside

co = casing outside

e = earth

es = earth static

fit = fitting

g = gas

i = index for summation

ins = insulation

L = liquid

n = n^{th} time index

t = tubing

ti = tubing inside

to = tubing outside

ts = tubing saturated

References

1. Gilbert, W.E.: "Flowing and Gas-Lift Well Performance," *Drill. and Prod. Prac.*, API (1954) 126.

2. Brown, K.E. and Lea, J.F.: "Nodal Systems Analysis of Oil and Gas Wells," *JPT* (October 1985) 1751.

3. Mach, J., Proano, E., and Brown, K.E.: "A Nodal Approach for Applying Systems Analysis to the Flowing and Artificial Lift Oil or Gas Well," paper SPE 8025 available from SPE, Richardson, Texas (1979).

4. Brown, K.E. *et al.*: "Production Optimization of Oil and Gas Wells by Nodal Systems Analysis," *Technology of Artificial Lift Methods*, PennWell Publishing Co., Tulsa, Oklahoma (1984) Chap. 4, 87.

5. Vogel, J.V.: "Inflow Performance Relationships for Solution-Gas Drive Wells," *JPT* (January 1968) 83; *Trans.*, AIME, **243**.

6. Brill, J.P. and Mukherjee, H.: *Multiphase Flow in Wells*, Monograph Series, SPE, Richardson, Texas (1999) **17**, 86.

7. Economides, M.J., Hill, A.D., and Economides, C.A.: *Petroleum Production Systems*, Prentice-Hall, Englewood Cliffs, New Jersey (1994) 173.

8. Beggs, H.D.: *Production Optimization Using Nodal Analysis*, OGCI, Tulsa, Oklahoma (1991) Chap. 4, 133.

9. Hagedorn, A.R. and Brown, K.E.: "Experimental Study of Pressure Gradients Occurring During Continuous Two-Phase Flow in Small Diameter Vertical Conduits," *JPT* (April 1965) 475.

10. Chambers, K.T. *et al.*: "Characterization of a Carbonate Reservoir Using Pressure-Transient Tests and Production Logs: Tengiz Field, Kazakstan," *SPEREE* (August 2001) 250.

11. Kabir, C.S. *et al.*: "Combined Production Logging, Transient Testing, and Well-Performance Analysis," paper SPE 48965 presented at the 1998 SPE Annual Technical Conference and Exhibition, New Orleans, 27–30 September.

12. Hasan, A.R., Kabir, C.S., and Wang, X.: "Wellbore Two-Phase Flow and Heat Transfer During Transient Testing," *SPEJ* (June 1998) 174.

13. Ansari, A.M. *et al.*: "A Comprehensive Mechanistic Model for Upward Two-Phase Flow in Wellbores," *SPE Prod. & Facilities* (May 1994) 143.

14. Hasan, A.R. and Kabir, C.S.: "Two-Phase Flow in Vertical and Inclined Annuli," *Int. J. Multiphase Flow* (1992) **18**, No. 2, 279.

15. Poettmann, F.H. and Carpenter, P.G.: "The Multiphase Flow of Gas, Oil, and Water Through Vertical Flow Strings," *API Dril. and Prod. Prac.* (1952) 257.

16. Bertuzzi, A.F., Welchon, J.K., and Poettmann, F.H.: "Description and Analysis of an Efficient Continuous-Flow Gas-Lift Installation," *Trans.*, AIME (1953) **198**, 271.

17. Brown, K.E., Mach, J., and Proano, E.A.: "Application of Systems Analysis Techniques in Optimizing Gas Lift Installations," *J. Energy Resources Tech.*, ASME (June 1982) 157.

18. Kanu, E.P., Mach, J., and Brown, K.E.: "Economic Approach to Oil Production and Gas Allocation in Continuous Gas Lift," *JPT* (October 1981) 1887.

19. Mach, J.M., Proano, E.A., Mukherjee, H., and Brown, K.E.: "A New Concept in Continuous-Flow Gas-Lift Design," *SPEJ* (December 1983) 885.

20. Winkler, H.W.: *Petroleum Engineering Handbook*, H.B. Bradley (ed.), SPE, Richardson, Texas (1987) Chap. 5, 1.

21. Kirkpatrick, C.V.: "Advances in Gas-Lift Technology," *API Dril. and Prod. Prac.* (1959) 24.

22. Shiu, K.S. and Beggs, H.D.: "Predicting Temperatures in Flowing Oil Wells," *J. Energy Resources Tech.*, ASME (March 1980) 1.

23. Hasan, A.R. and Kabir, C.S.: "A Mechanistic Model for Computing Fluid Temperature Profiles in Gas-Lift Wells," *SPEPF* (August 1996) 179.

24. Ramey, H.J., Jr.: "Wellbore Heat Transmission," *JPT* (April 1962) 427; *Trans.*, AIME, **225**.

25. Chiu, K. and Thakur, S.C.: "Modeling of Wellbore Heat Losses in Directional Wells Under Changing Injection Conditions," paper SPE 22870 presented at the 1991 SPE Annual Technical Conference and Exhibition, Dallas, 6–9 October.

26. Hasan, A.R. and Kabir, C.S.: "Aspects of Wellbore Heat Transfer During Two-Phase Flow," *SPEPF* (August 1994) 211.

27. Kanu, E.P.: "Systems Analysis Hikes Well Performance," *Petroleum Engineer International* (May 1981) 96.

28. Sagar, R.K. *et al.*: "A Mechanistic Model of a Nitrogen-Charged, Pressure-Operated Gas-Lift Valve," paper SPE 24838 presented at the 1992 SPE Annual Technical Conference and Exhibition, Washington, DC, 4–7 October.

29. Acuna, H.G., Schmidt, Z., and Doty, D.R.: "Modeling of Gas Rates Through 1-in. Nitrogen-Charged Gas-Lift Valves," paper SPE 24839 presented at the 1992 SPE Annual Technical Conference and Exhibition, Washington, DC, 4–7 October.

30. Tang, Y. *et al.*: "Transient Dynamic Characteristics of the Gas-Lift Unloading Process," *SPEJ* (September 1999) 268.

31. Satter, A.: "Heat Losses of Steam Down a Wellbore," *JPT* (July 1965) 845; *Trans.*, AIME, **234**.

32. Earlougher, R.C., Jr.: "Some Practical Considerations in the Design of Steam Injection Wells," *JPT* (January 1969) 79; *Trans.*, AIME, **246**.

33. Pacheco, E.F. and Farouq Ali, S.M.: "Wellbore Heat Losses and Pressure Drop in Steam Injection," *JPT* (February 1972) 139.

34. Sugiura, T. and Farouq Ali, S.M.: "A Comprehensive Wellbore Steam/Water Flow Model for Steam Injection and Geothermal Applications," paper SPE 7966 presented at the 1979 SPE California Regional Meeting, Ventura, California, 18–20 April.

35. Griston, S. and Willhite, G.P.: "Numerical Model for Evaluating Concentric Steam Injection Wells," paper SPE 16337 presented at the 1987 SPE California Regional Meeting, Ventura, California, 8–10 April.

36. Hasan, A.R.: "Void Fraction in Bubbly and Slug Flow in Downward Two-Phase Flow in Vertical and Inclined Systems," *SPEPF* (August 1995) 172.

37. Beggs, H.D. and Brill, J.P.: "A Study of Two-Phase Flow in Inclined Pipes," *JPT* (May 1973) 607.

38. Argument, P.T.: "A Mechanistic Model of Multiphase Heat and Fluid Flow in Geothermal Wells," MS thesis, U. of North Dakota, Grand Forks, North Dakota (1996).

39. James, R.: "Steam-Water Critical Flow Through Pipes," *Proc.*, Inst. Mech. Engrs. (1962) **176,** 741.

40. James, R.: "Metering of Steam-Water Two-Phase Flow by Sharp-Edged Orifices," *Proc.*, Inst. Mech. Engrs. (1965) **180,** 549.

41. Hasan, A.R.: "Modifications of James Correlation for Predicting Mass Flux and Steam Quality in Geothermal Wells Containing Dissolved Gases and Solids," *Chem. Eng. Comm.* (1990) **97,** 1.

42. Hasan, A.R.: "Simultaneous Measurement of Mass Flux and Steam Quality in Geothermal Wells Using Homogeneous and Separated Flow Models," *Chem. Eng. Comm.* (1991) **105,** 185.

43. Chisholm, D.: "The Influence of Mass Velocity on Friction Pressure Gradients During Steam-Water Flow," paper 35 presented at the March 1968 Thermodynamics and Fluid Mechanics Convention, Inst. Mech. Eng., Bristol.

44. Chien, S.F. and Schrodt, J.L.G.: "Determination of Steam Quality and Flow Rate Using Pressure Data from an Orifice Meter and a Critical Flowmeter," paper SPE 24832 presented at the 1992 SPE Annual Technical Conference and Exhibition, Washington DC, 4–7 October.

45. King, R.C. and Crocker, S.: *Pipe Handbook,* fifth edition, McGraw-Hill Book Co. Inc., New York City (1967) Chap. 3, 59.

46. Chisholm, D.: "Pressure Losses in Bends and Tees During Steam-Water Flow," NEL Report (1967) No. 318.

47. Collier, J.G.: *Convective Boiling and Condensation*, second edition, McGraw-Hill Book Co. Inc., New York City (1981) 86–94.

48. Perry, J.H.: *Chemical Engineering Handbook,* third edition, McGraw-Hill Book Co. Inc., New York City (1950) 389.

49. Hong, K.C.: *Steamflood Reservoir Management*, PennWell Publishing Company, Tulsa (1994) 518.

50. Leontaritis, K.J. and Mansoori, G.A.: "Asphaltene Deposition: A Survey of Field Experiences and Research Approaches," *J. Pet. Sci. Eng.* (August 1988) **1**, 229.

51. Hasan, A.R., Kouba, G.E., and Wang. X.: "Transient Analysis to Locate and Characterize Plugs in Gas Wells," paper SPE 36553 presented at the 1996 SPE Annual Technical Conference and Exhibition, Denver, 5–9 October.

52. Massinon, R.V.J.: "A Real-Time Transient Hydraulic Model for Leak Detection and Batch Tracking on a Liquid Pipeline System," paper 88-39-93 presented at the 1988, Annual Technical Meeting of CIM, Calgary, AB, Canada, 12–16 June.

53. Kabir, C.S. *et al.*: "An Approach to Mitigating Wellbore Solids Deposition," paper SPE 71558 presented at the SPE 2001 Annual Technical Conference and Exhibition, New Orleans, 30 September–3 October.

54. Jamaluddin, A.K.M. *et al.*: "A Systematic Approach in Deepwater Flow Assurance Fluid Characterization," paper SPE 71546 presented at the SPE 2001 Annual Technical Conference and Exhibition, New Orleans, 30 September–3 October.

55. Hammami, A. and Raines, M.A.: "Paraffin Deposition From Crude Oils: Comparison of Laboratory Results With Field Data," *SPEJ* (March 1999).

56. Monger-McClure, T.G., Tackett, J.E., and Merrill, L.S.: "Comparisons of Cloud Point Measurement and Paraffin Prediction Methods," *SPEPF* (February 1999) 4.

57. Burger, E.D., Perkins, T.K., and Striegler, J.H.: "Studies of Wax Deposition in the Trans Alaska Pipeline," *JPT* (1981) 1075.

58. Weingarten, J.S. and Euchner, J.A.: "Methods for Predicting Wax Precipitation and Deposition," *SPEPE* (February 1988) 121.

59. Majeed, A., Bringedal, B., and Overa, S.: "Model Calculates Wax Deposition for North Sea Oils," *Oil & Gas J.*, **88** (1990) 63.

60. Brown, T.S., Niesen, V.G., and Erickson, D.D.: "Measurement and Prediction of the Kinetics of Paraffin Deposition," *JPT* (April 1995) 328.

61. Singh, P. *et al.*: "Formation and Aging of Incipient Thin Film Wax-Oil Gels," *AIChE J*, **46**, No. 5 (May 2000) 1059.

62. Leontaritis, K.J. and Mansoori, G.A.: "Asphaltene Flocculation During Oil Production and Processing: A Thermodynamic-Colloidal Model," paper SPE 16258 presented at the 1987 SPE International Symposium on Oil Field Chemistry, San Antonio, February 4–6.

63. Pan, H. and Firoozabadi, A.: "Thermodynamic Micellization Model for Asphaltene Aggregation and Precipitation in Petroleum Fluids," *SPEPF* (May 1998) 118.

64. MacMillan, D.J. *et al.*: "A Unified Approach to Asphaltene Precipitation: Laboratory Measurement and Modeling," *JPT* (September 1995) 788.

65. Nghiem, L.X. and Coombe, D.A.: "Modeling Asphaltene Precipitation During Primary Depletion," *SPEJ* (June 1997) 170.

66. Barker, K.M.: "Formation Damage Related to Hot Oiling," paper SPE 16230 presented at the 1987 SPE Production Operations Symposium, Oklahoma City, Oklahoma, 8–10 March.

67. Mansure, A.J. and Barker, K.M.: "Insights Into Good Hot Oiling Practices," paper SPE 25484 presented at the 1993 SPE Production Operations Symposium, Oklahoma City, 21–23 March.

68. Jamaluddin, A.K.M., Nozarko, T.W., and Sills, S.: "De-asphalted Oil: A Natural Asphaltene Solvent," *SPEPF* (August 1996) 161.

69. Kabir, C.S. and Jamaluddin, A.K.M.: "Asphaltene Characterization and Mitigation in South Kuwait's Marrat Reservoir," *SPEPF* (November 2002).

SI Metric Conversion Factors

Btu × 1.055 056	E + 00	= kJ
Btu/lbm × 2.326*	E + 03	= J/kg
Btu/(lbm-°F) × 4.186 8*	E + 03	= J/(kg·K)
cp × 1.0*	E – 03	= Pa s
ft × 3.048*	E – 01	= m
ft² × 9.290 304*	E – 02	= m²
°F (°F – 32)/1.8		= °C
in. × 2.54*	E + 00	= cm
lbf × 4.448 222	E + 00	= N
lbm × 4.535 924	E – 01	= kg
lbm/ft³ × 1.601 846	E + 01	= kg/m³
psi × 6.894 757	E + 00	= kPa

*Conversion factor is exact.

Chapter 10
Production Logging

10.1 Introduction

Production logs (PLs) have the potential for providing an array of valuable information throughout the life of a well. This array of information includes well performance evaluation, workover and completion evaluation, and reservoir performance monitoring.

Conventional production logging as practiced today traces its origin to the introduction of temperature logs in 1937[1] and, subsequently, to the use of other sensors in 1965.[2] Over the past three decades, continuous enhancement of sensor resolution paved the way for improved downhole diagnosis. One cornerstone to the early success lay in the ability to run multiple sensors in one run, although surface transmission of only one sensor response at a time was permitted in 1971.[3] About a decade later, simultaneous transmission[4] of signals from all sensors to the surface became possible. Advances in data gathering techniques and instrumentation continue to this day. At the same time, our understanding of mechanics of gas/liquid and liquid/liquid flows in conduits of various orientations, as discussed in Chap. 4, has also matured over the years. Despite these advances, integration of mechanistic models with sensor responses have lagged behind. For instance, a holdup model may be used but without an explicit usage of the flow-pattern map associated with it. We also observe that the traditional approach of station-based analysis, dealing with a few data points, often does not explain anomalous flow behavior. Stated differently, one wonders whether certain sensor response is induced by the complex flow behavior, poor sensor resolution, logging speed, or a combination thereof.

In this chapter, we discuss a rigorous depth-indexed analysis of flowmeter response. Thereafter, we address how flow-pattern-based mechanistic models, discussed in Chaps. 3 and 4, can be integrated with log responses to gain superior understanding of flow mechanics and improved interpretation. Although the illustrative field examples involve oil/water flow, the principle can be extended to all flow situations.

For a detailed treatment of conventional topics, the reader is referred to other work, notably those of McKinley[5] and the SPE monograph by Hill.[6] Much of the material presented here is abstracted from Refs. 7 and 8, which consider examples from Kuwait's Burgan field.

10.2 PL Interpretation

10.2.1 Conventional Approach. The idealized spinner response owing to fluid influx at different tool velocities is illustrated by the synthetic Example A, shown in **Fig. 10.1.** Between the sets of perforations, spinner revolutions ideally remain constant. An increase in spinner response signifies fluid entry, while the decreased response suggests loss of fluid because of leak or injection into the formation. For each pass at a constant cable speed, a depth-dependent spinner profile or spinner response will develop. Ideally, each response will be parallel to one another. These data can be analyzed to quantify the amount of fluid produced, injected or cross-flowed within the wellbore.

As shown in Fig. 10.1, at each depth (A, B, C, and D), a linear regression of the data yields a slope and an x-axis intercept. Fluid density, viscosity and the spinner bearing friction affect the slope and the position of the line in the calibration plot. However, with constant fluid properties, the slope of the lines will be theoretically parallel to one another between the 100 and 0% flow intervals, as illustrated in **Fig. 10.2.** Here, Depth D represents the no-flow interval below all perforations, while Depth A represents the maximum flow above all fluid entry from the formation.

Typically, log presentation includes a static and dynamic spinner calibration plot. The static calibration may be derived from logging passes below all contributing perforations or sump area in the well during flowing conditions or from passes over the entire interval during well shut-in. In contrast, the dynamic calibration plot is usually generated from the data collected during flowing conditions at specific depth intervals above the sump. The selection of depth intervals is arbitrary and is ordinarily left to the discretion of the onsite log analyst.

10.2.2 Depth-Indexed Analysis. PL interpretation can be improved by generating depth-indexed flowmeter response quality traces (FRQT). The FRQT basically consist of three tracks that present the statistics in terms of the x-axis intercept, the slope's correlation coefficient, and the slope of the line at each depth. Performing a regression analysis of spinner velocity vs. cable velocity generates the spinner calibration response statistics at every depth or small interval. This analysis is a significant departure from the norm, which

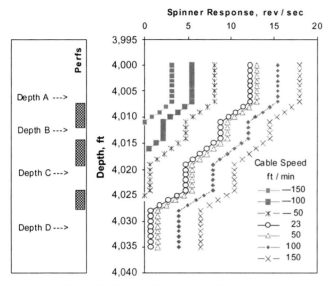

Fig. 10.1—Production spinner, Example A.

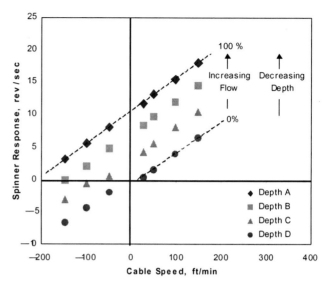

Fig. 10.2—Combined static and dynamic spinner calibration plot.

relies on the use of a spinner response chart for a small group of selected intervals. Details of the calculations are provided in Appendix F.

Using FRQT, an analyst can identify logging intervals that are appropriate for interpretation. For instance, poor correlation coefficients shed light on the behavior of fluids in the wellbore, reflecting turbulence or jetting effects, changes in fluid viscosity at the new entry point, and abrupt changes in cable speed. This approach allows us to distinguish poor data quality from true system response.

In Example A, data were evaluated at four depth intervals. This method provides only an indication of the flow rate change between intervals and not over the complete logged interval. Performing a linear regression on a continuous basis at small discrete intervals, through the logged section, yields additional information on flow behavior. For instance, the subtle spinner changes that occur during the logging passes are easier to recognize. If all logging passes at constant cable speeds result in parallel spinner response curves, as presented in Fig. 10.1, then the slopes and correlation coefficients will remain constant. Plotting this information of Example A, **Fig. 10.3** replaces the traditional plot in Fig. 10.2. That is because generating a conventional single calibration plot for all discrete depth intervals will produce an illegible graph. Fig. 10.3 improves display of the data, which, in turn, may improve the confidence in interpretation.

The spinner response at each depth is consistent with the tool velocity, provided the correlation coefficient is one and at least two tool passes are available. The relative fluid velocity is the same for each pass at a given depth. To obtain meaningful correlation coefficients, a minimum of four passes at different logging speeds, preferably in increments of 30 ft/min is recommended. Correlation coefficients less than one may be a result of many factors that are discussed later.

Evaluating the slope of the line at each discrete depth, while considering the correlation coefficient, can assist in interpretation. Changing slopes throughout the complete log interval may indicate changing fluid properties or possibly poor data correlations. For the entire log section, checking the

trends and values of the FRQT, reviewing the collected pressure, temperature, and specific gravity data, and knowing the characteristics of the produced fluids may help explain the anomalous response.

We find the x-axis intercept and, hence, the rate to be highly dependent on the slope. When both the correlation coefficient and the slope are continuously changing, the calculated rates from the x-axis intercept may vary significantly. Consequently, interpretation becomes difficult. In these cases, one may identify certain intervals from the revised spinner calibration plot that best represents flow in the well. Other alternatives include increasing the interval by considering several discrete intervals together or by smoothing anomalous and severe data spikes. Regenerating the revised spinner calibration plot will determine the effectiveness of the selected approach.

Similarly, the individual spinner response curves for each cable speed can be normalized to overlay each other, as illustrated by the spinner response overlay, Example A, as shown

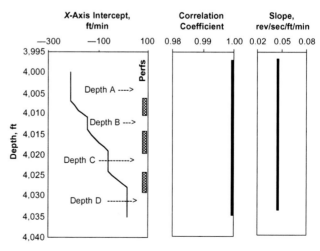

Fig. 10.3—FRQT calibration plot, Example A.

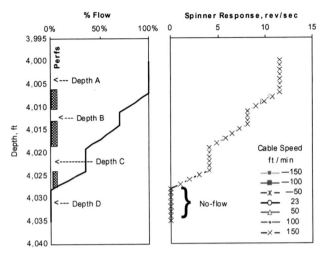

Fig. 10.4—Spinner response overlay, Example A.

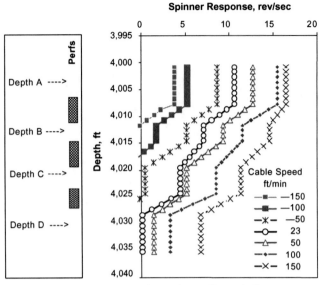

Fig. 10.5—Production spinner, Example B.

in **Fig. 10.4.** In the static or no-flow interval as shown, the spinner response should be zero.

Now, consider the case when the spinner response curves are not parallel to each other over the logged section, as shown in **Fig. 10.5** for Example B. Possible dynamic attributes, such as inclined segregated flow, changing flow regimes, significant slip velocities, perforation flow eddies, poor depth control or spinner mechanical deficiencies may result in incongruous spinner curves. Repeat logging using the same PL tools may not improve interpretation. However, understanding the wellbore flow mechanics and reservoir performance may provide insights into the nature of the problem.

Fig. 10.6 (FRQT calibration plot, Example B) shows the revised spinner calibration plot generated from the synthetic data in Fig 10.5. Note the apparent degradation in the correlation coefficient and an increasing variation in values of slope or spinner rotation. The FRQT provides a qualitative indication that flow measurement and, therefore, interpretation require careful attention.

Although the spinner response curves are parallel between the perforation sets, the correlation coefficients are less than unity. Because the slopes vary, selecting the appro-

priate x-axis intercept is difficult. This observation implies that the rate determination has some associated errors.

Fig. 10.7 presents the overlay of spinner response curves and the fluid contribution profile for Example B. By comparing Figs. 10.4 and 10.7, we note with interest that interpretation of the percentage flow contribution profile did not change significantly between Examples A and B. This is so because the 100% flow rate occurs at the minimum x-axis intercept and the minimum flow rate occurs near zero on the x-axis intercept. Because the x-axis intercept profiles are similar in both cases, the calculated percentage flow yields profiles that are nearly the same.

In some instances, logging programs forego the shut-in passes when a dead area or sump is available in a flowing well. Log interpreters use this assumed static interval to calibrate the no-flow spinner response. Useful pressure, temperature and density information are sacrificed and, as a result, comparisons cannot be made between flowing and static conditions. Often, subtle temperature and density differences

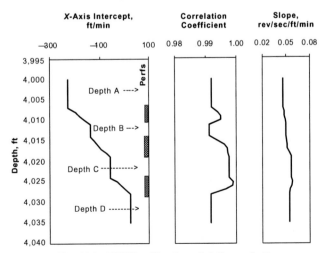

Fig. 10.6—FRQT calibration plot, Example B.

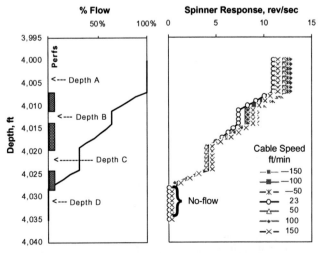

Fig. 10.7—Spinner response overlay, Example B.

　　　　　　　　　　　　　　　　　　　FLUID FLOW AND HEAT TRANSFER IN WELLBORES

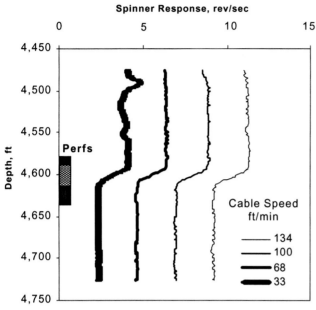

Fig. 10.8—Spinner response at different cable speeds.

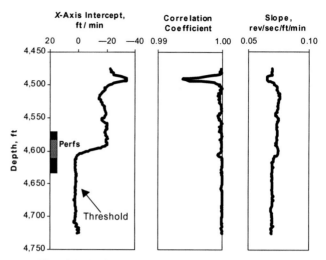

Fig. 10.9—FRQT spinner calibration plot, Well A-22.

between these conditions can help identify flow behind pipe or bottom flow in the well. Additionally, false indication of formation fluid densities can occur when heavier drilling fluids, used in well-kill operations, segregate out in the sump interval. Without the shut-in pressure data, the static reservoir pressure and, hence, the drawdown can only be estimated. As a result, systems-performance analysis may not provide the desired accuracy. By having both flowing and shut-in passes, even when sumps exist, corroborative information from various sensors can provide additional insights to improve interpretation.

10.2.3 Field Examples.

Well A-22. A production log was run in this well to identify the water entry point and any potentially leaking squeezed perforations. From a pulsed neutron capture (PNC) log, ran several years earlier, the oil/water contact (OWC) was found to be 16 ft below the open perforations. The OWC conceivably had risen into the squeezed perforations and could have been partially leaking. This perceived OWC movement accounted for the increasing water production after PNC logging operations were completed. During the PL operation, portable separator testing showed that the well was producing at 1,274 STB/D with a 54% water cut.

In **Fig. 10.8,** four different cable speeds in the downward direction are presented in the flowing condition for this well. The line pattern is parallel except near the top, above 4,500 ft. The significant change in spinner rotation for each line consistently occurs across the interval of open perforations, 4,588 to 4,611 ft. The darkened set of squeezed perforation above and below the open perforations do not appear to be leaking.

Here, shut-in passes were not taken because the sump was considered to be of insufficient length, thereby minimizing the deferred production. After generating the spinner calibration plot from below the point of fluid entry at 4,611 ft, the static threshold intercept is approximately 2.13 ft/min, as illustrated in Example A, shown in **Fig. 10.9.** This value is

realistic and is well within the range of those typically observed in many cases during static conditions and is interpreted as a no-flow condition.

An anomalous spike develops owing to the spinner rotation inconsistency, as seen near the top of the 33 ft/min pass in Fig. 10.8. Data collected above this point should not be considered in the rate calculation because it will suggest additional fluid entry with possible crossflow. The correlation coefficient values in Fig. 10.9 support this notion. Values closer to unity suggest better data consistency between passes. Correspondingly, the changing slope cause the x-intercept and, therefore, the rate calculation to change. Interpretation of data above 4,500 ft is cautioned. Note the slope values increase slightly above the sump zone. This observation may possibly be attributed to a combination of tool friction effects, in addition to viscosity and density difference between the formation water and the produced fluids.

Developing a frequency plot for the correlation coefficient over the entire logged section for the upflowing passes and downflowing passes, as shown in **Fig. 10.10,** provides an indication of consistency of the correlation. Clearly, about 95% of the data in both cases have a correlation better than 0.998. This observation is significant, considering that there are over 250 individual-depth regression analyses for this well at four different logging speeds. The degradation in the downflowing pass occurs because of the anomalous spike in the spinner response. Static pass correlations are not presented because they were unavailable.

Plotting other data, such as specific gravity, temperature and pressure, can provide additional support for this conclusion. In **Fig. 10.11,** the temperature and specific gravity plots indicate major fluid entry just below 4,600 ft, while a noticeable change in temperature or specific gravity is not observed above 4,500 ft. This suite of data supports the notion that there is no fluid entry near the top of the logged interval. Although not shown, the same conclusion was drawn from the upflowing pass interpretation.

The flowing bottomhole pressure of 1,960 psia is above the bubblepoint pressure, which is estimated at approximately 1,600 psia. The producing mixture specific gravity

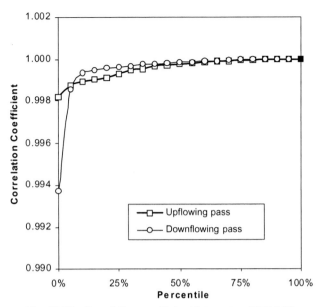

Fig. 10.10—Correlation coefficient frequency, Well A-22.

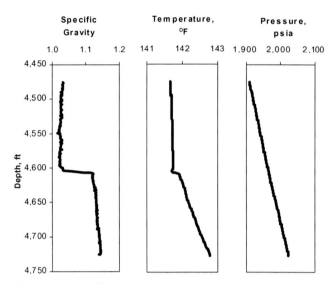

Fig. 10.11—Specific gravity, temperature, and pressure, Well A-22.

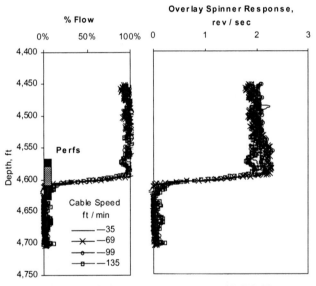

Fig. 10.12—Spinner response overlay, Well A-22.

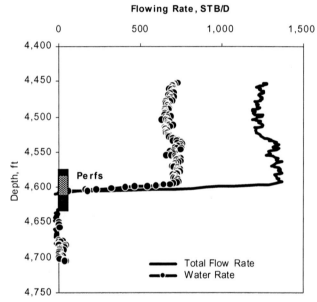

Fig. 10.13—Spinner interpretation, Well A-22.

values are not significantly lowered and, therefore, do not reflect gas evolution.

Knowing the geothermal gradient, as discussed in Sec. 8.2, and the water specific gravity, we can conclude that below 4,600 ft the geothermal gradient exists, and the formation water has segregated into the sump. However, static passes would have provided additional data for comparison, thereby revealing conclusively whether any fluid was channeling behind the pipe from below the bottom perforations.

Although not presented, the flow profile interpretation for the up/down passes is similar, with the exception of the interval above 4,500 ft, where the anomaly is not repeated. Discounting the spinner rotation spike in **Fig. 10.12,** the maximum or 100% flow is observed just above the open perforations. Accounting for the cable speeds, the upward spinner response overlay is generated to normalize the spinner rotation. Using the corresponding spinner data, the calculated

surface rates of approximately 1,325 STB/D from the downhole spinner rotation are similar to the independently measured field surface rates of 1,274 STB/D. Corroborating the rate measurements from various sources can be beneficial, particularly when the flow rates are less than 1,000 STB/D. If available, use should be made of the continuous flowmeter inside the tubing to substantiate the rate measurements, as discussed in Chap. 9, Sec. 9.1.

In **Fig. 10.13,** the total and water rates for the upflowing pass are shown. Assuming the water-specific gravity to be 1.13 and the oil gravity to be 0.77, the calculated surface water cut from the measured mixture specific gravity yields a value ranging between 47 and 62%, depending on the slip model used. The flow regime map and the slip model are discussed in detail in the next section.

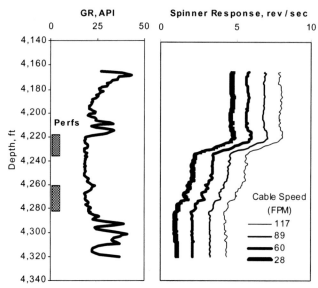

Fig. 10.14—Spinner response at different cable speeds, Well B-325.

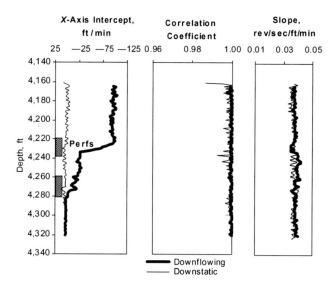

Fig. 10.15—FRQT spinner calibration plot, Well B-325.

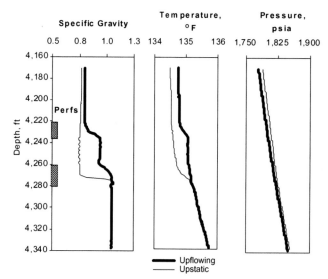

Fig. 10.16—Specific gravity, temperature, and pressure, Well B-325.

Based on results of the interpretation, the well was plugged back at a later date when the increasing water cut had finally killed the well and prevented flow. A through-tubing bridge plug was set at 4,580 ft, and cement was dumped on top, up to 4,573 ft. New perforations were added just above the plugback depth, which resulted in dry oil production of 950 STB/D.

Well B-325. When the water cut reached approximately 30%, the well was logged with a memory PL tool to identify the water source. Because there were two sets of perforations within a large sand body, the lower set was suspected as the main water contributor. This sand profile is presented in **Fig. 10.14.** This graph also includes the downflowing pass spinner response profile at different cable speeds to illustrate the congruent nature of the lines, as well as, to provide a preliminary indication of the flow contribution over the perforated interval.

For this well, the survey included both static and flowing passes in memory mode. The FRQT spinner calibration plot, shown in **Fig. 10.15,** combines both flowing and static FRQT spinner calibration plots for comparison. The x-axis intercept in the static condition is approximately zero. Because the two curves overlay each other below the bottom perforations, a sump is clearly indicated. When the two curves separate, fluid entry is observed near the bottom perforation set. Significant separation occurs over the upper perforation set, where the majority of the well's production occurs.

The slope values over the discrete intervals are fairly realistic and constant for the entire logged interval for both the static and flowing conditions. Additionally, the values of the correlation coefficients are close to unity, indicating favorable interpretable data over the entire interval. This is discussed in more detail with the frequency plots presented later.

In **Fig. 10.16,** both density and temperature data suggest a static sump below the bottom perforation interval.

After the well was shut-in, the fluids segregated, leaving oil above the water-filled sump. As a result, the temperature shows a cooling effect as the water migrates downward from higher up in the wellbore. When the flow resumed, separation occurred between the curves in each track. The flowing density data shows two distinct changes over the perforated intervals. Similarly, the temperature curve also reflects two points of fluid entry in the wellbore.

In **Fig. 10.17,** the spinner response overlay for Well B-325 confirms the profile suggested from earlier graphs. Both the static and the flowing passes overlay each other respectively. Based on the downward cable speeds, the curves were shifted accordingly. The static passes are aligned along the y-axis indicating static conditions. Approximately, 30% of the flow originates from the bottom set of perforations and the remaining 70% from the top set.

For the upflowing passes, there are sections in the individual spinner response traces that are slightly nonparallel. The resulting FRQT display in **Fig. 10.18** indicates between 4,225 ft and 4,275 ft, the uppass flowing correlation coefficient drops to 0.98 with a spike to approximately 0.92. Although the latter correlation is fairly good; nonetheless, it suggests that the data and spinner response passes need

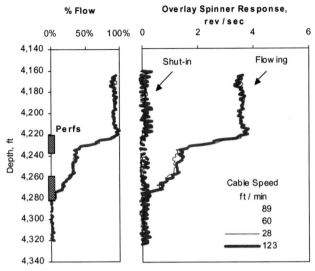

Fig. 10.17—Spinner response overlay, Well B-325.

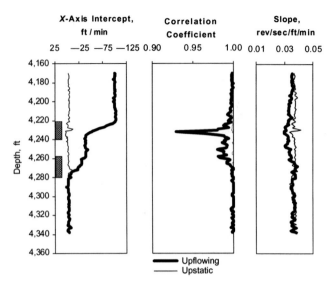

Fig. 10.18—FRQT spinner calibration plot, Well B-325.

reviewing to confirm that they are parallel for the entire dataset. Further, in the same graph, the slope values over the interval change slightly, possibly affecting the intercept values and, hence, the rate.

For the static conditions, the FRQT plots for the up and downpass, in both flowing and shut-in conditions, still yield basically the same interpretation. However, more confidence can be placed on the downpass interpretation. **Fig. 10.19,** displaying the frequency plot, mirrors this reality. Here, we observe that the correlation coefficients for downpasses are closer to unity than uppasses.

Similarly, the frequency plot for the slope in **Fig. 10.20** shows consistency in the shut-in passes in both directions. This behavior is expected because the spinner tool should encounter the same nonmoving fluid profile over the logged section. The flowing passes yield different slopes; however, the downflowing pass has a smaller range of values and, overall, is closer to the static slope values.

The production rate measured downhole using the spinner tool and converted to surface condition matches the sur-

face portable separator measurement within engineering accuracy. For instance, the spinner tool rate, in **Fig. 10.21,** of 4,075 STB/D compares favorably with 4,293 STB/D, measured by a surface separator. The calculated water cuts from the different slip models yield values between 0 and 21%, while the surface sample shake-out varied from 24 to 30%.

A PNC log was run, and the OWC was verified in the middle of the bottom perforations at 4,270 ft. Based on the results of PL interpretation and the PNC log, the well was recommended for a plugback, thereby isolating the bottom set of perforations. Closing the lower set will eliminate the unnecessary water production. Subsequently, a through-tubing bridge plug was set at 4,250 ft, and cement was dumped on top up to 4,240 ft. As a result, the well is producing approximately 4,900 STB/D with no water cut, thereby stressing the usefulness of the FRQT traces. Increased confidence in the interpretation of PL data was thus gained.

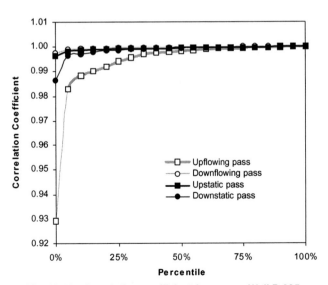

Fig. 10.19—Correlation coefficient frequency, Well B-325.

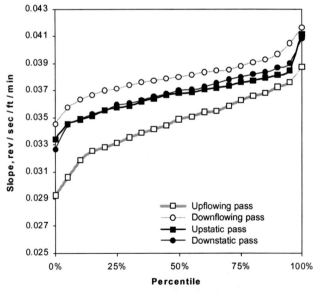

Fig. 10.20—Spinner response slope frequency, Well B-325.

FLUID FLOW AND HEAT TRANSFER IN WELLBORES

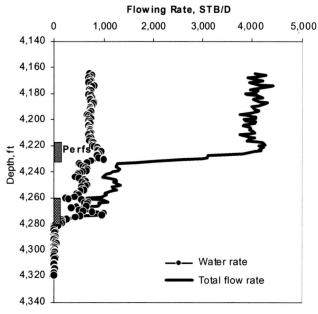

Fig. 10.21—Spinner interpretation, Well B-325.

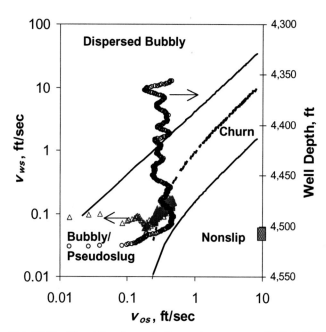

Fig. 10.22—Churn flow impacts flowmeter response, Well A-55.

10.3 Flow-Pattern Maps For PL Analysis

Traditional interpretation procedures do not normally make explicit use of the flow-pattern maps; instead, they establish slip velocity at each station using an empirical correlation. For example, Choquette[9] correlated slip velocity with density difference between the two phases, with water holdup as the parameter. Although this approach has served the industry quite well, we will discuss an alternative method that provides insights into the mechanics of flow and its impact on the flowmeter response.

We illustrate some of these points with field examples. In all cases, we used the Flores *et al.*[10] map, as adapted by Hasan and Kabir,[11] and the holdup model of Hasan and Kabir.[11]

10.3.1 Field Examples.

Well A-55. In this well, the fluid entry occurs through a single interval over 4,500 to 4,510 ft. We graphed the individual phase velocities in **Fig. 10.22.** As shown by the triangles, increases in oil velocity with shallower depth cause most of the flow to occur in the churn-flow regime. The chaotic nature of flow, associated with the churn-flow pattern, triggers an oscillatory response of the flowmeter, shown in circles. The secondary *y*-axis, representing the depth, shows the flowmeter response.

Fig. 10.23 displays the raw spinner response curves for uppasses. The oscillatory response is evident at all cable speeds, thereby confirming the notion that the churning motion of fluids caused this unusual behavior. This type of flow behavior remained unexplained in the past. Clearly, the flow-pattern map helped identify the root cause of this anomalous response.

An analyst often assigns a single value for the velocity-profile correction factor for all production zones. However, this practice may lead serious errors in PL analysis because the correction factor, which is the inverse of the flow parameter, C_o, depends on the local Reynolds number. As we dis-

cussed in Chaps. 3 and 4, the value of the flow parameter depends on the bubble concentration profile and the mixture velocity profile. Indeed, Govier and Aziz[12] presented an elegant analysis for rigorous calculation of C_o when the velocity and concentration profiles are available. In practice, such rigor is unwarranted given the uncertainties involved in the data. Assuming that the bubbles flow mostly through the channel center simplifies the C_o computation because the mixture-velocity profile can be expressed readily as a function of fluid Reynolds number. The essence of this discussion is that the use of a single value for the velocity-profile correction factor is often incorrect because changes in flow velocity occur with fluid entry. **Fig. 10.24** illustrates this point for the A-55 well. We used this depth-depended correction factor to

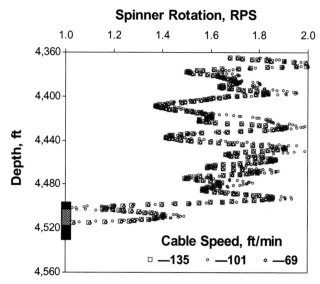

Fig. 10.23—Uppass spinner overlay shows consistent trend, Well A-55.

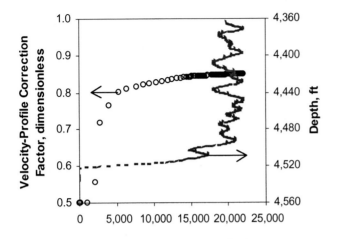

Fig. 10.24—Depth-dependent velocity-profile correction factor, Well A-55.

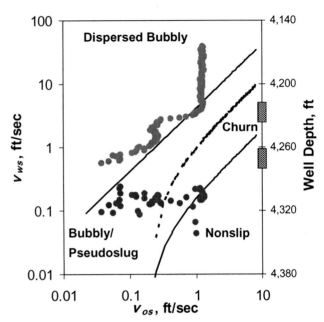

Fig. 10.25—Flowmeter response insensitive to flow regimes, Well B-325.

compute velocity of each phase, thereby avoiding any prior assumption in all examples presented here.

Well B-325. This example was discussed earlier in the previous section. Fluid entry occurs through two sets of perforations in this well, as depicted in **Fig. 10.25.** Bubbly and pseudoslug flows dominate the entry from the bottom set, (4,260 to 4,280 ft) while homogeneous flow (zero slip) is prevalent above the top set (4,220 to 4,235 ft) of perforations. Increased oil influx from the upper interval leads to a no-slip situation; that is, $H_w < 0.30$. Smooth response of the flowmeter is not very surprising. That is because gentle flow is observed in the laboratory for these two flow patterns. Note that transition through the churn-flow pattern occurs over short vertical distance; therefore, it does not present any problem, like the previous case.

To shed light on sensor response, we compared the measured holdup with those computed from two models[11,13] in **Fig. 10.26.** Overall, the agreement between measurement and models is quite good. However, both models tend to overestimate the holdup following the fluid entry. We suspect that the flowmeter had difficulties in responding to the turbulent eddies. That is because sharp excursions to the right occur only for the velocity-based sensor (model-derived values),

but not for the density-based sensor (data). In other words, inaccuracies in flow measurements precipitate this mismatch.

Well A-22. This well was also discussed in the previous section. Here, the velocity of the fluid entry occurring through a single interval (4,570 to 4,610 ft) is low enough to cause bubbly flow only. **Fig. 10.27** illustrates this point. The higher velocity associated with the uppass presents an unambiguous flowmeter trace. In contrast, the downpass exhibits a spike at the top because of spinner resolution at a low velocity. This point is made clear by the overlay of downpass spinner response, as shown in **Fig. 10.28.** Only the data corresponding to the lowest cable speed (33 ft/

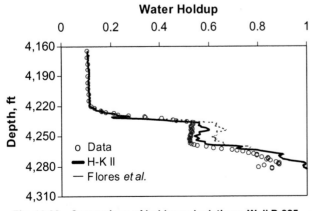

Fig. 10.26—Comparison of holdup calculations, Well B-325.

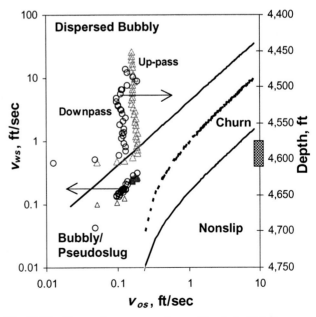

Fig. 10.27—Flowmeter response insensitive to bubbly flow, Well A-22.

FLUID FLOW AND HEAT TRANSFER IN WELLBORES

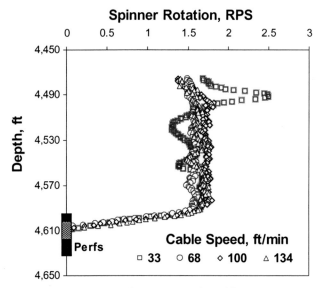

Fig. 10.28—Downpass spinner overlay identifies the problem pass, Well A-22.

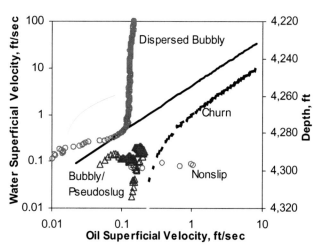

Fig. 10.29—Flowmeter response insensitive to bubbly flow, Well B-175.

min), which is the trace in question, departs from the norm. Therefore, flow-pattern-induced problems can be ruled out safely in this case. As we stressed in the previous section, one must examine all traces for quality control before including them in flow interpretation.

Well B-175. In this example, we illustrate the goodness of model-derived water holdup results with those obtained from two independent measurements. **Fig. 10.29** shows that the bubbly/pseudoslug flow pattern is observed in this well. Comparisons of holdup calculations are made with those obtained from differential manometer-type tool and the bubble-imaging sensor. **Fig. 10.30** compares the performance of the Hasan-Kabir model[11] with the two independent measurements.

The general overestimation by the imaging sensor is explained by the fact that the four low-frequency resistivity probes are mounted around the tool's periphery; that is, near the casing wall. Consequently, fewer bubbles are observed by the probes because the bubbles have the tendency to flow through the center of the channel. In other words, positioning of the probes leads us to observe disproportionately higher volume of the continuous phase, which is water. Thus, in a vertical wellbore, we should expect to observe a somewhat higher H_w value, if water is the continuous phase. Conversely, we would observe a lower H_w value than that measured by a centralized manometer-type tool, if oil is the continuous phase. Bear in mind that neither the water-cut measurement at surface nor the in-situ density measurement has enough precision for a perfect agreement of all three traces. Nonetheless, the agreement shown here is rather reassuring.

10.4 Discussion

Specifying the logging data requirements and suitably presenting the information is an important aspect of making an appropriate PL interpretation. If data are not analyzed over the entire log section, some significant well behavior may be overlooked. In particular, turbulence within the wellbore, jetting through perforations, flow channeling from below,

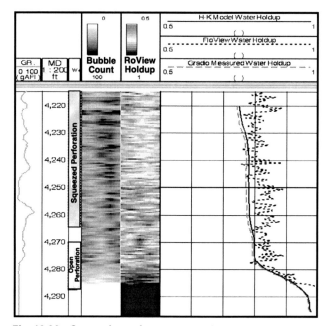

Fig. 10.30—Comparison of measured and computed holdup, Well B-175.

changes in fluid properties, and mechanical problems of a spinner tool may not be evident from limited and specific depth interpretations. In some instances, poor spinner response can be identified and prevented from influencing the PL interpretation. As illustrated in the first field example, we could have incorrectly interpreted the anomalous spinner response spike as crossflow or flow contribution.

By generating the FRQT display, in lieu of the traditional calibration plot, an improved assessment of the flow profile may be achieved through increased understanding. Reviewing specific data over the intervals of lower correlation coefficients and changing spinner response slopes can help discern poor data quality from inherent well producing characteristics. Through repeated application of this procedure, an analyst can quickly perform a quality check of the log, as well as, gain an improved understanding of the well and field performance characteristics.

The use of flow-pattern-based models; that is, those of Hasan and Kabir[11] and Flores et al.,[13] allow understanding of flow regimes prevalent in downhole conditions. For instance, one can conceivably adjust flow conditions to minimize churn flow while logging. We have also identified that smooth holdup response may be derived from a manometer-type tool. However, when the same information is obtained from a flowmeter using a two-phase flow model, overestimation may occur because of the uncertainties in the tool response, in the wake of fluid entry. The intrinsic idea is to collect unambiguous information that can be aided by onsite usage of a flow-pattern map and holdup computation. Imaging sensor is a welcome addition to the PL's tool inventory. One, however, must understand the measurement principle before comparing with the standard tool response.

Summary

In this chapter, we presented two elements to improve understanding of tool response and flow mechanics in PL interpretation. The first element involves the use of a systematic procedure, called the FRQT analysis. This approach makes use of the full suite of data in that the continuous-depth spinner calibration plot can identify intervals over which data are suspect and requires exclusion from interpretation. We recommend simultaneous plotting of data from static, constituting the baseline, and flowing passes. In other words, presenting density, pressure, and temperature of both passes on the same graph facilitates and confirms PL interpretation. The frequency plots of spinner response slopes and correlation coefficients provide a measure of data quality and consistency.

The second element revolves around integrating flow-pattern maps in PL interpretation. Use of a flow-pattern map helps discern fluid entry points, which, in turn, reveals much information about the prevailing flow regimes and anomalies in flowmeter response. Above all, it provides insights into mechanics of flow. For instance, holdups, derived from either the density-based or the velocity-based sensor, will have a different response.

Nomenclature

v_{os} = superficial oil velocity, ft/sec
v_{ws} = superficial water velocity, ft/sec

References

1. Schlumberger, M., Doll, H.G., and Perebinossoff, A.: "Temperature Measurements in Oil Wells," *J. Inst. Pet. Technologists* (January 1937) **23**, No. 159.
2. Wade, R.T. *et al.*: "Production Logging–The Key to Optimum Well Performance," *JPT* (February 1965) 137.
3. Meunier, D., Tixier, M.P., and Bonnet, J.L.: "The Production Combination Tool–A New System for Production Monitoring," *JPT* (May 1971) 603.
4. Anderson, R.A. *et al.*: "A Production Logging Tool With Simultaneous Measurements," *JPT* (February 1980) 191.
5. McKinley, R.M.: "Production Logging," paper SPE 10035 presented at the 1982 SPE Intl. Petroleum Exhibition and Technical Symposium, Beijing, 18–26 March.
6. Hill, A.D.: *Production Logging–Theoretical and Interpretative Elements*, Monograph Series, SPE, Richardson, Texas (1990) **14**.
7. Hoadley, S.F., Kabir, C.S., and Kamal, D.: "Continuous Depth-Indexed Analysis of Production-Log Data in Oil-Water Flow," paper SPE 68079 presented at the 2001 SPE Middle East Oil Show, Bahrain, 17–20 March.
8. Kabir, C.S., Hoadley, S.F., and Kamal, D.: "Use of Flow-Pattern-Based Models for Interpreting Oil-Water Flow in Production Logging," paper SPE 68468 presented at the 2001 SPE Middle East Oil Show, Bahrain, 17–20 March.
9. Choquette, S.P.: *Vertical Two-Phase Flow Systems and Interpretation of the Flowmeter and the Gradiomanometer Production Log Interpretation*, MS Report, Stanford U., Stanford, California (May 1975).
10. Flores, J.G., Chen, X.T., Sarica, C., and Brill, J.P.: "Characterization of Oil-Water Flow Patterns in Vertical and Deviated Wells," *SPEPF* (May 1999) 102.
11. Hasan, A.R. and Kabir, C.S.: "A Simplified Model for Oil-Water Flow in Vertical and Deviated Wellbores," *SPEPF* (February 1999) 56.
12. Govier, G.W. and Aziz, K.: *The Flow of Complex Mixtures in Pipes*, van Nostrand Reinhold Company, New York City (1972) 159.
13. Flores, J.G., Sarica, C., Chen, T.X., and Brill, J.P.: "Investigation of Holdup and Pressure Drop Behavior for Oil-Water Flow in Vertical and Deviated Wells," *SPEJ* (March 1998) **120**; *Trans.*, ASME (1991) **8**, 14.

SI Metric Conversion Factors

°API	141.5/(131.5 + °API)	= g/cm^3
dyne/cm × 1.0	E + 00	= mN/m
ft × 3.048*	E – 01	= m
ft/min × 5.080*	E – 03	= m/s
ft/sec × 3.048*	E – 01	= m/s
ft/sec^2 × 3.048*	E – 01	= m/s^2
°F	(°F – 32)/1.8	= °C
lbm/ft^3 × 1.601 846	E + 01	= kg/m^3
psia × 6.895	E + 00	= kPa

*Conversion factor is exact.

Appendix A
Overall Heat Transfer Coefficients for Wellbores

Radial heat transfer between the wellbore fluid and the formation occur by overcoming various resistances in series, as shown in Fig. 5.4. As pointed out earlier, at steady state, the rate of heat flow through a wellbore per unit length of the well, Q, can be expressed as

$$Q = -2\pi r_{to} U_{to} \left(T_f - T_{wb} \right) \cdot \qquad \text{(A-1)}$$

In Eq. A-1, U_{to} is defined as the overall-heat-transfer coefficient, based on the tubing outside surface area, $2\pi r_{to}$, and the temperature difference between the wellbore fluid and the wellbore/formation interface, $(T_f - T_{wb})$.

We assume heat transfer to be at steady state; hence, heat flowing through each of the elements must be the same. This assumption of steady heat transfer allows us to write the rate of heat transfer across each element in terms of the temperature difference across the element and the resistance offered by that element. Thus, the rate of heat transfer between the flowing fluid and inside the tubing wall is

$$Q = -2\pi r_{ti} h_t \left(T_f - T_{ti} \right) \cdot \qquad \text{(A-2)}$$

Eq. A-2 may be rewritten for the temperature drop across this element (fluid bulk) as

$$T_f - T_{ti} = -\frac{Q}{2\pi r_{ti} h_t} \cdot \qquad \text{(A-3)}$$

Noting that the sum of the temperature drops across all these elements is equal to the temperature difference between the fluid and the wellbore/earth interface, we write

$$T_f - T_{wb} = -\frac{Q}{2\pi} \left[\frac{1}{r_{ti} h_t} + \frac{\ln(r_{to}/r_{ti})}{k_t} + \frac{\ln(r_{ins}/r_{to})}{k_{ins}} \right]$$
$$- \frac{Q}{2\pi} \left[\frac{1}{r_{ins}(h_c + h_r)} + \frac{\ln(r_{co}/r_{ci})}{k_c} + \frac{\ln(r_{wb}/r_{co})}{k_{cem}} \right],$$
$$\qquad \text{(A-4)}$$

or $T_f - T_{wb} = -\frac{Q}{2\pi r_{to} U_{to}} \cdot \qquad \text{(A-5)}$

Eq. A-5 is another form of Eq. 5.16, where U_{to} is given by

$$\frac{1}{U_{to}} = \frac{r_{to}}{r_{ti} h_t} + \frac{r_{to} \ln(r_{to}/r_{ti})}{k_t} + \frac{r_{to} \ln(r_{ins}/r_{to})}{k_{ins}}$$
$$+ \frac{r_{to}}{r_{ins}(h_c + h_r)} + \frac{r_{to} \ln(r_{co}/r_{ci})}{k_c} + \frac{r_{to} \ln(r_{wb}/r_{co})}{k_{cem}} \cdot$$
$$\qquad \text{(A-6)}$$

Not all of the components shown in Fig. 5.4 are present in all well configurations, although some elements offer negligible resistance to heat flow even when they are present. Thus, for a typical well, tubing insulation is absent, thereby allowing us to drop the term involving k_{ins} in Eq. A-6. One may also assume that the fluid heat-transfer coefficient is so high that T_f may be assumed to be equal to T_{ti}. The high values of conductivity of metals, coupled with relatively thin tubing and casing walls, allow us to make the assumption that temperature drop across both the tubing and casing walls may be neglected; that is, $T_{ti} = T_{to}$, and $T_{ci} = T_{co}$. Therefore, a U_{to} for a typical well may be calculated from

$$\frac{1}{U_{to}} = \frac{1}{(h_c + h_r)} + \frac{r_{to} \ln(r_{wb}/r_{co})}{k_{cem}} \cdot \qquad \text{(A-7)}$$

The resistance to heat transfer offered by the annulus, represented by the first term in Eq. A-7 (the fourth term in Eq. 5.17), may involve radiative and natural-convective heat-transfer mechanisms.

A.1 Radiative Heat Transfer
The radiative heat transfer coefficient, h_r, is obtained from

$$h_r = \frac{\sigma \left(T_{ins}^{*2} + T_{ci}^{*2} \right) \left(T_{ins}^{*} + T_{ci}^{*} \right)}{\dfrac{1}{\varepsilon_{ins}} + \dfrac{r_{ins}}{r_{ci}} \left(\dfrac{1}{\varepsilon_{ins}} - 1 \right)}, \qquad \text{(A-8)}$$

where the asterisks denote absolute temperatures, σ represents the Stefan-Boltzmann constant with a value of 1.713×10^{-9}/ft^{2}hr°R^4, and ε_{ins} and ε_{ci} are the emissivities of the external surface of the insulation layer and the inside surface of the casing. It is difficult to obtain accurate values of the emissivities, which depend on surface finish and view factor, among other variables. In addition, an iterative solution procedure becomes necessary because casing inside temperature and the insulation outside temperature are needed. In most cases of petroleum production, the temperature difference across the annulus, and therefore h_r, is usually very small.

A.2 Convective Heat Transfer in Annuli

When a fluid at a given temperature is in contact with a surface at a different temperature, heat transfer takes place not only because of conduction, but also because of a phenomenon known as natural convection. Natural convection arises because fluid density depends on its temperature. The temperature difference, and therefore the density difference, between the bulk fluid and fluid close to the surface causes fluid circulation, which, in turn, enhances heat transfer. Unfortunately, very little work on natural convection in vertical annular geometry is reported in the literature. Willhite[1] and Hasan and Kabir[2] adapted the correlation proposed by Dropkin and Sommerscales[3] for heat-transfer coefficients for natural convection in fluids between two vertical plates. Their correlation for h_c, expressed for cylindrical geometry, is

$$h_c = \frac{0.049(\text{Gr}\,\text{Pr})^{0.333}\,\text{Pr}^{0.074}\,k_a}{r_{\text{ins}}\ln\left(r_{ci}/r_{\text{ins}}\right)} \quad \cdots\cdots\cdots (A\text{-}9)$$

The Grashof number, Gr, in Eq. A-9 is defined as

$$\text{Gr} = \left(r_{ci} - r_{\text{ins}}\right)^3 g\rho_a^2\beta\left(T_{\text{ins}} - T_{ci}\right)/\mu_a^2 \quad \cdots\cdots (A\text{-}10)$$

and reflects the extent of motion of the annular fluid owing to natural convection. The density of the heated fluid next to the insulation layer is less than that next to the casing, creating a buoyancy force. The viscous force, working against the buoyancy, generates a circular motion of the fluid in the annulus. In Eq. A-9, Prandtl number, Pr, defined as $c_p\mu_a/k_a$, is a measure of the interaction between the hydrodynamic boundary layer and the thermal boundary layer. For gases, the value of the Prandtl number is usually close to 1.0 (1.06 for steam and 0.69 for air); typical values for liquids range from one to ten.

A more appropriate correlation for the annuli Nusselt number was presented by Fishenden and Saunders[4] in a graphical form, in terms of Grashof and Prandtl numbers and the annular diameter ratio, d_{ci}/d_{to}. The following equation can be used to represent those curves.[2]

$$\text{Nu} \equiv \frac{hd}{k} = 0.10\left(\frac{d_{ci}}{d_{to}}\right)^{0.15}(\text{Gr}\text{Pr})^{0.3}, \quad \cdots\cdots (A\text{-}11)$$

where Pr is defined the same way as before. However, Nu and Gr are defined in terms of the inner pipe diameter, d_{to}, giving the correlation for h_c, which is written as

$$h_c = 0.10(d_{ci}/d_{to})^{0.15}\left(\frac{\rho_a^2\beta g(T_{\text{ins}} - T_{ci})}{\mu_a^2}\right)^{0.3}k_a d_{to}^{-0.1}(\text{Pr})^{0.3}\cdot$$
$$\cdots\cdots\cdots\cdots (A\text{-}12)$$

Eq. A-12 shows a slight dependence of h_c on the inner-pipe diameter; whereas, Eq. A-9 does not. Eq. A-12 also generally yields much lower h_c values than that of Eq. A-9.

Direct application of either Eq. A-12 or Eq. A-9, developed from short tubes in the laboratories, to wells that are orders of magnitude taller, is doubtful. That is because the natural convection cells that are supposed to set up in the annulus are probably suppressed by the weight of the fluid in tall columns. Indeed, attempts have been made to incorporate an L/d ratio in correlating annulus natural convective heat transfer data.[5]

$$\text{Nu} = a\text{Gr}^b\,\text{Pr}_c\left(L/d\right)^{-n}\cdot\quad\cdots\cdots\cdots\cdots (A\text{-}13)$$

Sheriff[5] used a value of $n=\frac14$ to express Nu data that he gathered with carbon dioxide in short vertical annuli. Unfortunately, such an approach is inapplicable in wells with very large values of L/d. Our experience generally indicates that inclusion of the full value of h_c, calculated from either Eqs. A-9 or A-12, and often leads to significant underestimation of wellbore fluid temperature. We have found a value of 25% of h_c, calculated from A-12 to mimic field data well. Therefore, until data become available from really tall columns mimicking wellbores, we recommend the use of $0.25\,h_c$.

For forced convective-heat transfer for turbulent flow in pipes and wells, we recommend the empirical correlation by Sieder-Tate.[6]

$$\text{Nu} \equiv \frac{hd}{k} = 0.023\left(\frac{dv\rho}{\mu}\right)^{0.8}\left(c_p\mu/k\right)^{0.33}\left(\mu/\mu_w\right)^{0.14}$$
$$\cdots\cdots\cdots\cdots (A\text{-}14)$$

where the unsubscripted property values represent those of the bulk fluid, and μ_w represents the viscosity of the fluid at the wall temperature. The correction represented by the last term is often neglected but becomes important for highly viscous fluids.

Nomenclature

d = pipe or well diameter, in.

d_c, d_t = casing or tubing diameter, in.

g = acceleration owing to gravity, ft/sec^2

Gr = Grashof number (defined by Eq. A-10), dimensionless

h_c = convective heat-transfer coefficient, Btu/($^\circ$F-hr-ft^2)

h_a, h_t = convective heat-transfer coefficient for annular or tubing fluid, Btu/($^\circ$F-hr-ft^2)

k_a = conductivity of annular fluid, Btu/(hr-ft-$^\circ$F)

k_c = conductivity of casing material, Btu/(hr-ft-$^\circ$F)

k_{cem} = conductivity of cement, Btu/(hr-ft-$^\circ$F)

L = total measured well depth, ft

Nu = Nusselt number [=hd/k], dimensionless

Pr = Prandtl number [=$c_p\mu/k$], dimensionless

Q = heat transfer rate per unit length of wellbore, Btu/hr-ft

r_D = dimensionless radial distance [$=r/r_w$], dimensionless

r_w = wellbore radius, ft

T = temperature, °F

T_a, T_t = temperature of annulus or tubing fluid, °F

T_{ai}, T_{ti} = inlet-temperature of annular or tubing fluid, °F

T_{ci} = casing inside temperature, °F

T_{ei}, T_e = formation temperature at initial condition or at any radial distance, °F

T_f = fluid temperature, °F

T_{ins} = insulation temperature, °F

T_{wb} = temperature at wellbore/formation interface, °F

U = overall heat transfer coefficient, Btu/(hr-ft²-°F)

β = fluid thermal expansion coefficient, 1/°F

μ = oil viscosity, cp

ρ = density, lbm/ft³

Subscripts

a = annulus

c = casing

cem = cement

g = gas

ins = insulation

L = liquid

o = oil

t = tubing

ta = tubing to annulus for heat-transfer coefficient

ti = tubing inside

to = tubing outside

wb = wellbore

References

1. Willhite, G.P.: "Overall Heat Transfer Coefficients in Steam and Hot Water Injection Wells," *JPT* (May 1967) 607.
2. Hasan, A.R. and Kabir, C.S.: "Aspects of Heat Transfer During Two-phase Flow in Wellbores," *SPEPF* (August 1994) 211.
3. Dropkin, D., and Sommerscales, E.: "Heat Transfer by Natural Convection in Liquids Confined by Two Parallel Plates Inclined at Various Angels with respect to the Horizontal," *J. Heat Transfer, Trans.* ASME, Series C (February 1965) **87**, 77.
4. Fishenden, M. and Saunders, O.A.: *An Introduction to Heat Transfer*, first edition, Oxford U. Press, London (1950) 103.
5. Sheriff, N.: "Experimental Investigation of Natural Convection in Single and Multiple Vertical Annuli with High Pressure Carbon Dioxide," *Proc.*, Third Intl. Heat Transfer Conference, Houston, Texas (1966) **2**, 132.
6. McCabe, W.L., Smith, J.C., and Harriott, P.: *Unit Operations of Chemical Engineering*, sixth edition, McGraw-Hill Book Co. Inc., New York City (2001) 347.

SI Metric Conversion Factors

Btu × 1.055 056	E + 00	= kJ
cp × 1.0*	E − 03	= Pa s
ft × 3.048*	E − 01	= m
ft² × 9.290 304*	E − 02	= m²
ft/sec² × 3.048*	E − 01	= m/s²
°F (°F − 32)/1.8		= °C
lbm/ft³ × 1.601 846	E + 01	= kg/m³

* Conversion factor is exact.

Appendix B
Working Equations for Multiple String Completions

B.1 Production Through Tubing and Annulus

Eq. 6.9 is a second-order linear differential equation in which the solution is given by Eqs. 6.12 and 6.13. The constants of Eqs. 6.12 and 6.13 are given by

$$\lambda_{ls} = \frac{L_R B''}{2B'} - \frac{L_R B''}{2B'} \sqrt{1 - \frac{4B'}{L_R B''^2}} , \quad \dots\dots\dots \text{(B-1)}$$

$$\lambda_{ss} = \frac{L_R B''}{2B'} + \frac{L_R B''}{2B'} \sqrt{1 - \frac{4B'}{L_R B''^2}} , \quad \dots\dots\dots \text{(B-2)}$$

$$\alpha = \frac{(1 - \lambda_{ss}B')\left(T_{tbh} - T_{es} - g_G L_{ss}\sin\theta - B''g_G\sin\theta\right)}{B'(\lambda_{ls} - \lambda_{ss})\exp(\lambda_{ls}L_{ss})}$$
$$- \frac{T_{abh} - T_{es} - g_G L_{ss}\sin\theta - (B'' - B')g_G\sin\theta}{B'(\lambda_{ls} - \lambda_{ss})\exp(\lambda_{ls}L_{ss})} , \quad \dots\dots\dots \text{(B-3)}$$

$$\beta = -\frac{(1 - \lambda_{ls}B')\left(T_{tbh} - T_{es} - g_G L_{ss}\sin\theta - B''g_G\sin\theta\right)}{B'(\lambda_{ls} - \lambda_{ss})\exp(\lambda_{ss}L_{ss})}$$
$$+ \frac{T_{abh} - T_{es} - g_G L_{ss}\sin\theta - (B'' - B')g_G\sin\theta}{B'(\lambda_{ls} - \lambda_{ss})\exp(\lambda_{ss}L_{ss})} , \quad \dots\dots\dots \text{(B-4)}$$

$$L_R \equiv \frac{2\pi}{c_{Pa}w_a}\left[\frac{r_c U_c k_e}{k_e + (r_c U_c T_D)}\right] , \quad \dots\dots\dots \text{(B-5)}$$

$$B = \frac{w_a c_{pa}}{2\pi r_t U_t} , \quad \dots\dots\dots \text{(B-6)}$$

$$B' = \frac{w_t c_{pt}}{2\pi r_t U_t} , \quad \dots\dots\dots \text{(B-7)}$$

$$\text{and } B'' = B' + \frac{B'}{L_R B} + \frac{1}{L_R} . \quad \dots\dots\dots \text{(B-8)}$$

B.2 Production Through Two Tubing Strings

The relaxation length, L_R, has the same form as defined by Eq. B-5 with an appropriate U. However, the total heat-transfer coefficient should be calculated from the annulus instead from the tubing, giving

$$\frac{1}{U_a} = \frac{r_{wb}\ln(r_{caseo}/r_{casein})}{k_{caseo}} + \frac{r_{wb}\ln(r_{cemt}/r_{caseo})}{k_{cemt}} , \quad \dots \text{(B-9)}$$

$$\text{and } L_R \equiv \frac{2\pi}{c_{Pls}w_{ls}}\left[\frac{r_{wb}U_a k_e}{k_e + (r_{wb}U_a T_D)}\right] . \quad \dots\dots\dots \text{(B-10)}$$

The parameters in the governing-differential equations, Eqs. 6.23 through 6.25, are

$$a_1 = 2\pi r_{ls}U_{ls} , \quad \dots\dots\dots\dots\dots\dots \text{(B-11)}$$

$$a_2 = -\left(2\pi r_{ls}U_{ls} + 2\pi r_{ss}U_{ss} + L_R w_{ls}c_{pls}\right) , \quad \dots\dots \text{(B-12)}$$

$$a_3 = 2\pi r_{ss}U_{ss} , \quad \dots\dots\dots\dots\dots\dots \text{(B-13)}$$

$$a_4 = -L_R w_{ls}c_{pls}g_G\sin\theta , \quad \dots\dots\dots\dots \text{(B-14)}$$

$$a_5 = L_R T_{lsbh}w_{ls}c_{pls} , \quad \dots\dots\dots\dots\dots \text{(B-15)}$$

$$a_6 = -\frac{2\pi r_{ls}U_{ls}}{c_{ls}w_{ls}} , \quad \dots\dots\dots\dots\dots\dots \text{(B-16)}$$

$$\text{and } a_7 = -\frac{2\pi r_{ss}U_{ss}}{c_{ss}w_{ss}} . \quad \dots\dots\dots\dots\dots \text{(B-17)}$$

Omitting the tedious derivation, we present the final differential equation for T_{ls} as

$$b_1\frac{d^2 T_{ls}}{dz^2} + b_2\frac{dT_{ls}}{dz} + b_3 T_{ls} = b_4 z + b_5 , \quad \dots\dots\dots \text{(B-18)}$$

where parameters $b_1 = -a_2$, and $b_2, b_3, b_4,$ and b_5 are defined as

$$b_2 = a_7(a_2 + a_3) - a_6(a_1 + a_2) , \quad \dots\dots\dots \text{(B-19)}$$

$$b_3 = a_6 a_7 (a_1 + a_2 + a_3) \, , \quad \cdots\cdots\cdots\cdots\cdots \text{(B-20)}$$

$$b_4 = a_4 a_6 a_7 \, , \quad \cdots\cdots\cdots\cdots\cdots\cdots\cdots \text{(B-21)}$$

and $b_5 = a_3 a_7 \phi_{ls} + a_3 a_6 \phi_{ss} - a_4 a_6$

$$\qquad + a_7 (a_2 \phi_{ls} - a_5 a_6) - a_4 a_6 a_7 L \cdot \quad \cdots\cdots\cdots\cdots \text{(B-22)}$$

The particular solution for Eq. B-18 is

$$T_{lp} = \frac{b_4}{b_3} z + \frac{b_3 b_5 - b_2 b_4}{b_3^2} \cdot \quad \cdots\cdots\cdots\cdots\cdots \text{(B-23)}$$

The general solution becomes

$$T_{ls} = c_1 e^{\lambda_{ls} z} + c_2 e^{\lambda_{ss} z} + \frac{b_4}{b_3} z + \frac{b_3 b_5 - b_2 b_4}{b_3^2} \, , \quad \cdots\cdots \text{(B-24)}$$

where $\lambda_{ls} = \dfrac{-b_2 + \sqrt{b_2^2 - 4 b_1 b_3}}{2 b_1} \, , \quad \cdots\cdots\cdots\cdots \text{(B-25)}$

and $\lambda_{ss} = \dfrac{-b_2 - \sqrt{b_2^2 - 4 b_1 b_3}}{2 b_1} \cdot \quad \cdots\cdots\cdots\cdots \text{(B-26)}$

By substituting Eq. B-24 into Eqs. B-12 and B-13 and eliminating T_a, one can obtain the final expression for T_{ss} as

$$T_{ss} = d_1 c_1 e^{\lambda_{ls} z} + d_2 c_2 e^{\lambda_{ss} z} + d_3 z + d_4 \, , \quad \cdots\cdots\cdots\cdots \text{(B-27)}$$

where $d_1 = -\left(\dfrac{a_2 \lambda_{ls}}{a_3 a_6} + \dfrac{a_1 + a_2}{a_3} \right) \, , \quad \cdots\cdots\cdots\cdots \text{(B-28)}$

$$d_2 = -\left(\frac{a_2 \lambda_{ss}}{a_3 a_6} + \frac{a_1 + a_2}{a_3} \right) \quad \cdots\cdots\cdots\cdots\cdots \text{(B-29)}$$

$$d_3 = \frac{a_4}{a_3} - \frac{a_1 + a_2}{a_3} \frac{b_4}{b_3} \, , \quad \cdots\cdots\cdots\cdots\cdots\cdots \text{(B-30)}$$

and $d_4 = \dfrac{a_2 \phi_1 - a_5 a_6 - a_4 a_6 L}{a_3 a_6} - \dfrac{a_2 b_4}{a_3 a_6 b_3}$

$$\qquad - \frac{a_1 + a_2}{a_3} \frac{b_3 b_5 - b_2 b_4}{b_3^2} \cdot \quad \cdots\cdots\cdots\cdots \text{(B-31)}$$

The integration constants, c_1 and c_2, are evaluated from known bottomhole temperatures. Thus, $z = L_{ss}$, and $T_{ss} = T_{ssbh}$.

We use Eq. 5.39 to estimate the longer string's fluid temperature, $T_{ls} = T_{lsbh}$, at the same depth, $z = L_{ss}$. These two boundary conditions are used in Eqs. B-24 and B-27 to derive the following expressions for calculating c_1 and c_2.

$$c_1 e^{\lambda_{ls} L_{ss}} (d_2 - d_1) = d_2 T_{lsbh} - T_{ssbh}$$

$$\qquad + d_4 - \frac{d_2 b_4 L_{ss}}{b_3} + d_3 L_{ss} - \frac{d_2}{b_3^2} (b_3 b_5 - b_2 b_4) \, , \quad \cdots\cdots \text{(B-32)}$$

and $c_2 e^{\lambda_{ss} L_{ss}} (d_1 - d_2) = d_1 T_{lsbh} - T_{ssbi}$

$$\qquad + d_4 - \frac{d_1 b_4 L_{ss}}{b_3} + d_3 L_{ss} - \frac{d_1}{b_3^2} (b_3 b_5 - b_2 b_4) \cdot \quad \cdots\cdots \text{(B-33)}$$

B.3 Production and Injection Through Common Wellbores

As stated earlier in the text, the governing differential equations, Eqs. 6.23 through 6.25, and the expressions for fluid temperatures, Eqs. 6.26 through 6.28, also apply to the case of production and injection through two tubing strings. In this case, however, the integration constants c_1 and c_2 are different because of different boundary conditions. Unlike the previous case, we now know the inlet temperature of the injected fluid in the long string. Thus, using the boundary conditions at $z = 0$, $T_{ls} = T_{lsi}$, $z = L_{ss}$, and $T_{ss} = T_{ssbh}$, we obtain

$$T_{lsi} = c_1 + c_2 + \frac{b_3 b_5 - b_2 b_4}{b_3^2} \, , \quad \cdots\cdots\cdots\cdots \text{(B-34)}$$

and $T_{ssbh} = d_1 c_1 e^{\lambda_{ls} L_{ss}} + d_2 c_2 e^{\lambda_{ss} L_{ss}} + d_3 L_{ss} + d_4 \cdot$

$$\qquad \cdots\cdots\cdots\cdots\cdots \text{(B-35)}$$

The solutions for c_1 and c_2 are given by

$$c_1 = \frac{d_2 e^{\lambda_{ss} L_{ss}} \left(T_{lsi} - \dfrac{b_3 b_5 - b_2 b_4}{b_3^2} \right) - T_{ssbh} + d_3 L_{ss} + d_4}{d_2 \exp(\lambda_{ss} L_{ss}) - d_1 \exp(\lambda_{ls} L_{ss})}$$

$$\qquad \cdots\cdots\cdots\cdots \text{(B-36)}$$

and $c_2 = \dfrac{d_1 e^{\lambda_{ls} L_{ss}} \left(T_{lsi} - \dfrac{b_3 b_5 - b_2 b_4}{b_3^2} \right) - T_{ssbh} + d_3 L_{ss} + d_4}{d_1 \exp(\lambda_{ls} L_{ss}) - d_2 \exp(\lambda_{ss} L_{ss})}$

$$\qquad \cdots\cdots\cdots\cdots \text{(B-37)}$$

B.4 Input Parameters for Field Examples

TABLE B-1—INPUT PARAMETERS FOR FIELD EXAMPLES

Parameters	Well A28	Well C39
Producing rates (ls/ss), STB/D	4,088/352	2,698/1,138
Gas/Oil ratio (ls/ss), scf/STB	489/489	449/449
Oil density (ls/ss), lbm/ft^3	54/54	57/57
Gas gravity (ls/ss), (air=1)	0.85/0.85	0.85/0.85
Cement-Sheath diameter, in.	16.0	16.0
Length of strings (ls/ss), ft	5,194/4,984	5,151/4,984
Casing ID, in.	10.0	10.0
Tubing ID (ls/ss), in.	3.0	3.0
Geothermal gradient, °F/ft	0.012	0.012
Tubular thermal conductivity, Btu/(hr-ft-°F)	30.0	30.0
Formation thermal conductivity, Btu/(hr-ft-°F)	3.33	3.33
Tubular Field thermal conductivity, Btu/(hr-ft-°F)	0.07	0.07
Cement thermal conductivity, Btu/(hr-ft-°F)	0.38	0.38
Formation Density, lbm/ft^3	135.0	135.0
Formation heat capacity, Btu/(lbm-°F)	0.625	0.625
Pipe roughness, ft	0.000018	0.000018
Reservoir pressure, psi	2,011	2,147

Nomenclature

B_a = parameter defined by Eq. B-6 (also Eq. 6.2), ft/lbm

B' = parameter defined by Eq. B-7 (also Eq. 6.8), ft

B'' = parameter defined by Eq. B-7 (also Eq. 6.10), ft

c_p = heat capacity of fluids, Btu/(lbm-°F)

k_e = earth or formation conductivity, Btu/(hr-ft-°F)

L = well length, ft

L_R = relaxation distance parameter, 1/ft

r = radius of flow string, L

T = fluid or formation temperature, °F

T_D = dimensionless temperature $\{=2\pi k_e \Delta T/Q\}$

U = overall heat-transfer coefficient for a string, Btu/(hr-ft^2-°F)

z = variable well depth from surface, ft

α = parameter defined by Eq. B-3 (also Eq. 6.12), °F

β = parameter defined by Eq. B-4 (also Eq. 6.12), °F

ϕ = parameter used in Eq. B-22 (also Eq. 6.20), °F/ft

γ = parameter defined by Eqs. B-1 and B-2, ft^{-1}

Subscripts

a = annulus

bh = bottomhole

$casein$ = casing inside

$caseo$ = casing outside

$cemt$ = cement

es = earth static

ls = long string

lsi = wellhead condition of long string

ss = short string

t = tubing

wb = wellbore

SI Metric Conversion Factors

Btu × 1.055 056	E + 00 = kJ
ft × 3.048*	E – 01 = m
°F (°F – 32)/1.8	= °C
in. × 2.54*	E + 00 = cm
lbm × 4.535 924	E – 01 = kg
lbm/ft^3 × 1.601 846	E + 01 = kg/m^3
psi × 6.894 757	E + 00 = kPa

* Conversion factor is exact.

Appendix C
Finite-Difference Equations for Wellbore Fluid Temperature

C.1 Single-Phase Gas Flow

Using j to denote spatial coordinate, the finite-difference form of Eq. 7.9 is

$$\frac{\rho v}{A}\left(c_p L_R^{l+1}\left((T_{ei})_j - (T_f)_j^{l+1}\right) + \sigma_j^l\right) = \rho_j^l \frac{\Delta H}{\Delta t} - \rho_j^l R \frac{\Delta(ZT_f)}{\Delta t}$$

$$+\left(H_j^l - R\frac{Z(T_f)_j^l}{M}\right)\left(\frac{\rho_j^{l+1} - \rho_j^l}{\Delta t}\right)$$

$$+\frac{(w)_{j+1}^l}{A\Delta z}\left(H^l + \frac{(v^l)^2}{2} + gz\sin\theta\right)_{j+1}$$

$$-\frac{(w)_{j-1}^l}{A\Delta z}\left(H^l + \frac{(v^l)^2}{2} + gz\sin\theta\right)_{j-1}, \quad \ldots\ldots\ldots \text{(C-1)}$$

where $\Delta H = -C_J c_p^l R\left[(Z\rho T_f)_j^{l+1} - (Z\rho T_f)_j^l\right]$

$$+c_p^l\left[(T_f)_j^{l+1} - (T_f)_j^l\right]/M, \quad \ldots\ldots\ldots \text{(C-2)}$$

and $\Delta[Z(T_f)] = Z_j^{l+1}(T_f)_j^{l+1} - Z_j^l(T_f)_j^l \cdot \quad \ldots\ldots\ldots \text{(C-3)}$

Eqs. C-1 and C-2 do not show any conversion factors that might be needed to retain unit consistency. For example, T_f in these equations is in °R, whereas the measurements are reported in °F. The left side of Eq. C-1 may be written in the following form with Eqs. C-2 and C-3.

$$\rho_j^l c_p^l \frac{(T_f)_j^{l+1} - (T_f)_j^l}{\Delta t} - \frac{C_J \rho_j^l c_p^l (p_j^{l+1} - p_j^l)}{\Delta t}$$

$$-R\rho_j^l \frac{Z_j^{l+1}(T_f)_j^{l+1} - Z_j^l(T_f)_j^l}{\Delta t} + \psi_j^l$$

$$= \xi_j^l\left((T_f)_j^{l+1} - (T_f)_j^l\right) - \lambda_j^l T_{fj}^{l+1} + \omega_j^l + \psi_j^l. \quad \ldots\ldots \text{(C-4)}$$

We can now write an explicit expression for $(T_f)_j^{l+1}$ as

$$(T_f)_j^{l+1} = \frac{(\sigma_j^l/A) - \psi_j^l + \left(\rho v T_{ei} c_p L_R\right)_j^{l+1} + \xi_j^l(T_f)_j^l + \omega_j^l}{\left(\rho v c_p L_R\right)_j^{l+1} + \xi_j^l - \lambda_j^l},$$

$$\ldots\ldots\ldots\ldots \text{(C-5)}$$

which is the same as Eq. 7.11. In Eq. C-5,

$$\lambda_j^l = \frac{R\rho_j^l Z_j^{l+1}}{\Delta t}\left(1 + C_J c_p^l \rho_j^{l+1}\right), \quad \ldots\ldots\ldots \text{(C-6)}$$

$$\psi_j^l = \left(H_j^l - \frac{p_j^l}{\rho_j^l}\right)\left(\frac{\rho_j^{l+1} - \rho_j^l}{\Delta t}\right)$$

$$+\frac{(w)_{j+1}^l}{A\Delta z}\left(H^l + \frac{(v^l)^2}{2} + gz\sin\theta\right)_{j+1}$$

$$-\frac{(w)_{j-1}^l}{A\Delta z}\left(H^l + \frac{(v^l)^2}{2} + gz\sin\theta\right)_{j-1}, \quad \ldots\ldots\ldots \text{(C-7)}$$

$$\xi_j^l = \frac{c_p^l \rho_p^l}{\Delta t}, \quad \ldots\ldots\ldots\ldots\ldots \text{(C-8)}$$

and $\omega_j^l = \dfrac{RC_J c_p^l\left(\rho_j^l\right)^2 Z_j^l(T_f)_j^l}{\Delta t} + \dfrac{R\rho_j^l Z_j^l(T_f)_j^l}{\Delta t} \quad \ldots\ldots \text{(C-9)}$

C.2 Single-Phase Oil Flow

The development of the finite difference equations for the case of oil wells is very similar to that for gas wells described in the previous section. We only present the final expression for the fluid temperature here, the details are found in Ref. 1.

$$(T_f)_j^{l+1} = \frac{(\sigma_j^l/A) - \psi_j^l + \left(\rho v T_{ei} c_p L_R\right)_j^{l+1} + \xi_j^l(T_f)_j^l + \omega_j^l}{\left(\rho v c_p L_R\right)_j^{l+1} + \xi_j^l}.$$

$$\ldots\ldots\ldots\ldots \text{(C-10)}$$

In Eq.C-10, as in Eq. C-5, ψ_j is still given by Eq. C-7. However, other parameters of Eq. C-10 are somewhat different from their counterpart in Sec. C.1. Therefore,

$$\psi_j^l = \left(H_j^l - \frac{p_j^l}{\rho_j^l}\right)\left(\frac{\rho_j^{l+1} - \rho_j^l}{\Delta t}\right) - \rho_j^l\left(\frac{(p/\rho)_j^{l+1} - (p/\rho)_j^l}{\Delta t}\right)$$

$$+ \frac{(w)_{j+1}^l}{A\Delta z}\left[H^l + \frac{(v^l)^2}{2} + gz\sin\theta\right]_{j+1}$$

$$- \frac{(w)_{j-1}^l}{A\Delta z}\left[H^l + \frac{(v^l)^2}{2} + gz\sin\theta\right]_{j-1}, \quad \ldots\ldots\ldots(C-11)$$

$$\text{and } \omega_j^l = \frac{\left(1 - \beta(T_f)_j^l\right)\left(p_j^{l+1} - p_j^{l+1}\right)}{\Delta t}. \quad \ldots\ldots\ldots\ldots(C-12)$$

C.3 Two-Phase Gas/Oil Flow

The development of the finite difference equations for the case of two-phase flow is very similar to that for gas or oil wells described in previous sections of this appendix. We only present the final expression for the fluid temperature here; the details are found in Ref. 2.

The final finite-difference form of the energy-balance equation in terms of the fluid temperature is given by

$$\left(T_f\right)_j^{l+1} = \frac{(\sigma_j^l / A) - \psi_j^l + \left(\rho v T_{ei} c_p L_R\right)_j^{l+1}}{\left(\rho v c_p L_R\right)_j^{l+1} + \phi_j^l + \gamma_j^l(c_{pg})_j^l}$$

$$+ \frac{\phi_j^l(T_f)_j^l + \Gamma_j^l - \eta_j^l + \gamma_j^l(c_{pg})_j^l(T_f)_j^l}{\left(\rho v c_p L_R\right)_j^{l+1} + \phi_j^l + \gamma_j^l(c_{pg})_j^l}, \quad \ldots(C-13)$$

$$\text{where } \psi_j^l = \left(H_j^l - \frac{p_j^l}{\rho_j^l J}\right)\frac{(\rho_j^{l+1} - \rho_j^l)}{\Delta t}$$

$$+ \frac{(\rho v)_{j+1}^l}{\Delta z}\left[H^l + \frac{1}{2}(v^l)^2 + gz\sin\theta\right]_{j+1}$$

$$- \frac{(\rho v)_j^l}{\Delta z}\left[H^l + \frac{1}{2}(v^l)^2 + gz\sin\theta\right]_j \quad , \quad \ldots(C-14)$$

$$\xi_j^l = \frac{c_p^l \rho_j^l}{\Delta t} + \frac{\rho' c'}{\Delta t}, \quad \ldots\ldots\ldots\ldots\ldots\ldots\ldots\ldots(C-15)$$

$$\gamma_j^l = \frac{\rho_j^l x_j^l}{\Delta t}, \quad \ldots\ldots\ldots\ldots\ldots\ldots\ldots(C-16)$$

$$\phi_j^l = \rho_j^l(1 - x_j^l)\frac{(c_{pl})_j^l}{\Delta t} + \frac{\rho' c'}{\Delta t}, \quad \ldots\ldots\ldots(C-17)$$

$$\eta_j^l = \rho_j^l(H_{gj}^l - H_{Lj}^l)\frac{x_j^{l+1} - x_j^l}{\Delta t}, \quad \ldots\ldots\ldots\ldots(C-18)$$

$$\text{and } \Gamma_j^l = \frac{\rho_j^l\left[1 - x_j^l c_{pgj}^l C_{Jgj}^l - (1 - x_j^l)c_{plj}^l C_{Jlj}^l\right](p_j^{l+1} - p_j^l)}{\Delta t}.$$
$$\ldots\ldots\ldots\ldots\ldots\ldots(C-19)$$

These equations lead to a tridiagonal matrix, which is solved by using the two-step Gaussian elimination method.

Nomenclature

A = cross-sectional area for flow, ft^2
c_p = heat capacity of fluids, Btu/lbm-°F
C_J = Joule-Thompson coefficient, °F/psi
E = internal energy, Btu/lbm
g = gravitational acceleration, ft/sec^2
h = formation thickness, ft
H = enthalpy, Btu/lbm
j = depth index for discretization, dimensionless
k_e = earth or formation conductivity, Btu/(hr-ft-°F)
l = time index for discretization, dimensionless
L = cell length, L
L_R = inverse relaxation distance, 1/ft
M = molecular weight, lbm/lbmole
p = pressure, psia
R = universal gas-law constant, psia-ft^3/lbmole-°R
t = time, hr
T = temperature, °F
T_{ei} = initial or static earth temperature
T_f = fluid temperature in the wellbore, °F
v = velocity, ft/sec
w = mass rate of fluid, lbm/hr
x = mass fraction of gas, dimensionless
Z = gas-law deviation factor, dimensionless
α = well angle from horizontal, degree
ρ = fluid density, lbm/ft^3

References

1. Hasan, A.R., Kabir, C.S., and Wang, X.: "Development and Application of a Wellbore/Reservoir Simulator for Testing Oil Wells," *SPEFE* (September 1997) 182.
2. Hasan, A.R., Kabir, C.S., and Wang, X.: "Wellbore Two-Phase Flow and Heat Transfer During Transient Testing," *SPEJ* (June 1998) 174.

SI Metric Conversion Factors

Btu × 1.055 056	E + 00 = kJ
ft × 3.048*	E – 01 = m
ft^2 × 9.290 304*	E – 02 = m^2
ft^3 × 2.831 685	E – 02 = m^3
ft/sec^2 × 3.048*	E – 01 = m/s^2
°F (°F – 32)/1.8	= °C
lbm × 4.535 924	E – 01 = kg
psi × 6.894 757	E + 00 = kPa

* Conversion factor is exact.

Appendix D
Models Related to Drilling Operations

D.1 Constants for the Reverse- and Forward-Circulation Models

Use of appropriate boundary conditions leads one to obtain the following expressions for the constants, as shown in Refs. 1 and 2. For the reverse-circulation case (flow down the annulus), the appropriate boundary condition is $T_a = T_{as}$ at $z=0$ and $dT/dz=0$ at the well bottom, $z=L$.

$$\alpha = -\frac{(T_{as} - T_{es})\lambda_2 e^{\lambda_2 L} + g_G \sin\theta(1-\lambda_2 B)}{\lambda_1 e^{\lambda_1 L}(1-\lambda_2 B) - \lambda_2 e^{\lambda_2 L}(1-\lambda_1 B)} \quad \ldots \ldots \text{(D-1)}$$

$$\beta = \frac{(T_{ai} - T_{es})\lambda_1 e^{\lambda_1 L} + g_G \sin\theta(1-\lambda_1 B)}{\lambda_1 e^{\lambda_1 L}(1-\lambda_2 B) - \lambda_2 e^{\lambda_2 L}(1-\lambda_1 B)} \quad \ldots \ldots \text{(D-2)}$$

$$\lambda_1 = -\frac{L_R}{2} + \frac{L_R}{2}\sqrt{1 + 4(r_c U_c T_D + k_e)\frac{r_t U_t}{r_c U_c k_e}} \quad \ldots \text{(D-3)}$$

$$\lambda_2 = -\frac{L_R}{2} - \frac{L_R}{2}\sqrt{1 + 4(r_c U_c T_D + k_e)\frac{r_t U_t}{r_c U_c k_e}} \quad \ldots \text{(D-4)}$$

The constants for the forward-circulation case are somewhat different than those for reverse circulation and are given by the expressions,

$$\alpha = -\frac{(T_{ts} - T_{es} + Bg_G \sin\theta)\lambda_2 e^{\lambda_2 L} + g_G \sin\theta}{\lambda_1 e^{\lambda_1 L} - \lambda_2 e^{\lambda_2 L}},$$
$$\ldots \ldots \ldots \ldots \text{(D-5)}$$

$$\beta = \frac{(T_{ti} - T_{es} + Bg_G \sin\theta)\lambda_1 e^{\lambda_1 L} + g_G \sin\theta}{\lambda_1 e^{\lambda_1 L} - \lambda_2 e^{\lambda_2 L}}, \quad \ldots \text{(D-6)}$$

$$\lambda_1 = \frac{L_R}{2} + \frac{L_R}{2}\sqrt{1 + 4(r_c U_c T_D + k_e)\frac{r_t U_t}{r_c U_c k_e}}, \quad \ldots \text{(D-7)}$$

$$\text{and } \lambda_2 = \frac{L_R}{2} - \frac{L_R}{2}\sqrt{1 + 4(r_c U_c T_D + k_e)\frac{r_t U_t}{r_c U_c k_e}} \quad \ldots \text{(D-8)}$$

D.2 Constants for the Variable-Heat Flux Model

The superposition principle accounts for the variable heat flow rate. To do so, the entire production period is divided into small time steps. Variables having subscript i refer to any given time period, and those with n suggest the last time period. The solutions for the tubing- and annular-fluid temperatures are the same as those for the constant-heat flux; that is, Eqs. 8.5 and 8.6 apply. However, the expressions for the constants are different. For the case of reverse circulation, the constants are given by

$$\alpha = -\frac{\left(T_{ti} - T_{es} + B\Lambda + |\omega_2 - \omega_1|_{z=0}\right)\lambda_2 e^{\lambda_2 L} + |\Lambda|_{z=L}}{\lambda_1 e^{\lambda_1 L} - \lambda_2 e^{\lambda_2 L}},$$
$$\ldots \ldots \ldots \ldots \text{(D-9)}$$

$$\beta = \frac{\left(T_{ai} - T_{es} + B\Lambda + |\omega_2 - \omega_1|_{z=0}\right)\lambda_1 e^{\lambda_1 L} + |\Lambda|_{z=L}}{\lambda_1 e^{\lambda_1 L} - \lambda_2 e^{\lambda_2 L}},$$
$$\ldots \ldots \ldots \ldots \text{(D-10)}$$

$$\Lambda = g_G + \frac{F_{n-1}}{2\pi k_e} - \frac{w}{2\pi k_e}$$

$$\sum_{i=1}^{n-1}(F_i - F_{i-1})T_D(t_{D,n} - t_{D,i-1}), \quad \ldots \ldots \ldots \text{(D-11)}$$

$$\omega_1 = \frac{Q_{n-1}}{2\pi k_e}T_D(t_{D,n} - t_{D,n-1}), \quad \ldots \ldots \ldots \text{(D-12)}$$

$$\text{and } \omega_2 = \frac{1}{2\pi k_e}\sum_{i=1}^{n-1}(Q_i - Q_{i-1})T_D(t_{D,n} - t_{D,n-1}),$$
$$\ldots \ldots \ldots \ldots \text{(D-13)}$$

where F is the change in heat flux (Q) per unit well depth (z) and the subscripts, i and n, are values of the variable for the ith and n^{th} (last) superposition time.

The constants, α and β, for the forward-circulation case are somewhat different than that for reverse circulation and are given by the expressions,

$$\alpha = -\frac{\left(T_{ti} - T_{es} + |\omega_2 - \omega_1|_{z=0}\right)\lambda_2 e^{\lambda_2 L} + |\Lambda|_{z=L}(1-\lambda_2 B)}{\lambda_1 e^{\lambda_1 L}(1-\lambda_2 B) - \lambda_2 e^{\lambda_2 L}(1-\lambda_1 B)}$$
$$\ldots \ldots \ldots \ldots \text{(D-14)}$$

and $\beta = \dfrac{\left(T_{ai} - T_{es} + |\omega_2 - \omega_1|_{z=0}\right)\lambda_1 e^{\lambda_1 L} + |\Lambda|_{z=L}\left(1 - \lambda_1 B\right)}{\lambda_1 e^{\lambda_1 L}\left(1 - \lambda_2 B\right) - \lambda_2 e^{\lambda_2 L}\left(1 - \lambda_1 B\right)}$.

$$\dots\dots\dots\dots\dots\dots\dots\text{(D-15)}$$

The expressions for λ_1 and λ_2 remain the same as in Eqs. D-3 and D-4 for the reverse-circulation case and Eqs. D-7 and D-8 for the forward-circulation case.

D.3 Transient Heat Transfer From Mud to Formation

We base our analysis on one foot of well, containing mass (M) of mud at a temperature, T_{ws}. The heat loss per unit time, per unit length of wellbore, is given by

$$Q = M c_p \frac{dT_{ws}}{dt} \ . \qquad\dots\dots\dots\dots\dots\dots\text{(D-16)}$$

Eq. D-16 shows that heat gained by (or lost from) the mud is a direct consequence of its change in temperature. Because the mud temperature, T_{ws}, will gradually approach the static formation temperature, T_{ei}, the driving force and, hence, the heat-transfer rate, Q, decreases with time. Therefore, T_{ws} is also a function of time. In addition, for any finite well diameter, the mud temperature will vary from well center to the wall because the mud has ceased to circulate. Here, we assumed that the mud temperature available is that at the center of the wellbore.

Applying Fourier's law of heat conduction, we can also relate the rate of heat gain to the temperature difference between the well center and the wall, $T_{ws} - T_{wb}$, and the overall-heat-transfer coefficient for the wellbore, U, as

$$Q = -2\pi r U\left(T_{ws} - T_{wb}\right) \ . \qquad\dots\dots\dots\dots\text{(D-17)}$$

Note that, in this case, mud is the only element of resistance to heat transfer in the well. Therefore, U, in this case, represents free convection in the wellbore; that is, $U = h$.

Similarly, we can relate heat transfer to the temperature difference between the well wall, T_{wb}, (at well/formation interface) and the undisturbed formation temperature, T_{ei}, as[3]

$$Q = -2\pi k_e \frac{\left(T_{wb} - T_{ei}\right)}{T_D} , \qquad\dots\dots\dots\dots\dots\text{(D-18)}$$

where T_D represents the solution of the thermal diffusivity equation obtained by using the cylindrical-source well.[3]

Combining Eqs. D-9 and D-10

$$Q = -2\pi\left[\frac{rUk_e}{k_e + rUT_D}\right]\left(T_{ws} - T_{ei}\right) \ . \qquad\dots\dots\dots\text{(D-19)}$$

Combining Eqs. D-8 and D-11, we get the differential equation for the variation of mud temperature with time,

$$\frac{dT_{ws}}{dt} = -\left(\frac{2\pi}{Mc_p}\right)\left[\frac{rUk_e}{k_e + rUT_D}\right]\left(T_{ws} - T_{ei}\right) = -L_R'\left(T_{ws} - T_{ei}\right),$$

$$\dots\dots\dots\dots\dots\dots\dots\text{(D-20)}$$

where the relaxation time parameter, L_R', as given by

$$L_R' \equiv \left(\frac{2\pi}{Mc_p}\right)\left[\frac{rUk_e}{k_e + rUT_D}\right], \qquad\dots\dots\dots\dots\text{(D-21)}$$

is similar to the relaxation parameter L_R, discussed in Chap. 5, to relate wellbore flowing fluid temperature.

As discussed in Chap. 5, T_D in Eq. D-17 may be approximated by the equations,

$$T_D = 1.1282\sqrt{t_D}\left[1 - 0.3\sqrt{t_D}\right], \quad\text{for } t_D < 1.5 \ , \quad\dots\text{(D-22)}$$

and $T_D = \left(0.4063 + 0.5\ln t_D\right)\left[1 + \dfrac{0.6}{t_D}\right], \quad\text{for } t_D > 1.5$.

$$\dots\dots\dots\dots\dots\dots\dots\text{(D-23)}$$

Eq. D-20 may be rearranged and integrated to yield[3]

$$-\ln\left[T_{ei} - T_{ws}\right] = C_o + \left(\frac{2\pi}{Mc_p}\right)\left(rUk_e\right)\int\frac{dt}{\left(k_e + rUT_D\right)} ,$$

$$\dots\dots\dots\dots\dots\dots\text{(D-24)}$$

where the constant of integration C_o indicates the initial temperature difference between the mud and formation. Noting that the value of the integral is zero at $t = 0$, and denoting the initial mud temperature by T_{wso}, we may write

$$C_o = -\ln\left(T_{ei} - T_{wso}\right) \ . \qquad\dots\dots\dots\dots\dots\text{(D-25)}$$

Eq. D-24 will be difficult to integrate with T_D given by Eq. D-23. Even if such operations were possible, the final form will probably be too complex to be useful for graphical analysis. However, for most cases of mud circulation the elapsed time is small and Eq. D-22 is perhaps adequate. In that case, we can rewrite Eq. D-24 as

$$-\ln\left(T_{ei} - T_{ws}\right) = C_o$$

$$+ \left(\frac{2\pi}{Mc_{pm}}\right)\left(rUk_e\right)\left(\frac{r^2}{a}\right)\int\frac{dT_D}{k_e + rU\left[1.1282\sqrt{t_D}\left(1 - 0.3\sqrt{t_D}\right)\right]}$$

$$= -C_o - C_1 I \ , \qquad\dots\dots\dots\dots\dots\dots\text{(D-26)}$$

where $I = \int\dfrac{dT_D}{1 + C_2\sqrt{t_D} - C_3 t_D} , \qquad\dots\dots\dots\dots\text{(D-27)}$

$$C_1 = \left(\frac{2\pi}{Mc_p}\right)\left(rU\right)\left(\frac{r^2}{a}\right), \qquad\dots\dots\dots\dots\dots\text{(D-28)}$$

$$C_2 = 1.1282\left(\frac{rU}{k_e}\right), \qquad\dots\dots\dots\dots\dots\dots\text{(D-29)}$$

and $C_3 = 0.3385\left(\dfrac{rU}{k_e}\right) = 0.3C_2$. $\qquad\dots\dots\dots\dots\text{(D-30)}$

The integral, I, was evaluated by using partial fractions[3] giving the solution,

$$T_{ws} = T_{ei} - C_{o''}\left[\frac{\left(\dfrac{f_1(t_D)}{f_2(t_D)}\right)^{\left(\frac{5.555}{aC_2}\right)}}{f_3(t_D)^{\left(\frac{3.333}{C_2}\right)}}\right]^{-C_1}$$

$$= T_{ei} - C_{o''}F(t_D) , \quad \dotfill (D\text{-}31)$$

where $f_1(t_D) = a + \sqrt{t_D} - 1.667 , \quad \dotfill (D\text{-}32)$

$f_2(t_D) = a - \sqrt{t_D} + 1.667 , \quad \dotfill (D\text{-}33)$

$f_3(t_D) = 1 + C_2\sqrt{t_D} - 0.3 C_2 t_D , \quad \dotfill (D\text{-}34)$

$C_{o''} = T_{ei} - T_{wso} , \quad \dotfill (D\text{-}35)$

and $a = \left[\left(\dfrac{C_2^2}{4C_3^2}\right) + \left(\dfrac{1}{C_3}\right)\right]^{0.5} = \left[2.777 + \left(\dfrac{3.333}{C_2}\right)\right]^{0.5} .$

$$\dotfill (D\text{-}36)$$

Nomenclature

$B =$ parameter defined by Eq. 8.4, ft
$c_e =$ specific heat of earth or formation, Btu/(lbm-°F)
$c_{fl} =$ specific heat of fluid, Btu/(lbm-°F)
$c_p =$ specific heat of mud, Btu/(lbm-°F)
$C_o =$ constant defined by Eq. D-25, dimensionless
$C_1 =$ constant defined by Eq. D-28, dimensionless
$C_2 =$ constant defined by Eq. D-29, dimensionless
$C_3 =$ constant defined by Eq. D-30, dimensionless
$f_1(t_D) =$ function defined by Eq. D-32, dimensionless
$f_2(t_D) =$ function defined by Eq. D-33, dimensionless
$f_3(t_D) =$ function defined by Eq. D-34, dimensionless
$F =$ change of heat flux per unit well depth, Btu/(hr-ft²)
$g_G =$ geothermal gradient, °F/ft
$h =$ heat transfer coefficient, Btu/(hr-ft²-°F)
$I =$ integral defined by Eq. D-27
$k_e =$ earth or formation thermal conductivity, Btu/(hr-ft-°F)
$k_m =$ thermal conductivity of mud, Btu/(hr-ft-°F)
$L =$ total well length, ft
$L'_R =$ relaxation time parameter defined by Eq. D-21, 1/hr
$L_R =$ relaxation length, ft⁻¹
$M =$ mass of fluid in a one-foot length of well, lbm
$q =$ liquid flow rate, STB/D
$Q =$ heat flow rate per unit well length, Btu/(hr-ft)
$r_c =$ casing radius, ft
$r_t =$ tubing radius, ft
$r, r_w =$ wellbore radius, ft
$t =$ time after circulation, hr
$t_D =$ dimensionless circulation time ($= k_m t_p / \rho c_{fl} r_w^2$)
$t_p =$ circulation time, hr
$T =$ fluid temperature at any point in the well, °F
$T_a =$ annular-fluid temperature, °F
$T_{ae} =$ annular-fluid exit temperature, °F
$T_{ai} =$ annular-fluid inlet temperature, °F
$T_{as} =$ annular-fluid temperature at surface, °F
$T_D =$ dimensionless temperature [$= 2\pi k_e(T_{wb}-T_{ei})/Q$]
$T_{ei} =$ formation static temperature at bottomhole, °F
$T_{es} =$ formation static temperature at surface, °F
$T_t =$ tubing/drillpipe fluid temperature, °F
$T_{ti} =$ fluid temperature entering the wellbore, °F
$T_{wb} =$ wellbore temperature, °F
$T_{ws} =$ sandface shut-in temperature, °F
$T_{wso} =$ initial wellbore temperature, °F
$\Delta t =$ shut-in time, hr
$\Delta t_D =$ dimensionless shut-in time
$U =$ overall heat-transfer coefficient, Btu/(hr-ft²-°F)
$U_a =$ overall heat-transfer coefficient for annulus, Btu/(hr-ft²-°F)
$U_t =$ overall heat-transfer coefficient for tubing, Btu/(hr-ft²-°F)
$w =$ mass flow rate of fluid, lbm/hr
$z =$ any well length, ft
$\alpha =$ constant defined by Eqs. D-1, D-5, and D-9, °F
$\beta =$ constant defined by Eqs. D-2, D-6, and D-10, °F
$\lambda_1, \lambda_2 =$ constants defined by Eqs. D-3, D-4, D-7, and D-8, ft⁻¹
$\Lambda =$ parameter defined by Eq. D-11, °F/ft
$\mu =$ fluid viscosity, cp
$\rho, \rho_e =$ bulk density of earth or formation, lbm/ft³
$\rho_{fl} =$ density of fluid, lbm/ft³
$\omega_1, \omega_2 =$ parameters defined by Eqs. D-12 and D-13, °F

Subscripts

$c =$ casing
$i =$ time index for superposition
$m =$ fluid mixture
$n =$ last time step for superposition
$t =$ tubing
$w =$ wall of tubulars

References

1. Kabir, C.S. *et al.*: "Determining Circulating Fluid Temperature in Drilling, Workover, and Well Control Operations," *SPEDC* (June 1996) 74.
2. Hasan, A.R. *et al.*: "A Mechanistic Model for Circulating Fluid Temperature," *SPEJ* (June 1996) 133.
3. Hasan, A.R. and Kabir, C.S.: "Static Reservoir Temperature Determination From Transient Data After Mud Circulation," *SPEDC* (March 1994) 17.

SI Metric Conversion Factors

Btu × 1.055 056	E+00	= kJ
Btu/(hr-ft²-°F) × 5.678 263	E+00	= W/(m²·K)
Btu/lbm × 2.326*	E+03	= J/kg
Btu/(lbm-°F) × 4.186 8*	E+03	= J/(kg·K)
cp × 1.0*	E−03	= Pa s
ft × 3.048*	E−01	= m
ft² × 9.290 304*	E−02	= m²
ft³ × 2.831 685	E−02	= m³
°F (°F−32)/1.8		= °C
lbm/ft³ × 1.601 846	E+01	= kg/m³
lbm/hr × 1.259 979	E−04	= kg/s

*Conversion factor is exact.

Appendix E
Models Related to Production Operations

E.1 Superposition Equations for Multirate Tests

Considering rate-dependent skin, we can write the generalized expression for a constant-rate test as

$$p_i - p_{wf} = m^* q \left\{ p_D(t_D) + s + Dq \right\}, \quad \ldots \ldots \ldots \text{(E-1)}$$

where $p_D(t_D)$ is the reservoir model; s is the static skin; and D is the rate-dependent or non-Darcy skin parameter.

For a two-rate test, one obtains the expression by applying the principle of superposition in time, which is written as

$$p_i - p_{wf2} = m^* q_1 \left\{ p_D(t_{D2}) + s + Dq_1 \right\}$$
$$+ m^* (q_2 - q_1) \left\{ p_D(t_{D2} - t_{D1}) + s + Dq_2 \right\} . \quad \ldots \ldots \text{(E-2)}$$

For the nth period in a multirate test, we can write

$$p_i - p_{wfn} = m^* q_1 \left\{ p_D(t_{Dn}) + s + Dq_1 \right\}$$
$$+ m^* (q_2 - q_1) \left\{ p_D(t_{Dn} - t_{Dn-1}) + s + Dq_2 \right\} + \ldots$$
$$+ m^* (q_n - q_{n-1}) \left\{ p_D(t_{Dn} - t_{Dn-1}) + s + Dq_n \right\},$$
$$\ldots \ldots \ldots \ldots \ldots \ldots \text{(E-3)}$$

or $p_i - p_{wfn} = m^* \left\{ \sum_{i=1}^{n} (q_i - q_{i-1}) \left[p_D(t_{Dn} - t_{Di-1}) + s + Dq_i \right] \right\},$
$$\ldots \ldots \ldots \ldots \ldots \text{(E-4)}$$

where $t_{D0} = 0$ and $q_0 = 0$. For a nonequilibrium initial condition, $p_i = p_{wf1}$; q_1 is the prevailing flow rate; and $Dq_i = |D(q_1 - q_{i-1})|$.

Assuming constant flow rate after timestep k and that buildup starts at timestep $n+1$, we can write the expression for buildup at time, t_m, as

$$p_i - p_{wm} = m^* \left\{ q_1 \left[p_D(t_{Dm}) + s + Dq_1 \right] + (q_2 - q_1) \right.$$
$$\left[p_D(t_{Dm} - t_{D1}) + s + Dq_2 \right] + \ldots + (q_k - q_{k-1})$$
$$\left[p_D(t_{Dm} - t_{Dk-1}) + s + Dq_k \right] + \ldots + (q_{n+1} - q_n)$$
$$\left[p_D(t_{Dm} - t_{Dn}) + s + Dq_{n+1} \right] + \ldots + (q_m - q_{m-1})$$
$$\left. \left[p_D(t_{Dm} - t_{Dm-1}) + s + Dq_m \right] \right\}$$

$$= m^* \sum_{i=1}^{k} (q_i - q_{i-1}) \left[p_D(t_{Dm} - t_{Di-1}) + s + Dq_i \right]$$
$$+ m^* \sum_{j=n+1}^{m} (q_j - q_{j-1}) \left[p_D(t_{Dm} - t_{Dj-1}) + s + Dq_j \right] .$$
$$\ldots \ldots \ldots \ldots \ldots \text{(E-5)}$$

To obtain an expression for rate, Eq. E-4 is rearranged to obtain

$$q_n = q_{n-1} + \frac{p_i - p_{wn}}{m^* \left[p_D(t_{Dn} - t_{Dn-1}) + s + Dq_n \right]}$$
$$- \frac{\sum_{i=1}^{n-1} (q_i - q_{i-1}) \left[p_D(t_{Dn} - t_{Di-1}) + s + Dq_i \right]}{p_D(t_{Dn} - t_{Dn-1}) + s + Dq_n} . \quad \ldots \text{(E-6)}$$

Similarly, Eq. E-5 can be rearranged to obtain the expression for after flow rate during buildup, which is written as

$$q_m = q_{m-1} + \frac{p_i - p_{wm}}{m^* \left[p_D(t_{Dm} - t_{Dm-1}) + s + Dq_m \right]}$$
$$- \frac{\sum_{i=1}^{k} (q_i - q_{i-1}) \left[p_D(t_{Dm} - t_{Di-1}) + s + Dq_i \right]}{p_D(t_{Dm} - t_{Dm-1}) + s + Dq_m}$$
$$- \frac{\sum_{j=n+1}^{m-1} (q_j - q_{j-1}) \left[p_D(t_{Dm} - t_{Dj-1}) + s + Dq_j \right]}{p_D(t_{Dm} - t_{Dm-1}) + s + Dq_m} .$$
$$\ldots \ldots \ldots \ldots \ldots \text{(E-7)}$$

E.2 Temperature Models for Gas-Lift (Solution of Eq. 9.14)

At the wellhead, the gas injection temperature, T_{ai}, is known and forms one boundary condition for Eq. 9.14 ($T_a = T_{ai}$, when $z=0$). The bottomhole condition takes into account the formation fluid entering the production string and mixing with the injected gas. The tubing-fluid temperature at the gas injection point can be obtained from a simple energy balance, given by

$$T_{tbh} = \frac{w_t - w_a}{w_t} c_{pt} T_{ebh} + \frac{w_a}{w_t} c_{pa} T_{abh} \cdot \quad \cdots\cdots\cdots \quad \text{(E-8)}$$

The particular solution to Eq. 9.14 is

$$T_{tp} = g_G z \sin\theta + T_{ew} + B'' g_G \sin\theta \quad \cdots\cdots\cdots \quad \text{(E-9)}$$

The characteristic polynomial equation for the complementary solution becomes

$$p(\lambda) = AB'\lambda^2 - B''\lambda - 1 = 0 \;, \quad \cdots\cdots\cdots \quad \text{(E-10)}$$

with the two roots,

$$\lambda_1 = -\frac{B''}{2AB'} + \frac{B''}{2AB'}\sqrt{1 + \frac{4AB'}{B''^2}} \quad \cdots\cdots\cdots \quad \text{(E-11)}$$

and

$$\lambda_2 = -\frac{B''}{2AB'} - \frac{B''}{2AB'}\sqrt{1 + \frac{4AB'}{B''^2}} \cdot \quad \cdots\cdots \quad \text{(E-12)}$$

The complete solution, obtained by adding the particular and the complementary solutions, is

$$T_t = \alpha e^{\lambda_1 z} + \beta e^{\lambda_2 z} + g_G z \sin\theta + B'' g_G \sin\theta + T_{es} + D' \;, \\ \cdots\cdots\cdots \quad \text{(E-13)}$$

and

$$\begin{aligned} T_a &= T_t - B' \frac{dT_t}{dz} \\ &= (1 - \lambda_1 B')\alpha e^{\lambda_1 z} + (1 - \lambda_2 B')\beta e^{\lambda_2 z} \\ &\quad + g_G \sin\theta(B'' - B') + g_G z \sin\theta + T_{es} + D' - B'\frac{D_t}{c_{pt}} \cdot \\ &\qquad\qquad\qquad\qquad\qquad\qquad \cdots\cdots\cdots \quad \text{(E-14)} \end{aligned}$$

To obtain the constants, α and β, we apply the first boundary condition to Eq. E-14.

$$\begin{aligned} T_a = T_{ai} &= (1 - \lambda_1 B')\alpha \\ &\quad + (1 - \lambda_2 B')\beta + g_G \sin\theta(B'' - B') + T_{es} + D' - B'\frac{D_t}{c_{pt}} \cdot \\ &\qquad\qquad\qquad\qquad\qquad\qquad \cdots\cdots\cdots \quad \text{(E-15)} \end{aligned}$$

By applying the second boundary condition and using T_{tbh} from Eq. E-8 into Eq. E-13, we obtain

$$T_{tbh} = \alpha e^{\lambda_1 L_j} + \beta e^{\lambda_2 L_j} + g_G L_j \sin\theta + B'' g_G \sin\theta + T_{es} + D' \cdot \\ \cdots\cdots\cdots \quad \text{(E-16)}$$

Therefore, $\alpha = \dfrac{T_{tbh} - T_{es} - D' - \beta e^{\lambda_2 L_j \sin\theta} - g_G \sin\theta L_j - B'' g_G \sin\theta}{e^{\lambda_1 L_j}} \cdot$

$$\cdots\cdots\cdots \quad \text{(E-17)}$$

By substituting this expression for α into Eq. E-15 and rearranging, we obtain

$$\beta = \frac{\left(T_{ai} - T_{ew} - D' + \dfrac{B'D_t}{c_{pt}}\right)e^{\lambda_1 L_j} + (1 - \lambda_1 B')(g_G L_j \sin\theta + B'' g_G \sin\theta + T_{es} + D' - T_{tbh})}{e^{\lambda_1 L_j}(1 - \lambda_2 B') - e^{\lambda_2 L_j}(1 - \lambda_1 B')}$$

$$- \frac{g_G \sin\theta e^{\lambda_1 L_j}(B'' - B')}{e^{\lambda_1 L_j}(1 - \lambda_2 B') - e^{\lambda_2 L_j}(1 - \lambda_1 B')} \cdot \quad \cdots\cdots\cdots \quad \text{(E-18)}$$

E.3 Models for Solids Remediation

E.3.1 Development of Fluid Circulation Model—Tubing Fluid.
During steady-state flow, tubing fluid loses energy to the surrounding annular fluid, which causes a decrease in the tubing fluid's enthalpy, kinetic energy, and/or potential energy. Therefore, we can write

$$Q_1 = w_f \left[\frac{dH_f}{dz} + v_f \frac{dv_f}{dz} + g\sin\theta \right], \quad \cdots\cdots\cdots \quad \text{(E-19)}$$

where w_f is the fluid mass flow rate; H_f is its enthalpy; v_f is its velocity; and θ is the inclination angle of the wellbore with horizontal. Enthalpy can be expressed as a function of pressure and temperature by

$$\frac{dH_f}{dz} = c_f \frac{dT_f}{dz} - C_J c_f \frac{dp}{dz}, \quad \cdots\cdots\cdots \quad \text{(E-20)}$$

where c_f is the heat capacity at constant pressure, and C_J $\{=(-1/c_f)(\partial H/\partial p)_T\}$ is the Joule-Thompson coefficient of the fluid in the producing string. Combining Eqs. E-19 and E-20, we have

$$Q_1 = w_f \left[c_f \frac{dT_f}{dz} - C_J c_f \frac{dp}{dz} + v_f \frac{dv_f}{dz} + g\sin\theta \right] \cdot \\ \cdots\cdots\cdots \quad \text{(E-21)}$$

The heat loss to (or gain from) the annulus per unit length of tubing, Q_1, can be expressed in terms of a heat-transfer coefficient, U_1, and temperature difference, $T_f - T_a$, as

$$Q_1 = U_1(2\pi r_{to})(T_f - T_a) \cdot \quad \cdots\cdots\cdots \quad \text{(E-22)}$$

The heat-transfer coefficient, U_1, depends on the convective-heat-transfer coefficient, h_{to}, of the tubing fluid and the thermal conductivity of the tubing wall, which is given by

$$\frac{1}{U_1} = \frac{r_{to}\ln(r_{to}/r_{ti})}{k_t} + \frac{r_{to}}{r_{ti}h_{to}} + \frac{1}{h_a} \cdot \quad \cdots\cdots\cdots \quad \text{(E-23)}$$

We define a relaxation parameter, L_{R1}, in terms of U_1, as

$$L_{R1} = U_1 \frac{2\pi r_{to}}{w_f c_f} \cdot \quad \cdots\cdots\cdots \quad \text{(E-24)}$$

By combining Eq. E-24 with Eq. E-21 and simplifying, we obtain an expression for the tubing and annular fluid temperatures, which is written as

$$\frac{dT_f}{dz} = L_{R1}\left(T_f - T_a\right) + \phi_f , \quad\quad\quad\quad \text{(E-25)}$$

where $\phi_f = C_J \dfrac{dp}{dz} - \dfrac{v}{c_f}\dfrac{dv}{dz} - \dfrac{g\sin\theta}{c_f} .$ .... (E-26)

For single-phase liquid flow, the Joule-Thompson coefficient is negligible, as is the change in kinetic energy. Therefore, the parameter, ϕ_f, for liquid flow is equal to $-g\sin\theta/c_f$.

Circulating Fluid. Differential equations governing the temperatures of the fluid (water) in the circulating string, T_w, is derived in a manner similar to the derivation shown for the tubing fluid. Heat transferred from the annular fluid to the circulating fluid, Q_2, is given by expressions similar to Eqs. E-21 and E-22. Thus, temperature of water in the circulating string flowing in the downward direction, is governed by

$$\frac{dT_w}{dz} = \left(2\pi r_{jo} U_2\right)\left(T_a - T_w\right)/\left(w_w c_w\right) + \phi_w , \quad \text{(E-27)}$$

where $\dfrac{1}{U_2} = \dfrac{r_{jo}\ln\left(r_{jo}/r_{ji}\right)}{k_j} + \dfrac{r_{jo}}{r_{ji}h_{jo}} + \dfrac{1}{h_a} .$ .... (E-28)

Using the relaxation parameter, $L_{R2} = (U_2)(2\pi r_{jo})/(w_w c_w)$, we obtain

$$\frac{dT_w}{dz} = L_{R2}\left(T_a - T_w\right) + \phi_w . \quad\quad\quad \text{(E-29)}$$

In Eq. E-29, the parameters ϕ_w and L_{R2} are given by

$$\phi_w = C_J \frac{dp}{dz} - \frac{v}{c_w}\frac{dv}{dz} - \frac{g\sin\theta}{c_w} , \quad\quad\quad \text{(E-30)}$$

and $L_{R2} = \dfrac{2\pi r_{to}}{w_w c_w\left(\dfrac{r_{jo}\ln\left(r_{jo}/r_{ji}\right)}{k_j} + \dfrac{r_{jo}}{r_{ji}h_{jo}} + \dfrac{1}{h_a}\right)} .$

$$\quad\quad\quad\quad\quad\quad\quad \text{(E-31)}$$

Annular Fluid. The fluid in the annulus moves upward and exchanges energy with the fluid flowing inside the production tubing and that in the circulating string. In addition, the annular fluid exchanges energy with the surrounding formation. We can write the energy balance equation as

$$Q_1 - Q_2 - Q_3 = -w_a\left[\frac{dH_a}{dz} + v_a\frac{dv_a}{dz} + g\sin\theta\right]. \quad \text{(E-32)}$$

Following the treatment presented in Chap. 5, we can write the expression for heat lost by the annular fluid to the formation, per unit length of the well, as

$$Q_3 = c_a w_a L_{R3}\left(T_a - T_{ei}\right), \quad\quad\quad\quad \text{(E-33)}$$

where L_{R3} is given by

$$L_{R3} = \frac{2\pi r_{to} U_{to} k_e}{c_a w_a\left(k_e + r_{to}U_{to}T_D\right)} . \quad\quad\quad\quad \text{(E-34)}$$

In Eq. E-34, T_D is the dimensionless temperature distribution function and is discussed in Ref. 1, and also in Chap. 5. The overall-heat-transfer coefficient, U_{to}, used in Eq. E-34 is given by

$$\frac{1}{U_{to}} = \frac{r_{to}\ln\left(r_{co}/r_{ci}\right)}{k_c} + \frac{r_{to}\ln\left(r_{cmo}/r_{cmi}\right)}{k_{cm}} + \frac{r_{to}}{r_{ci}h_a} ,$$

$$\quad\quad\quad\quad\quad\quad\quad \text{(E-35)}$$

where h_a is the forced-convective-heat-transfer coefficient for the annular fluid. In offshore, where casing is exposed to cold seawater, the expression for L_{R3} changes to

$$L_{R3} = \frac{2\pi r_{to} U_{tc}}{c_a w_a} . \quad\quad\quad\quad\quad\quad \text{(E-36)}$$

In Eq. E-36, the overall-heat-transfer coefficient accounting for the effect of seawater cooling, U_{tc} is given by

$$\frac{1}{U_{tc}} = \frac{r_{to}\ln\left(r_{co}/r_{ci}\right)}{k_c} + \frac{r_{to}}{r_{co}h_c} + \frac{r_{to}}{r_{ci}h_a} . \quad\quad \text{(E-37)}$$

Natural current will make forced convection as the most likely mode of heat transfer in offshore. We suggest the use of the Fishenden-Saunders[2] correlation for flow across long vertical pipes, which is

$$h_c = 0.26\left(k_c/d_{co}\right)^{0.6}\left(d_{co}v_c\rho_c/\mu_c\right)\left(c_c\mu_c/k_c\right)^{0.3} .$$

$$\quad\quad\quad\quad\quad\quad\quad \text{(E-38)}$$

Subscript c in Eq. E-38, indicates properties for seawater. Similar to Eqs. E-25 and E-29, the governing differential equation for the annular fluid is written as

$$\frac{dT_a}{dz} = -L_{R1}\left(T_f - T_a\right)\frac{c_f}{c_a} + L_{R2}\left(T_a - T_w\right)\frac{c_w}{c_a}$$

$$+ L_{R3}\left(T_a - T_{ei}\right) + \phi_a , \quad\quad\quad \text{(E-39)}$$

where $\phi_a = C_J \dfrac{dp}{dz} - \dfrac{v}{c_a}\dfrac{dv}{dz} - \dfrac{g\sin\theta}{c_a} .$ .... (E-40)

Note that simultaneous solution of Eqs. E-25, E-29 and E-39 should give the expressions for fluid temperatures in the three conduits of the system. The resulting third-order-differential equation does not lend itself to analytic solution. The numerical solution procedure is discussed in the next section. In this derivation, we assumed that the inlet temperature of the circulating fluid remains constant. In case one wishes to circulate the fluid using a surface tank, the tank-fluid temperature will asymptotically approach the final annular-fluid exit temperature in a manner very similar to that described for mud circulation, discussed in Chap. 8, Sec. 8.1.

E.3.2 Solution of Fluid Circulation Model.

The known wellhead-injection-fluid temperature forms one of the boundary conditions. At the point of injection, the annular fluid temperature is the same as the injection fluid temperature; that is, $T_{aj}=T_{wj}$ is the second boundary condition. The tubing fluid temperature at $z=L_j$ can be estimated from the known bottomhole temperature using the method presented in Chap. 5 and forms the last boundary condition needed to solve the system of equations.

We introduce the fractional parameter, ξ, to write the difference equations in terms of the value of the variable (temperatures) at the jth node and the $(j+1)^{th}$ node. Thus, the difference equation for the tubing fluid temperature from Eq. 9.40 is given by

$$\frac{T_{fj+1}-T_{fj}}{\Delta z} = L_{R1}$$
$$\left[\xi\left(T_{fj}-T_{aj}\right)+(1-\xi)\left(T_{fj+1}-T_{aj+1}\right)\right]+\phi_{fj} . \quad \ldots \ldots (E\text{-}41)$$

Similarly, for the fluid in the circulating string, we have

$$\frac{T_{wj+1}-T_{wj}}{\Delta z} = L_{R2}$$
$$\left[\xi\left(T_{aj}-T_{wj}\right)+(1-\xi)\left(T_{aj+1}-T_{wj+1}\right)\right]+\phi_{wj} , \quad \ldots \ldots (E\text{-}42)$$

and, for the annular fluid,

$$\frac{T_{aj+1}-T_{aj}}{\Delta z} = -\frac{L_{R1}c_f}{A_1c_a}\left\{\xi\left(T_{fj}-T_{aj}\right)+(1-\xi)\left(T_{fj+1}-T_{aj+1}\right)\right\}$$
$$+\frac{L_{R2}c_w}{A_2c_a}\left\{\xi\left(T_{aj}-T_{wj}\right)+(1-\xi)\left(T_{aj+1}-T_{wj+1}\right)\right\}$$
$$+L_{R3}\left\{\xi T_{aj}+(1-\xi)T_{aj+1}-T_{eij}\right\}+\phi_{aj} . \quad \ldots \ldots (E\text{-}43)$$

We rearrange these three equations by moving the variables $T_{f\,j+1}$, $T_{a\,j+1}$, and $T_{w\,j+1}$ to the right side of the equation and obtain the expressions,

$$b_1T_{fj+1}+b_2T_{aj+1}=b_3 , \quad \ldots \ldots (E\text{-}44)$$

$$C_1T_{aj+1}+C_2T_{wj+1}=C_3 , \quad \ldots \ldots (E\text{-}45)$$

and $d_1T_{fj+1}+d_2T_{aj+1}+d_3T_{wj+1}=d_4 . \quad \ldots \ldots (E\text{-}46)$

Further rearrangement gives the expressions for fluid temperatures in the three conduits at the $(j+1)^{th}$ node in terms of temperature at the jth node and other parameters, which are

$$T_{fj+1}=\frac{b_3C_1d_3+b_2C_2d_4-C_2d_2b_3-b_2C_3d_3}{b_1C_1d_3+b_2C_2d_1-C_2d_2b_1} , \quad \ldots \ldots (E\text{-}47)$$

$$T_{aj+1}=\frac{b_1C_3d_3+b_3C_2d_1-C_2d_4b_1}{b_1C_1d_3+b_2C_2d_1-C_2d_2b_1} , \quad \ldots \ldots (E\text{-}48)$$

and $T_{wj+1}=\frac{b_1C_1d_4+b_2C_3d_1-b_3C_1d_1-b_1C_3d_2}{b_1C_1d_3+b_2C_2d_1-C_2d_2b_1} . \quad \ldots \ldots (E\text{-}49)$

The parameters used in Eqs. E-47 through E-49 are

$$b_1=1-L_{R1}\Delta z(1-\xi) , \quad \ldots \ldots (E\text{-}50)$$

$$b_2=L_{R1}\Delta z(1-\xi) , \quad \ldots \ldots (E\text{-}51)$$

$$b_3=L_{R1}\Delta z\xi\left(T_{fj}-T_{aj}\right)+T_{fj}+\phi_j , \quad \ldots \ldots (E\text{-}52)$$

$$C_1=-L_{R2}\Delta z(1-\xi) , \quad \ldots \ldots (E\text{-}53)$$

$$C_2=1+L_{R2}\Delta z(1-\xi) , \quad \ldots \ldots (E\text{-}54)$$

$$C_3=L_{R2}\Delta z\xi\left(T_{aj}-T_{wj}\right)+T_{wj} , \quad \ldots \ldots (E\text{-}55)$$

$$d_1=\frac{L_{R1}\Delta zc_f}{c_a}(1-\xi) , \quad \ldots \ldots (E\text{-}56)$$

$$d_2=\left\{1-\frac{L_{R1}\Delta zc_f}{c_a}(1-\xi)-\frac{L_{R2}\Delta zc_w}{c_a}(1-\xi)-L_{R3}\Delta z(1-\xi)\right\} , \quad \ldots \ldots (E\text{-}57)$$

$$d_3=\frac{L_{R2}\Delta zc_w}{c_a}(1-\xi) , \quad \ldots \ldots (E\text{-}58)$$

and $d_4=L_{R2}\Delta z\frac{c_w\xi}{c_a}\left(T_{aj}-T_{wj}\right)+L_{R1}\Delta z\frac{c_f\xi}{c_a}\left(T_{fj}-T_{aj}\right)$
$$+L_{R3}\Delta z\xi T_{aj}-L_{R3}\Delta zT_{eij}+T_{aj}+\phi_{aj}\Delta z . \quad \ldots \ldots (E\text{-}59)$$

E.3.3 Constants of the Solvent Injection Model.

In Eqs. 9.44 through 9.46, α_1 and α_2 are the constants of integration that require two boundary conditions. The circulating fluid temperature at the wellhead, T_{ww}, and the fluid temperature at the point of injection, T_{ff}, constitute the two boundary conditions. Substituting $T_w=T_{ww}$ at the wellhead and $T_f=T_{ff}$ at L_j in Eq. 9.46, we obtain

$$T_{ff}=\alpha_1 e^{\lambda_1 L_j}+\alpha_2 e^{\lambda_2 L_j}+\frac{\beta_4}{\beta_3}L_j+\frac{\beta_3\beta_5-\beta_2\beta_4}{\beta_3^2} , \quad \ldots \ldots (E\text{-}60)$$

and $T_{ww}=\omega_1\alpha_1+\omega_2\alpha_2+\omega_4 . \quad \ldots \ldots (E\text{-}61)$

Therefore, α_1 and α_2 are given by

$$\alpha_1=\frac{e^{\lambda_2 L_j}\left(T_{ww}-\omega_4\right)-\omega_2\left[T_{ff}-\frac{\beta_4}{\beta_3}L_j-\frac{\beta_3\beta_5-\beta_2\beta_4}{\beta_3^2}\right]}{\omega_1 e^{\lambda_2 L_j}-\omega_2 e^{\lambda_1 L_j}} , \quad \ldots \ldots (E\text{-}62)$$

$$\text{and } \alpha_2 = \frac{\omega_1\left(T_{ff} - \frac{\beta_4}{\beta_3}L_j - \frac{\beta_3\beta_5 - \beta_2\beta_4}{\beta_3^2}\right) - e^{\lambda_1 L_j}\left(T_{ww} - \omega_4\right)}{\omega_1 e^{\lambda_2 L_j} - \omega_2 e^{\lambda_1 L_j}}.$$

$$\dots\dots\dots\dots\dots\text{(E-63)}$$

The parameters βi ($i=1, 2,\dots5$) are defined by the expressions,

$$\beta_1 = 2\pi r_{to}U_1 + 2\pi r_{jo}U_2 + L_{R3}w_a c_a , \quad \dots\dots\dots\text{(E-64)}$$

$$\beta_2 = \left(4\pi^2 r_{to}r_{jo}U_1 U_2\right)\left(\frac{1}{w_w c_w} - \frac{1}{w_f c_f}\right)$$
$$- L_{R3}2\pi w_a c_a\left(\frac{r_{to}U_1}{w_f c_f} - \frac{r_{jo}U_2}{w_w c_w}\right), \quad \dots\dots\dots\text{(E-65)}$$

$$\beta_3 = \frac{4\pi^2 r_{to}r_{jo}U_2 U_1 w_a c_a L_{R3}}{w_f w_w c_f c_w} , \quad \dots\dots\dots\dots\text{(E-66)}$$

$$\beta_4 = -\frac{4\pi^2 r_{to}r_{jo}U_1 U_2 w_a c_a L_{R3}g_G \sin\theta}{w_f w_w c_f c_w} , \quad \dots\dots\text{(E-67)}$$

$$\text{and } \beta_5 = \frac{2\pi r_{jo}U_2\phi_f}{w_w c_w}\left(2\pi r_{to}U_1 + L_{R3}w_a c_a\right)$$
$$- \frac{2\pi r_{to}U_1}{w_f c_f}\left(2\pi r_{jo}U_2\phi_w + w_a c_a L_{R3}g_G \sin\theta\right)$$
$$- \frac{2\pi r_{to}U_1}{w_f c_f}\left(\frac{2\pi r_{jo}U_2 w_a c_a\left(T_{bh} - Lg_G \sin\theta\right)L_{R3}}{w_w c_w}\right).$$

$$\dots\dots\dots\dots\dots\text{(E-68)}$$

λ_1 and λ_2 are given by

$$\lambda_1 = \frac{-\beta_2 + \sqrt{\beta_2^2 - 4\beta_1\beta_3}}{2\beta_1} , \quad \dots\dots\dots\dots\text{(E-69)}$$

$$\text{and } \lambda_2 = \frac{-\beta_2 - \sqrt{\beta_2^2 - 4\beta_1\beta_3}}{2\beta_1} . \quad \dots\dots\dots\dots\text{(E-70)}$$

The parameters for ω_i are

$$\omega_1 = -\frac{\left(2\pi r_{to}U_1 + 2\pi r_{jo}U_2 + L_{R3}w_a c_a\right)w_f c_f\lambda_1}{4\pi^2 r_{to}r_{jo}U_1 U_2}$$
$$+ \frac{2\pi r_{jo}U_2 + L_{R3}w_a c_a}{2\pi r_{jo}U_2} , \quad \dots\dots\dots\dots\text{(E-71)}$$

$$\omega_2 = -\frac{\left(2\pi r_{to}U_1 + 2\pi r_{jo}U_2 + L_{R3}w_a c_a\right)w_f c_f\lambda_2}{4\pi^2 r_{to}r_{jo}U_1 U_2}$$
$$+ \frac{2\pi r_{jo}U_2 + L_{R3}w_a c_a}{2\pi r_{jo}U_2} , \quad \dots\dots\dots\dots\text{(E-72)}$$

$$\omega_3 = \frac{2\pi r_{jo}U_2 + L_{R3}w_a c_a}{2\pi r_{jo}U_2}\frac{\beta_4}{\beta_3} - \frac{L_{R3}g_G \sin\theta w_a c_a}{2\pi r_{jo}U_2} ,$$

$$\dots\dots\dots\dots\dots\text{(E-73)}$$

$$\text{and } \omega_4 = -\frac{2\pi r_{to}U_1 + 2\pi r_{jo}U_2 + L_{R2}w_a c_a}{4\pi^2 r_{to}r_{jo}U_1 U_2}\frac{w_f c_f\beta_4}{\beta_3}$$
$$- \frac{2\pi r_{jo}U_1 T_{bh}L_{R3}w_a c_a}{4\pi^2 r_{to}r_{jo}U_1 U_2} - \frac{Lg_G \sin\theta L_{R3}w_a c_a}{2\pi r_{jo}U_2}$$
$$+ \frac{w_f c_f\phi_1\left(2\pi r_{to}U_1 + 2\pi r_{jo}U_2 + L_{R3}w_a c_a\right)}{4\pi^2 r_{to}r_{jo}U_1 U_2}$$
$$+ \frac{2\pi r_{jo}U_2 + L_{R3}w_a c_a}{2\pi r_{jo}U_2}\frac{\beta_3\beta_5 - \beta_2\beta_4}{\beta_3^2} . \quad \dots\dots\text{(E-74)}$$

Nomenclature

A = cross-sectional area for flow, ft^2

B = constant defined by Eq. 9.8, ft

B' = constant ($=Bw_t/w_a$) used in Eq. 9.15, ft

B'' = constant defined by Eq. 9.15, ft

c_a = annular-fluid heat capacity, Btu/(lbm-°F)

c_e = specific heat of earth or formation, Btu/(lbm-°F)

c_f, c_{flt} = specific heat of tubing fluid, Btu/(lbm-°F)

c_{ga} = specific heat of annular gas, Btu/(lbm-°F)

c_{pa} = specific heat of annular gas, Btu/lbm-°F

c_{pt} = specific heat of tubing fluid, Btu/lbm-°F

c_w = circulating-fluid heat capacity, Btu/(lbm-°F)

C_J = Joule-Thompson coefficient, °F/psi

C_c = contraction coefficient used in Eq. 9.34, dimensionless

d = pipe diameter, ft

D = non-Darcy flow coefficient, STB/D

D_a = constant defined by Eq. 9.11, Btu/(lbm-ft)

D_t = constant analogous to D_a for tubing fluid, Btu/(lbm-ft)

D' = constant defined by Eq. 9.16, °F

f = friction factor, dimensionless

f_L = liquid holdup, dimensionless

G = mass flux (mass flow rate/unit area), lbm/(hr-ft^2)

g = acceleration owing to gravity, ft/sec^2

g_c = conversion factor, 32.17 lbm-ft/lbf-sec^2

g_G = geothermal gradient, °F/ft

h = formation thickness, ft

h_a = forced-convection-heat-transfer coefficient for the annulus, Btu/(°F-hr-ft)

h_c = natural-convection-heat-transfer coefficient, Btu/(°F-hr-ft)

h_{jo} = forced-convection-heat-transfer coefficient for circulating string, Btu/(°F-hr-ft)

H, H_f = fluid enthalpy, Btu/lbm

J = conversion factor, 778 Btu/lbf

J_p = productivity index, STB/D-psi

k = formation permeability, md

k_c = casing material conductivity, Btu/(hr-ft-°F)

k_{cm} = cement conductivity, Btu/(hr-ft-°F)

k_e = earth or formation thermal conductivity, Btu/(hr-ft-°F)

k_j = conductivity of circulating string, Btu/(°F-hr-ft)

L = well depth, ft

L_e = equivalent length factor, dimensionless

L_R = relaxation length parameter, ft^{-1}

m^* = $kh/(141.2\mu B)$, md-ft/cp

p = pressure, psia

p_i = initial reservoir pressure, psia

p^* = Horner's extrapolated pressure, psia

Δp = pressure drop, psi

p_D = dimensionless pressure ($=\Delta p/141.2qB\mu$)

p_{wf} = flowing bottomhole pressure, psia

p_{ws} = shut-in bottomhole pressure, psia

$\bar{p}$ = average reservoir pressure, psia

q, q_{wh} = wellhead oil rate, STB/D

q_c = liquid circulation rate, STB/D

q_m = maximum or open-flow potential, STB/D

q_{sf} = sandface oil rate, STB/D

q_t = total (gas+liquid) volumetric fluid flow rate, STB/D

Q = heat flow from formation to annular fluid per unit well length, Btu/(hr-ft)

Q_{ta} = heat flow from annular to tubing fluid per unit well length, Btu/(hr-ft)

r_c, r_w = wellbore radius, ft

r_{co} = outside casing radius, ft

r_{jo} = outside injection-tubular radius, ft

r_{ti} = inside tubing radius, ft

r_{to} = outside tubing radius, ft

R_A = area ratio, A_2/A_1

s = damaged or static skin, dimensionless

s' = total skin ($=s+Dq$), dimensionless

t = producing time, hr

t_e = effective superposition time, hr

t, t_p = fluid production or injection time, hr

t_D = dimensionless production or injection time ($=2.64 \times 10^{-4}kt/\phi\mu c_t r_w^2$)

Δt = shut-in time, hr

T = fluid temperature, °F

T_a = annular-fluid temperature, °F

T_{ai} = annular-fluid temperature at surface, °F

T_{ei} = formation static temperature at bottomhole, °F

T_{es} = formation static temperature at surface, °F

T_f = tubing-fluid temperature, °F

T_t = tubing fluid temperature, °F

T_{tp} = particular solution of tubing-fluid temperature, °F

T_w = circulating water or fluid temperature, °F

T_{wb} = wellbore/formation interface temperature, °F

T_D = dimensionless temperature [$=2\pi k_e(T_{wb}-T_{ei})/q_F$]

U = overall-heat-transfer coefficient, Btu/(hr-ft^2-°F)

U_1 = overall-heat-transfer coefficient for tubing fluid, Btu/(hr-°F-ft)

U_{tc} = overall-heat-transfer coefficient for tubular in seawater, Btu/(hr-°F-ft)

U_{to} = overall-heat-transfer coefficient for annular fluid, Btu/(hr-°F-ft)

v, v_f = fluid velocity, ft/sec

w, w_f = mass rate of tubing fluid, lbm/hr

w_t = total mass flow rate of fluid stream in gas lift, lbm/hr

w_w = mass rate of circulating fluid, lbm/hr

x = mass fraction of gas in the tubing-fluid mixture, dimensionless

X = Lockhart-Martinelli parameter, dimensionless

z = any vertical depth, ft

Z = gas-law deviation factor, dimensionless

α = constant defined by Eq. E-17, °F

α_h = heat diffusivity of formation [$=k_e/c_e\rho_e$], ft^2/hr

β = constant defined by Eq. E-18, °F

θ = well inclination angle from horizontal, degree

λ_1, λ_2 = constants defined by Eqs. E-11, E-12, E-69 and E-70, °F

μ = oil viscosity, cp

ρ = fluid density, lbm/ft^3

ρ_e = bulk density of earth or formation, lbm/ft^3

ϕ = porosity, fraction

ϕ_f, ϕ_w = parameters defined by Eqs. E-26 and E-30, °F/ft

ω = lumped parameters, defined by Eqs. E-71 through E-74

Subscripts

1 = inlet state

2 = outlet state

a = annulus

bh = bottomhole

c = casing

cem = cement

ci = casing inside

co = casing outside

e = earth

es = earth static

f = fluid

fit = fitting

g = gas

ins = insulation

j = depth index

L = liquid

m = time index during buildup test

n = time index during drawdown test

t = tubing

ti = tubing inside

to = tubing outside

ts = tubing saturated

w = circulating string

References

1. Hasan, A.R. and Kabir, C.S.: "Aspects of Heat Transfer During Two-Phase Flow in Wellbores," *SPEPF* (August 1994) 211.

2. Fishenden, M. and Saunders O.A.: *An Introduction to Heat Transfer*, first edition., Oxford U. Press, London (1950) 103.

SI Metric Conversion Factors

Btu $\times$ 1.055 056	E + 00	= kJ
Btu/lbm $\times$ 2.326*	E + 03	= J/kg
Btu/(lbm-°F) $\times$ 4.186 8*	E + 03	= J/(kg·K)
cp $\times$ 1.0*	E − 03	= Pa s
ft $\times$ 3.048*	E − 01	= m
ft^2 $\times$ 9.290 304*	E − 02	= m^2
ft/sec^2 $\times$ 3.048*	E − 01	= m/s^2
°F (°F − 32)/1.8		= °C
lbf $\times$ 4.448 222	E + 00	= N
lbm $\times$ 4.535 924	E − 01	= kg
lbm/ft^3 $\times$ 1.601 846	E + 01	= kg/m^3
lbm/hr $\times$ 1.259 979	E − 04	= kg/s
psi $\times$ 6.894 757	E + 00	= kPa

*Conversion factor is exact.

Appendix F
Estimating Flow from Spinner Response

F.1 Least-Squares Spinner Slope Calculation

When the spinner response, f, at different cable speeds or tool velocities, v_T, is available, the spinner response slope, m, can be calculated at any particular depth in the well. Given a set of observations, (v_{T1}, f_1), (v_{T2}, f_2),...(v_{Tn}, f_n), in a particular logging direction, the formula for computing the spinner response slope is given by

$$m = \frac{\sum_{i=1}^{n}\left(v_{T_i} - \bar{v}_T\right)\left(f_i - \bar{f}\right)}{\sum_{i=1}^{n}\left(v_{T_i} - \bar{v}_T\right)^2} \quad \dots\dots\dots\dots \text{(F-1)}$$

The number of observations, n, is equivalent to the number of cable speeds taken in each direction. Down-pass cable speeds are conventionally considered positive and, therefore, v_T will be positive. Conversely, up-pass cable speeds will be negative for v_T. The spinner response can be negative or positive depending on the fluid movement relative to the tool. Ultimately, when fluids are produced from the well, the fluid velocity is positive.

After determining the slope, the y-axis intercept is calculated from the equation,

$$b = \bar{f} - m\bar{v}_T , \quad \dots\dots\dots\dots\dots\dots \text{(F-2)}$$

and therefore, the x-axis intercept can be determined as

$$v_T = \frac{-b}{m} . \quad \dots\dots\dots\dots\dots\dots\dots \text{(F-3)}$$

In this manner m and b are calculated for each depth with corresponding cable speeds and spinner responses.

Using the data collected in a static section of the well, the spinner response slope is calculated from the above equations. Within this no-flow interval, the extrapolated x-axis intercept should theoretically intersect the origin. However, the spinner does not rotate within a small range of fluid velocities in either flow direction because of tool frictional and viscous fluid properties. The point where rotation begins is referred to as the threshold velocity, v_{th}, and is the static x-axis intercept value. Ordinarily, a constant threshold velocity occurs for each direction of tool passes, meaning that they are of similar magnitude but opposite in sign.

Accounting for the bypass velocity, the fluid mixture velocity, v_m, at any depth can be calculated from equation

$$v_m = v_{th} - v_T . \quad \dots\dots\dots\dots\dots\dots \text{(F-4)}$$

To calculate the volumetric flow rate from fluid velocity, additional steps are required. These details are not covered in this text; however, they are easily available in the literature.[1,2]

F.2 Correlation Coefficient Calculation

When the sum of the squared distances of all the data points from the line is the lowest possible, a least square fit is obtained. A perfect fit or correlation is achieved when the measured paired data points fall on the line. The strength of the linear association between paired points is quantified by the correlation coefficient, r. We can generally define the strength of correlation as: perfect ($|r|=1$); strong ($|r|>0.8$); moderate ($0.5<|r|<0.8$); and weak ($|r|<0.5$).

The equation for computing the correlation coefficient in terms of spinner response and cable speed is given by

$$r = \frac{1}{n-1}\sum_{i=1}^{n}\left(\frac{v_{T_i} - \bar{v}_T}{s_{v_T}}\right)\left(\frac{f_i - \bar{f}}{s_f}\right) , \quad \dots\dots\dots \text{(F-5)}$$

$$\text{where } s_{v_T} = \sqrt{\frac{\sum_{i=1}^{n}v_{T_i}^2 - \frac{\left(\sum_{i=1}^{n}v_{T_i}\right)^2}{n}}{n-1}} , \quad \dots\dots\dots \text{(F-6)}$$

$$\text{and } s_f = \sqrt{\frac{\sum_{i=1}^{n}f_i^2 - \frac{\left(\sum_{i=1}^{n}f_i\right)^2}{n}}{n-1}} \quad \dots\dots\dots\dots \text{(F-7)}$$

Nomenclature

b = y-axis intercept, rev/sec

f = spinner response, rev/sec

m = spinner response slope, rev/ft

n = number of observations

r = least-squares regression coefficient, dimensionless

s_f = standard deviation for spinner response, defined by Eq. F-7

s_{vT} = standard deviation for tool velocity, defined by Eq. F-6

v_m = fluid mixture velocity, ft/sec

v_{th} = threshold velocity, ft/sec

v_T = tool velocity, ft/sec

Subscript

i = summation index

References

1. McKinley, R.M.: "Production Logging," paper SPE 10035 presented at the 1982 SPE Intl. Petroleum Exhibition and Technical Symposium, Beijing, 18–26 March.

2. Hill, A.D.: *Production Logging—Theoretical and Interpretative Elements*, Monograph Series, SPE, Richardson, Texas (1990) **14**.

SI Metric Conversion Factor

ft × 3.048*   E – 01 = m

*Conversion factor is exact.

Author Index

A

Alhmehaideb, R.A., 79
Ansari, A.M.
  horizontal wells and, 46, 52
  liquid holdup and, 25, 27–28
  multiphase flow and, 16, 21, 25, 27–28, 30–32, 46, 52
  production operations and, 117
Aziz, K., 20, 26, 29, 31, 53, 55, 147

B

Baker, O., 51
Baxendell, P.B., 10
Beck, A.E., 99, 102
Beggs, H.D.
  multiphase flow and, 31, 40–42, 46, 55–56
  production operations and, 122, 124
Beggs-Brill correlation, 40–42, 46
Bendiksen, K.H., 44
Bertuzzi, A.F., 117
Bird, R.B., 3
Blassius equation, 2, 11, 51
Bornea, D., 23, 38, 40, 50, 56
Brauner, N., 23
Brill, J.P., 55–56
  multiphase flow and, 28, 31, 40–42, 46
  production operations and, 124
Brown, K.E., 10, 13–15, 31, 113

C

Caetano, E.F., 4, 27, 29, 55–56
Carlsaw, H.S., 64
Carpenter, P.G., 10–11, 117
Chen, N.H., 3
Chien, S.F., 127
Chisholm, D., 127–128
Choquette, S.P., 147
Cicchiti, A., 10

Clark, A.R., 106, 108
Cobb, W.M., 97–100
Collier, J.G., 127–128
Crawford, T.J., 56
Crocker, S., 127
Cullender, M.H., 1

D

Darcy flow, 79, 113, 114–117
Darling, C.W.W., 4
Davies, R.M., 28
Davies, S.N., 95
Dikken, B.J., 53
Dimon, C.A., 55
Dowdle, W.L., 97–100
Dukler, A.E., 10, 23, 29, 51
Duns, H., 12–13
Duns, H. Jr., 31

E

Edwardson, M.J., 90
Eotvos number, 28, 43

F

Fancher, G.H., 10
Fanning friction factor, 2–3
Fernandes, R.C., 29
Fetkovich equation, 113
Findlay, J., 25
Fishenden, M., 152
Flores, J.G., 59, 147, 150
Forchheimer equation, 113
Fourier's law, 160
Froude numbers, 38, 41

G

Gaussian elimination method, 158
Gilbert, W.E., 113
Gipson, F.W., 55
Godbey, J.K., 55
Gomez, L.E., 31–32, 42–44, 51–52, 55
Govier, G.W., 20, 26, 29, 51, 147
Grashof number, 152
Gregory, G.A., 52
Griston, S., 124
Gunn, D.J., 4

H

Hagedorn, A.R., 10, 13–15, 31, 113
Hammami, A., 131
Hanratty, T.J., 53
Harmathy, T.Z., 25–26, 28, 57, 59
Hasan, A.R., iv, 30–32, 152
   deviated wells and, 39, 42–46, 54–57, 59
   flow pattern delineation and, 23
   heat transfer and, 64–66, 69
   liquid holdup and, 27
   production logging and, 147, 150
   production operations and, 117, 122, 124, 126–127
Henstock, W.H., 53
Hewitt, G.F., 20, 22–23
Hill, A.D., 140
Holmes, C.S., 90, 93
Horner, D.R., 97
Hughmark, G.A., 52
Hurst, W., 65

I

Idsinga, W., 12
Ihara, M., 53

J

Jaeger, J.C., 64
Jamaluddin, A.K.M., 131
James, R., 126–127
Jayanti, S., 23
Joule-Thompson effect, 64, 67, 70
   heat transfer and, 80
   oil heating and, 103
   solids remediation and, 163–164
   temperature profiles and, 118

K

Kabir, C.S., iv, 59, 152

deviated wells and, 39, 42–43, 45–46
drilling operations and, 90
heat transfer and, 64–66, 69
horizontal wells and, 54–55
production logging and, 147, 150
production operations and, 117, 122, 126
vertical wells and, 23, 27, 30–32
Kang, S.Y., 20, 38–40, 56
Kanu, E.P., 122
Kaya, A.S.
   deviated wells and, 40, 42–44
   flow pattern delineation, 23
   multiphase flow and, 23, 31–32, 40, 42–44, 52, 54–55
Kelessidis, V.C., 29
King, R.C., 127
Kutadelaze number, 38

L

Lockhart, R.W., 11–12
Lockhart-Martinelli correlation, 11–12, 49, 51, 56, 128

M

McAdams, W.H., 10
McKinley, R.M., 140
Mandhane, J.M., 51
Mao, Z.S., 23, 29
Martinelli, R.C., 11–12
Moody friction factor, 2–4
   horizontal wells and, 51
   separated flow models and, 11–15
Mukherjee, H., 28, 31

N

Nicklin, D.J., 22
Nicolas, Y., 59

O

Orkiszewski, J., 31
Ouyang, L., 4, 54–55

P

Patel, R., 43
Perkins, T.K., 106, 108
Podio, A.L., 55
Poettmann, F.H., 10–11, 117
Prandtl number, 152
Pucknell, J.K., 32

R

Ramey, H.J. Jr., 64, 66, 98–99, 124
Ramey function, 98–99
Reynolds number, 2–4, 10
  Duns-Ros correlation and, 13
  GLR and, 10–11
  horizontal wells and, 51
  intermittent flow and, 53
  production logging and, 147
  pseudo, 10
  steam injection and, 127
Roberts, D.N., 20, 22–23
Ros, N.C.J., 12–13, 31
Roux, B., 99–100

S

Sadatomi, M., 21
Sagar, R.K., 69–70
Satter, A., 125
Saunders, O.A., 152
Schlumberger, M., 64
Schmidt, Z., 28
Schrodt, J.L.G., 127
Scott, D.S., 52
Shah, Y.T., 57
Shen, P.Y., 99, 102
Sheriff, N., 152
Shiu, K.S., 122
Shoham, O., 22
Sieder-Tate coefficient, 152
Singh, P., 131
Smith, R.V., 1
Steen, D.A., 29–30
Stefan-Boltzmann constant, 151–152
Swaim, H.W., 55

Swift, S.C., 90, 93

T

Taitel, Y.
  deviated wells and, 37–38
  flow pattern and, 20, 22–23
  horizontal wells and, 47, 51, 55
Taylor, G., 28
Taylor bubbles, 18–19
  deviated wells and, 37–47
  horizontal wells and, 47–55
  liquid holdup and, 24–30
  rise velocity and, 43–45
  transitions and, 21–24
  upward inclines and, 37–38
Thomas, R., 10
Tragesser, A.F., 90

V

van Everdingen, A.F., 65
Vogel, J.V., 114

W

Wallis, G.B., 25, 28–30, 43–44
Weisman, J., 20, 38–40
Willhite, G.P., 124
Winterfeld, P.H., 79
Witterholt, E.J., 59

X

Xiao, J.J., 51

Y

Yuan, H.J., 4

Subject Index

A

annular flow, 3–4
  circulation model and, 132
  convective heat transfer and, 152
  countercurrent, 57–59
  defined, 19
  deviated wells and, 40, 45
  entrainment and, 29–30
  horizontal wells and, 48, 53
  liquid holdup and, 29–30
  multiple strings and, 154–155
  paraffin control and, 133–135
  solids remediation and, 164
  stratified transition and, 48–50
  tank-fluid temperature and, 90–92
  temperature profiles and, 74–75, 117–124
  transition and, 23–24
  two-phase, 55–56
  upward inclines and, 37–38
  wellbores and, 74–75
asphaltene
  flocculation envelope and, 132
  solids deposition and, 130–136

B

backpressure, 113
Beggs-Brill correlation, 40–42, 46
Blassius equation, 2, 11, 51
blowout
  analysis of, 105–106
  example of, 106–108
  bottomhole pressure and, 108–109
  fluid loss and, 109–110
  rate computation, 106
bottomhole pressure, 143–144
  blowout and, 108–109
  single-phase flow and, 79–86
  two-phase flow and, 86–88
bubbly flow
  countercurrent, 57–59
  defined, 18

deviated wells and, 37–47
dispersed, 22, 48, 53
elongated, 47–48
horizontal wells and, 47–55
intermittent transition and, 50–51
liquid holdup and, 24–26
momentum fluxes and, 20
nonconventional situations and, 55–59
slug flow and, 21–22, 26–29
upward inclines and, 37–38
buoyancy, 37

C

cased-hole data, 101–105
choke settings, 114–115
churn flow
  defined, 18–19
  deviated wells and, 40
  liquid holdup and, 29
  transition and, 22–24
  upward inclines and, 37–38
circulation temperature, 93–96, 164–165
conservation of momentum, 1
  balance in, 79
  fluxes in, 20
  steam injection and, 124–130
convection, 66, 68, 103–104, 152
  See also heat transfer
countercurrent two-phase flow, 57–59

D

Darcy flow, 79, 113, 114–117
deasphalted oil (DAO), 134
density
  gas, 1
  homogeneous models and, 9–11
  liquid holdup and, 24–30
  mixture, 9–10, 124, 127
  momentum fluxes and, 20
  pressure and, 1

openhole data analysis and, 97–101, 103–105
radiative, 151–152
relaxation parameter and, 67–68
single-phase gas flow and, 79–83
single-phase oil flow and, 83–86
solids remediation and, 163–164
tank-fluid temperature and, 90–92
temperature profiles and, 74–78, 117–124
(*see also* temperature)
two-phase gas/oil flow and, 86–88
wellbore coefficients and, 67, 151–153
wellbores and, 68–71, 74–78
homogeneous flow model, 9–11, 127
horizontal wells, 4–5, 54–55
   flow patterns in, 47–51
   holdup and, 51–53
   Moody friction factor and, 51
   pressure drop and, 51–53
   Reynolds number and, 51
   transition and, 48–51
hydrostatic gradient, 1
hyperbola method, 101–102

I

inclination factor, 53
incompressible flow, 1
inflow performance relationship (IPR), 114–117
injection, 136
   asphaltene and, 134–135
   dyes and, 8
   equations for, 155
   heat transfer and, 64–73
   in-situ velocity and, 7–9
   paraffin and, 133–135
   single-phase flow and, 124–130
   solvent, 132–133, 165–166
   steam, 55, 124–130
   superficial velocity and, 7–9
in-situ velocity, 7–9
intermittent flow, 50–53
inversion, 3, 92–93

J

James tubing, 126–127
Joule-Thompson effect, 64, 67, 70
   heat transfer and, 80
   oil heating and, 103
   solids remediation and, 163–164
   temperature profiles and, 118

K

kinetic energy
   solids remediation and, 163–164
   temperature profiles and, 117–124

wellbore heat transport and, 64–78
Kutadelaze number, 38

L

laminar flow, 3–4
least-squares spinner slope, 169
lift, 7
   temperature profiles and, 117–124, 162–163
liquid holdup, 8
   annular flow and, 29–30
   Beggs-Brill correlation and, 40–42
   bubbly flow and, 24–26
   churn flow and, 29
   deviated wells and, 40–47
   flow parameter and, 25–26
   Hagedorn-Brown method and, 13–15
   homogeneous models and, 9–11
   horizontal wells and, 51–53
   pressure drop and, 24–30
   transitional flow and, 23–24
liquids
   countercurrent flow and, 57–59
   heat transfer and, 69–70
   homogeneous models and, 10–11
   in-situ velocity and, 7–9
   multiphase flow and, 7–17 (*see also* multiphase flow)
   separated flow models and, 11–15
   superficial velocity and, 7–9
   transitional flow and, 21–24
   vertical wells and, 18–36
Lockhart-Martinelli correlation, 11–12, 49, 51, 56, 128
log-linear approximation, 98–99

M

mapping
   flow-pattern and, 19–24, 37–39, 47–51, 147–149
   transition and, 21–24
mass balance, 79
mass flux, 8
mass fraction, 8, 125
material balance, 79
mathematics
   Eotvos number, 28, 43
   exponential approach, 98
   Fourier's law, 160
   Froude number, 38, 41
   Grashof number, 152
   hyperbola method, 101–102
   Joule-Thompson effect, 64, 67, 70, 80, 103, 118, 163–164
   Kutadelaze number, 38
   log-linear approach, 98–99
   Prandtl number, 152
   Ramey function, 98–99
   Reynolds number, 2–4, 10–11, 13, 51, 53, 127, 147
   rigorous approach, 98

square-root time approximation, 99
Stefan-Boltzmann constant, 151–152
superposition, 98–99, 104
See also equations; models
mechanical energy. *See* energy balance
mechanistic models
  deviated wells and, 42–47
  vertical wells and, 18–36
metering, 130
  production logging and, 140–150
  steam, 126–127
mixtures
  analysis methods and, 9–10
  blowout and, 105–110
  density, 9–10, 124, 127
  homogeneous models and, 10–11
  separated flow models and, 11–15
  steam injection and, 124–130
  temperature profiles and, 117–124
  transitional flow and, 21–24
models
  application of, 133–135
  circulation, 132, 159, 165
  deviated wells and, 37–47
  drilling operation, 159–161
  Duns-Ros, 12–13
  empirical, 40–42
  exponential approach, 98
  fluid circulation, 132
  gas-lift temperature, 162–163
  Hagedorn-Brown, 13–15
  homogeneous flow, 9–11, 127
  horizontal wells and, 47–55
  liquid holdup and, 24–30
  Lockhart-Martinelli, 11–12
  log-linear approximation, 98–99
  mechanistic, 18–36, 42–47
  nonconventional situations and, 55–59
  production operations and, 162–168
  rigorous approach, 98
  separated flow, 9, 11–15
  single-phase gas flow and, 79–83
  single-phase oil flow and, 83–86
  solids remediation, 163–164
  solvent injection, 132–133, 165–166
  square-root time approximation, 99
  steam injection and, 55, 124–130
  systems analysis and, 113–117
  temperature profiles and, 74–78, 117–124
  two-phase gas/oil flow and, 86–88
  variable heat constants, 159–160
  vertical wells and, 18–36
  wellbores and, 74–78
momentum balance, 1, 79
  fluxes in, 20
  steam injection and, 55, 124–130
Moody friction factor, 2–4
  horizontal wells and, 51
  separated flow models and, 11–15

mud temperature, 160–161
  cased-hole data and, 101–105
  exponential approach, 98
  log-linear approach, 98–99
  openhole data and, 97–101, 103–105
  rigorous approach, 98
  square-root time approximation, 99
multiphase flow, 16–17, 35–36, 60–63
  analysis methods and, 9–15
  annular flow and, 23–24, 29–30, 55–56
  area and, 7
  bubbly flow and, 18, 21–22, 24–26
  churn flow and, 22–24, 29
  concurrent systems and, 18–19
  countercurrent, 57–59
  delineation and, 19–24
  deviated wells and, 37–47
  downward, 56–57
  Duns & Ros correlation and, 12–13
  flow pattern and, 7, 20
  gas-volume fraction and, 8–9
  Hagedorn & Brown method and, 13–15
  homogeneous models for, 10–11
  horizontal wells and, 47–55
  in-situ velocities and, 7–8
  liquid holdup and, 8–9
  Lockhart-Martinelli correlation and, 11–12
  mass flux and, 8
  mass fraction and, 8
  mechanistic approach to, 30–34
  oil/water, 59
  pressure drop and, 24–30
  separated flow models for, 11–15
  slip and, 8–9
  slug flow and, 18, 21–24, 26–29
  superficial velocities and, 7–8
  vertical wells and, 18–36
  volume fraction and, 8
  wellbore patterns and, 19
multiple strings
  equations for, 154–155
  temperature and, 74–78

N

non-Darcy flow, 79
nonisothermal systems, 3

O

oil, 1
  deasphalted, 134
  finite-difference equations and, 157–158
  Joule-Thompson effect and, 103
  multiphase flow and, 7–17 (*see also* multiphase flow)
  single-phase flow and, 83–86
  transitional flow and, 21–24
  water two-phase flow and, 59
oil/water contact (OWC), 143, 146

vertical wells, 35–36
  annular flow and, 19, 23–24, 29–30
  bubbly flow and, 18, 21–22, 24–26
  churn flow and, 18–19, 22–24, 29
  concurrent systems and, 18–19
  delineation and, 19–24
  flow-pattern maps and, 20
  liquid holdup and, 24–30
  mechanistic approach to, 30–34
  pressure drop and, 24–30
  slug flow and, 18, 21–24, 26–29
  wellbore patterns and, 19
viscosity, 10–11, 28
volume
  blowout and, 105–110
  fraction, 8
  heat transfer and, 80

W

water
  multiphase flow and, 7–17 (*see also* multiphase flow)
  oil contact and, 143, 146
  oil two-phase flow and, 59
  steam injection and, 124–130

wax crystallization temperature (WCT), 131
wellbores, 89
  blowout and, 105–110
  deviated wells and, 37–47
  diffusivity equation and, 64–66
  drilling operations and, 159–161
  energy balance for, 66–68
  finite-difference equations for, 157–158
  flow patterns in, 19
  fluid ingress and, 4–5
  heat transport and, 64–73, 151–153 (*see also* heat transfer)
  horizontal wells and, 4–5, 47–55
  injection and, 124–130, 136 (*see also* injection)
  multiphase flow and, 7–17 (*see also* multiphase flow)
  nonisothermal systems and, 3
  production logging and, 140–150
  single-phase gas flow and, 79–83
  single-phase oil flow and, 83–86
  solids deposition and, 130–136
  systems analysis and, 113–114
  temperature and, 68–71, 74–78, 93–96
  (*see also* temperature)
  two-phase gas/oil flow and, 86–88
  vertical wells and, 18–36
wellhead pressure, 82

CPSIA information can be obtained at www.ICGtesting.com
Printed in the USA
LVOW030050230512

282691LV00002BB/4/P